Frances Camp
2-3-1992

Frances
Smith

DRAFTING FUNDAMENTALS
Fourth Edition

DRAFTING FUNDAMENTALS
Fourth Edition

C. H. JENSEN
Technical Director,
R. S. McLaughlin Collegiate
and Vocational Institute,
Oshawa, Ontario

F. H. S. MASON
Technical Director,
Anderson Collegiate
and Vocational Institute,
Whitby, Ontario

McGRAW-HILL RYERSON LIMITED
Toronto   Montreal   New York   London   Sydney   Johannesburg
Mexico   Panama   Düsseldorf   Singapore   Rio de Janeiro
Kuala Lumpur   New Delhi

DRAFTING FUNDAMENTALS / Fourth Edition

ISBN 0-07-82436-3

12345678910 E P-76   109876

Printed and bound in Canada

PREFACE

THE NEED TO STANDARDIZE MEASUREMENT

The amount of goods and services traded between countries in today's world and the speed with which this trade is carried out has made it imperative that Canadian and American goods and services be usable by every country throughout the world. This exchange has brought about the necessity for a common system of measurement.

Through the centuries, many measurement systems have developed, evolving from numerous origins, convenient customs, and local adaptions. Most of these systems lacked rational structure. The *inch-pound system* — using the yard, quart, and pound — is an example. In this system each measurement is subdivided into smaller or larger units by using awkward numbers such as 12, 16, or 5280, etc.

There have been several metric systems used throughout the world. Each country developed metric names or units to suit its particular needs, and as such, caused unnecessary congestion and confusion. These metric systems would not serve a world that needed a universally understood measurement system.

Obviously, the nations of the world would have to get together and decide on a new system.

THE SI METRIC SYSTEM

In 1960, international discussions lead to the creation of a new system called SI, from the French name, Le Système International d'Unités. The SI system is now replacing all former systems of measurement, including former versions of the metric system. Like older metric systems SI is based on the decimal number system. Unit prefixes are related to each other by factors such as 10, 100, and 1000, and a great deal of arithmetic merely involves shifting the decimal marker. For example, to find the total length in millimetres of three parts which measure 3.7 m (metres), 46 cm (centimetres) and 15 mm (millimetres) respectively, the conversion of each part to millimetre sizes is easily carried out.

$$3.7 \times 1000 = 3700$$
$$46 \times 10 \ = \ 460$$
$$15$$
$$\overline{}$$
$$4175 \ \text{mm}$$

Standard prefixes for all metric units of measurements have been adopted. Thus the prefix "kilo", meaning one thousand, may be used for length (kilometre = one thousand metres), for mass (kilogram = one thousand grams), for volume (kilolitre = one thousand litres), and for other measurable quantities.

INDUSTRY AND METRICATION

Most large industries in Canada and the United States which enjoy world wide distribution of their products are now designing their parts and materials in metric sizes or are planning to do so in the very near future. Smaller companies, which rely on local distribution of their products, will probably continue to use the *inch-pound system* for the next few years. As their customers begin to ask for metric products, however, and as the raw materials to produce these products become available in metric sizes, these companies too will start designing to metric measurements.

DRAWING STANDARDS

Although the existing Engineering Drawing Standards B78.2 and ANSI YI4.5, produced by the Canadian Standards Association and the American National Standards Institute respectively, are in *inch-pound* units, committees are presently at work converting these Standards to SI. Tentative target dates in 1978 have been set for publication of the revised Standards.

An extensive list of standards of interest to draftsmen may be found in the Appendix and all drawings in this text conform to these standards. They are reproduced with the permission of the Canadian Standards Association, 178 Rexdale Boulevard, Rexdale, Ontario, and the American National Standards Institute, 1430 Broadway, New York, N.Y., 10018. Where quotes or illustrations taken from these Standards are used in the text, recognition as to the Standard used is shown.

In some areas of practice, such as Simplified Drafting, national standards have not yet been established. The authors have, in such cases, adopted the practices used by leading industries both in Canada and the United States.

DESIGNING IN METRIC UNITS

For engineering drawings the millimetre replaces the fractional and decimal inch units. The same basic rules which applied to drawings using inch measurements will apply to drawings using millimetre units except for two basic changes:

1. Dimensions less than unity, that is, less than one millimetre in size, will show a zero to the left of the decimal. Thus decimal two four millimetres will be shown as 0.24, not .24.
   Decimal three millimetres will be shown as 0.3, not .30.
2. Commas will not be used between groups of three numbers, as some nations now use the comma for a decimal marker. A space will be used in place of the comma. Examples:
   53 454.26 not 53,454.26
   4.175 03 not 4.175,03

Some drawings may be dual-dimensioned, that is, show both millimetre and inch equivalents, during the transition period. When such dimensioning is required, adhere to the techniques outlined in the dimensioning chapter.

The foot and inch measurements used for architectural drawings will be replaced by the metre and millimetre. Floor plans, room sizes, carpeting, etc. will be expressed in metres. Lumber sizes, such as 2 x 4's and stud spacings etc., will be given in millimetres.

Although all future designs should be in metric sizes, draftsmen will be required to make revisions to existing drawings dimensioned in inches or feet and inches. These revisions must be made in the same units of measurement as used on the original drawing. Therefore, students must be completely familiar with the *inch-pound* system of dimensioning. For this reason instructions and drawings in *inch-pound* units have been included in the Appendix.

CLARIFICATION OF DRAWING PROJECTION METHOD

The interchange of drawings with other nations using the same units of measurement has made it necessary to add the ISO symbol to drawings. This symbol identifies the method of drawing projection (first or third angle) used on the drawing. Some nations use first angle projection whereas other countries, such as Canada and the United States, use third angle projection for engineering drawings. All drawings in this text are drawn in third angle projection. They do not, therefore, show the ISO symbol.

C. JENSEN and F. MASON

CONTENTS

Page

CHAPTER ONE   **THE LANGUAGE OF INDUSTRY** 1

                    Review questions 4

CHAPTER TWO   **DEVELOPING DRAFTING SKILLS** 5

                    The parallel straight edge 5

                    Drafting tables and machines 6

                    The T square 6

                    Set squares 6

                    Drafting paper 8

                    Title strips and blocks 8

                    Fastening paper to the board 9

                    Drafting pencils 9

                    Drawing lines 10

                    The compass 11

                    Scales 12

                    Irregular curves 14

                    Templates 14

                    Dividers 14

                    Erasing shields 14

                    Brushes 14

                    Letters and figures 15

                    Lettering aids 15

                    Line work 16

                    Sketching 20

                          Review questions 21

                          Problems 22

CHAPTER THREE   **THEORY OF SHAPE DESCRIPTION** 29

                    Representing objects by views 29

                    Third angle projection 29

                    Views 31

                    Use of a miter line 33

                    Spacing the views 34

                          Review questions 34

                          Problems 35

CHAPTER FOUR   **BASIC DIMENSIONING** 42

                    Units of measurement 42

                    Working drawings 44

                    Dimensioning 44

                          Review questions 53

                    Surface symbols 54

                          Review questions 57

                          Problems 58

CHAPTER FIVE   **WORKING DRAWINGS AND CONVENTIONS** 64
    Assembly and detail drawings 64
    Bills of materials 68
    Tolerances and allowances 70
    Dimensioning of special features 72
    Conventional representation of common features 76
    Reproduction of drawings 82
        Review questions 82
        Problems 83

CHAPTER SIX   **SIMPLIFIED DRAFTING** 92
        Review questions 97
        Problems 97

CHAPTER SEVEN   **FASTENING DEVICES** 100
    Screw threads 100
    Thread classes and their applications 105
    Keys 108
        Review questions 109
        Problems 110

CHAPTER EIGHT   **SECTION VIEWS** 112
    The cutting-plane line 112
    Types of sections 114
    Placement of section views 118
    Section-lining 119
    Thin sections 119
    Large areas 120
    Sections through shafts, bolts, pins, keys, etc. 120
    Adjacent parts in section 120
    Dimensions 120
    Holes in section 121
    Ribs in section 121
    Webs and spokes in section 123
    Lugs in section 125
        Review questions 125
        Problems 125

CHAPTER NINE   **AUXILIARY VIEWS** 137
        Review questions 139
        Problems 140

CHAPTER TEN   **PICTORIAL DRAWING** 146
    Isometric projection 147
    Dimensioning isometric drawings 153
    Oblique projection 154
        Review questions 157
        Problems 158

CHAPTER ELEVEN   **DEVELOPMENT DRAWINGS AND INTERSECTIONS** 163
Straight line development 164
Parallel line development 167
Radial line development 170
Intersections 172
Review questions 174
Problems 174

CHAPTER TWELVE   **ARCHITECTURAL DRAFTING** 181
Presentation drawings 181
Working drawings 187
Lettering 187
Drawing scales 187
Drawing symbols 190
Dimensioning 195
Developing a house plan 196
Review questions 199
Problems 199
Problem 1, Summer Cottage 200
Problem 2, Bungalow No. 1 201
Problem 3, Bungalow No. 2 202
Problem 4, Bungalow No. 3 203

CHAPTER THIRTEEN   **ELECTRICAL DRAFTING** 205
Electrical requirements for the home 205
Location of outlets, lights and switches 206
Convenience outlets 207
Electrical circuits 208
Review questions 211
Problems 211
Problem 13.1   Summer Cottage No. 1 211
Problem 13.2   Summer Cottage No. 2 212
Problem 13.3   Bungalow No. 1 213
Problem 13.4   Bungalow No. 2 214
Problem 13.5   Summer Cottage No. 3 215

CHAPTER FOURTEEN   **BASIC METALLURGY AND SHOP PROCESSES** 216
Materials 216
Review questions 219
Manufacturing Processes 220
Review questions 225

CHAPTER FIFTEEN   **APPLIED GEOMETRY** 226

CHAPTER SIXTEEN   **PROBLEMS IN INTERPRETING MECHANICAL DRAWINGS** 232
Problem 16.1   Mounting block 232
Problem 16.2   Wedge block 233
Problem 16.3   Grooved slide block 233
Problem 16.4   Sliding V block 234
Problem 16.5   Dovetail bracket 234

Page

Problem 16.6   Knurled shoulder clamp 235
Problem 16.7   Tapered draw bar 235
Problem 16.8   Tapered shaft support 236
Problem 16.9   V belt pulley 236
Problem 16.10 Adjustable base plate 237
Problem 16.11 Flanged shaft support 237
Problem 16.12 Coupling 238
Problem 16.13 Adjustable shaft support 238
Problem 16.14 Locating piece 239
Problem 16.15 Base support 239
Problem 16.16 Vise body 240
Problem 16.17 Slide bracket 241
Problem 16.18 Guide block 242
Problem 16.19 V bracket 243
Problem 16.20 Step block 244
Surface identification problems 16.21 to 16.25 245
Problem 16.26 Swing bracket 248
Problem 16.27 Cradle bracket 248
Problem 16.28 Bearing guide 249
Problem 16.29 Vertical guide 249

APPENDIX   TABLE   1 ANSI and CSA publications 251
TABLE   2 ISO Metric Screw Threads 253
TABLE   3 Number and Letter-Size Drills 254
TABLE   4 Twist Drill Sizes 255
TABLE   5 Hexagon Head Bolts, Regular Series 256
TABLE   6 Hexagon Head Nuts 257
TABLE   7 Common Cap Screws 258
TABLE   8 Set Screws 259
TABLE   9 Common Washer Sizes 260
TABLE 10 Square and Flat Stock Keys 261
TABLE 11 Woodruff Keys 261
TABLE 12 Sheet Metal Gauges and Thicknesses 262
TABLE 13 Wire Gauges and Diameters 263
TABLE 14 Trigonometric Functions 264
TABLE 15 Function of Numbers 265
TABLE 16 Inch Screw Threads 266
TABLE 17 Abbreviations and Symbols 267

INDEX   269

ACKNOWLEDGMENTS

The authors wish to express their gratitude to the people responsible for supplying them with information essential to the development and success of this text. Most of these sources have been credited below the illustrations. In addition to these, we are indebted to the following organizations: the Canadian Standards Association, the American National Standards Institute, the American Society of Mechanical Engineers, the Canadian Government Specifications Board (for illustrations and text in Chapter 12), the Central Mortgage and Housing Corporation (also for illustrations and text appearing in Chapter 12), the Canadian Wood Council (for illustrations appearing in Chapter 12), and the publication *Machine Design* (for an illustration in Chapter 14).

World's Tallest Freestanding Structure, CN Tower, Toronto, Ontario, Canada   © CN Tower Limited 1973

CHAPTER ONE

THE LANGUAGE OF INDUSTRY

Since earliest times, man has used drawings to communicate ideas to his fellow man and to record those ideas so that they would not be forgotten. The earliest forms of writing, such as Egyptian hieroglyphics, were picture forms.

The word "graphic" means "dealing with the expression of ideas by lines or marks impressed on a surface". A drawing is a *graphic representation* of a real thing. Drafting, therefore, is a graphic language, because it uses *pictures* to communicate thoughts and ideas. Because these pictures are understood by men of different nations, drafting is referred to as a "universal language".

Man has developed drawing along two distinct lines, using each form for a different purpose. Artistic drawing is mainly concerned with the expression of real or imagined ideas of a cultural nature. Technical drawing, on the other hand, is concerned with the expression of technical ideas or ideas of a practical nature, and is the method used in all branches of technical industry.

Even highly developed word languages are inadequate for describing the size, shape, and relationships of physical objects. For every manufactured object there are drawings that describe its physical shape completely and accurately, communicating the draftsman's ideas to the workman. For this reason drafting is referred to as the "language of industry".

The Bettman Archive

The Drafting Office a Century Ago and Today

Addressograph-Multigraph

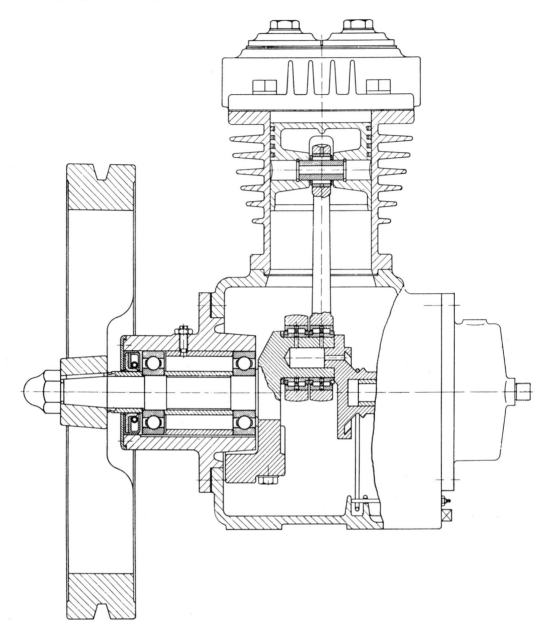

Mechanical Drafting   SKF

Throughout the long history of drafting, many symbols, terms, abbreviations, and practices have come into common use. It is essential that different draftsmen use the same practices if drafting is to serve as a reliable means of communicating technical theories and ideas. Through the Canadian Standards Association, and the American National Standards Institute representatives from government and industry engaged in mechanical engineering work have set forth recommended drafting practices in the publications *Mechanical Engineering Drawing Standards,* and the American National Standard Drawing Manual.

These standards were recently revised, and standard drawing conventions, such as threads, were modified slightly.

As there are many thousands of drawings at present being used in Canadian industries that follow the older Canadian drawing practices or the American drawing practices, it is the intent of this text also to acquaint the reader with these drawing conventions. It is recommended

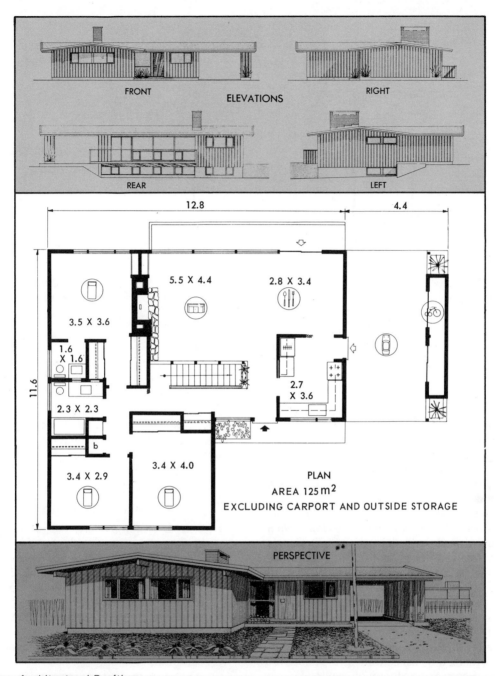

FRONT ELEVATIONS RIGHT

REAR LEFT

12.8 4.4

5.5 X 4.4 2.8 X 3.4

3.5 X 3.6

1.6
X 1.6

11.6

2.3 X 2.3

2.7
X 3.6

b

3.4 X 2.9 3.4 X 4.0

PLAN
AREA 125 m^2
EXCLUDING CARPORT AND OUTSIDE STORAGE

PERSPECTIVE

Architectural Drafting Central Mortgage and Housing Corporation

that any new drawings adhere to the most up-to-date drawing conventions. However, when a draftsman is called upon to make changes or revisions to a drawing already in existence, he must adhere to the drawing conventions that appear on the drawing being used.

Although the information given in this text is based on the CSA *Mechanical Engineering Drawing Standards B78*, and the American National Standard Drawing Manual Y-14, the problems found throughout the chapters may show any of the drawing conventions mentioned above.

Because a drawing is a set of instructions that the workman must follow, it must be clear, correct, accurate, and complete. The ability to draw does not in itself make a person a draftsman; a draftsman must have creative ability, a wide

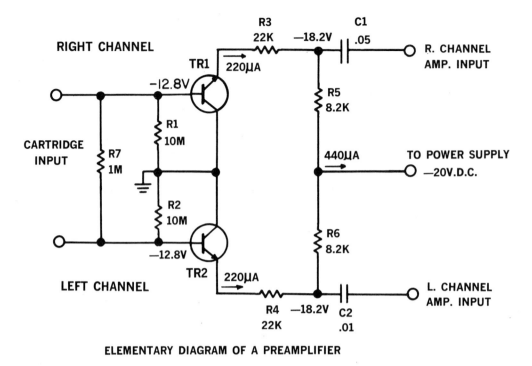

ELEMENTARY DIAGRAM OF A PREAMPLIFIER

Electrical Drafting   Canadian General Electric

range of technical knowledge, and specialized knowledge in his own field. The various specialized fields are as different as the branches of industry. Some of the main areas of drafting are mechanical, architectural, structural, and electrical drafting.

Technical drawing is the term applied to any drawings used to express technical ideas. When drawings are made with the use of instruments, they are referred to as instrumental drawings. If instruments are not used, drawings are referred to as sketches. The ability to sketch ideas and designs and to make accurate instrumental drawings is a fundamental part of this graphic language.

Only a small percentage of students taking a drafting course will make drafting a lifetime occupation. However, a thorough understanding of this precise language is necessary for anyone who intends to work in our increasingly complex and highly technical manufacturing and construction industries, and to anyone planning to become a professional engineer. Many more people are required to be able to *read* drawings than to *make* them. In everyday life a knowledge of drafting is very helpful in understanding house

plans; assembly, maintenance, and operating instructions for many manufactured products; and plans and specifications for many hobbies and spare-time activities.

Review Questions

1. Why is drafting referred to as a "universal language"?
2. What is the main difference between artistic drawing and technical drawing?
3. Why is drafting necessary to the functioning of modern industry?
4. Why are uniform drafting practices and standards important?
5. Name four requirements for a good technical drawing.
6. What are three requirements for a person to become a successful draftsman?
7. Name four main branches of drafting.
8. Name two forms in which technical drawings may be made.
9. Why should all students interested in technical careers learn the drafting language?
10. In what ways is a knowledge of drafting helpful in personal life?

CHAPTER TWO

DEVELOPING DRAFTING SKILLS

The drafting office is the starting point for all engineering work. Initial ideas and designs are often sketched freehand by the designer or engineer before final, accurate drawings are made with the use of instruments. The student should become proficient in making freehand sketches and must learn how to use drafting instruments with skill, accuracy, and speed.

THE PARALLEL STRAIGHT EDGE

The straight edge is fastened on each end to cords, which pass over pulleys. This arrangement permits movement of the straight edge up and down the board while maintaining a horizontal position of the straight edge. It is used primarily when drawing horizontal lines and for supporting set squares when drawing vertical and sloping lines.

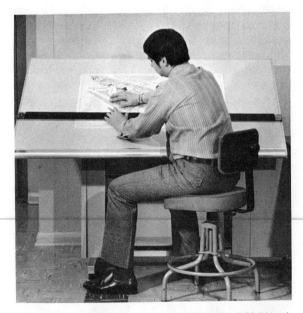

Addressograph-Multigraph

Using a Straight Edge

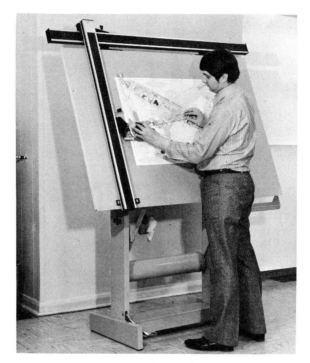

*Drafting Table
and Machine*

Addressograph-Multigraph

DRAFTING TABLES AND MACHINES

Many engineering offices are equipped with special drafting tables and drafting machines. The drafting machine takes the place of the T square or parallel straight edge, set squares, scale, and protractor. Use of the drafting machine reduces the time spent in the preparation of drawings, thus reducing cost. Left-handed drafting machines are available but are not common.

Addressograph-Multigraph

ADJUSTABLE SET SQUARE

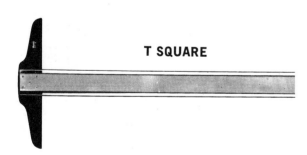

T SQUARE

THE T SQUARE

While you are using the T square, keep the head of the instrument firmly against the side of the board to ensure that the lines you draw will be parallel. The head will be on the left edge of the board if you are right-handed, and on the right if you are left-handed.

SET SQUARES

Set squares are used together with the parallel straight edge or T square when you are drawing vertical and sloping lines. The set squares most commonly used are the 60°—30° and the 45° set squares. Singly or in combination, these set squares can be used to form angles in all the multiples of 15°. For other angles, the protractor is used. *All* angles can be drawn with the *adjustable set square;* this instrument replaces the two common set squares and the protractor.

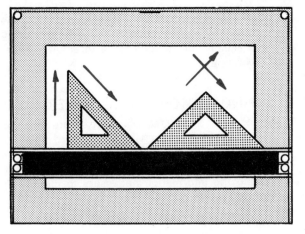
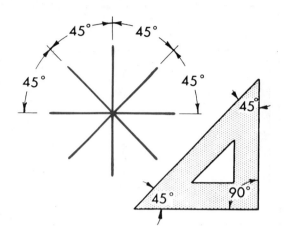

(A) THE 45° SET SQUARE

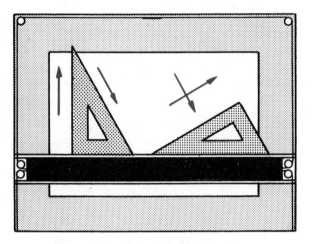

(B) THE 60° SET SQUARE

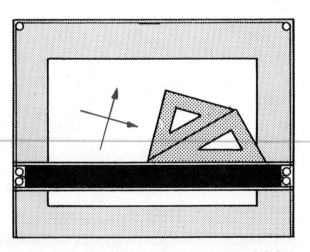

(C) THE SET SQUARES IN COMBINATION

Figure 2.1   The Set Squares

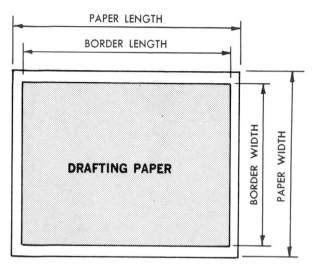

PAPER LENGTH

BORDER LENGTH

BORDER WIDTH

PAPER WIDTH

DRAFTING PAPER

METRIC SIZE DESIGNATION	PAPER SIZE IN MILLIMETRES	APPROXIMATE SIZE IN INCHES
A0	841 x 1189	33.1 x 46.8
A1	594 x 841	23.4 x 33.1
A2	420 x 594	16.5 x 23.4
A3	297 x 420	11.7 x 16.5
A4	210 x 297	8.3 x 11.7
A5	148 x 210	5.8 x 8.3

Figure 2.2   *Standard Metric (ISO) Sheet Sizes*

these tracings. In drafting classrooms, reproductions are not often necessary, so that drawings are usually made on white or buff-coloured drawing paper.

STANDARD DRAWING SHEET SIZES

Sheet sizes are based on approximate multiples of 148 x 210 mm, the size of standard notebook paper. Drawings normally have border lines on all four sides and a title strip or title block containing the information necessary to identify the drawing properly.

TITLE STRIPS AND BLOCKS

Although the needs and wishes of individual industrial firms or schools vary, information printed in the title strip or title block usually includes: Title, Drawing Number, Name of Company or School, Scale Used, Name of Draftsman, Date Drawn, Name of Checker or Supervisor. In order to save drafting time, many firms purchase their drawing paper cut to the standard sheet sizes, with the border lines and the title strip or title block of their own design already printed on the sheets.

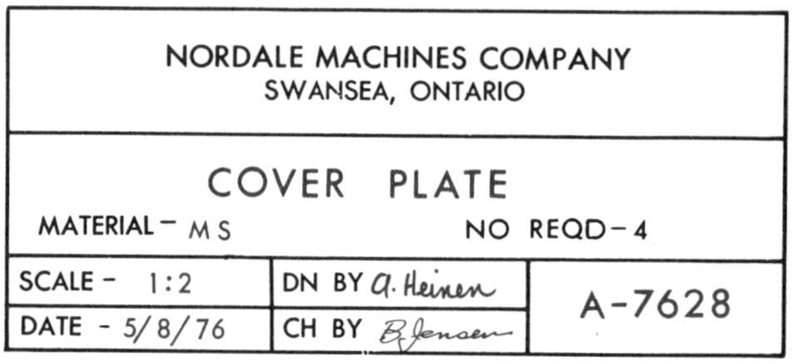

DRAFTING PAPER

In industry, several copies of each drawing are required; drawings are made, therefore, on a type of translucent paper, usually referred to as tracing paper. Reproductions in the form of blueprints or whiteprints can be made from

NORDALE MACHINES COMPANY SWANSEA, ONTARIO			
COVER PLATE			
MATERIAL – M S		NO REQD – 4	
SCALE – 1:2	DN BY *Q. Heinen*	A-7628	
DATE – 5/8/76	CH BY *B Jensen*		

Figure 2.3   *Typical Title Block*

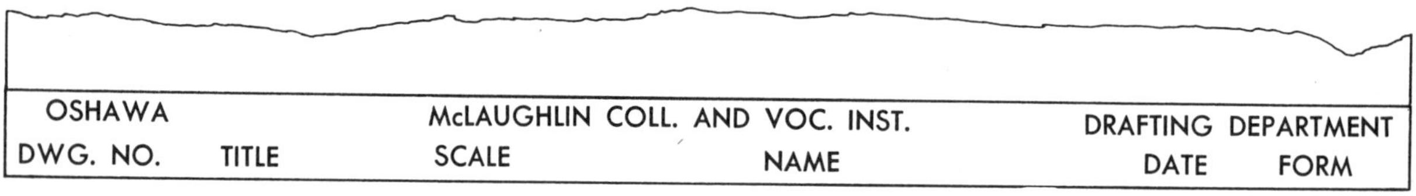

OSHAWA		McLAUGHLIN COLL. AND VOC. INST.		DRAFTING DEPARTMENT	
DWG. NO.	TITLE	SCALE	NAME	DATE	FORM

Figure 2.4   *Title Strip*

FASTENING PAPER TO THE BOARD

The draftsman in industry usually fastens the drawing paper to the board with staples or tape, and he does not remove it from the board until the drawing has been completed. In drafting classrooms, drawings are fastened to and removed from the boards so frequently that it is desirable to use fastening methods that permit easy removal of drawings without marking the board surface. Masking tape and spring clips are two methods that meet this requirement.

When you are fastening paper to the board, line up the bottom or top edge of the paper with the top horizontal edge of the T square, parallel straight edge, or horizontal scale of the drafting machine. When you are refastening a partially completed drawing, use lines rather than the edge of the paper for alignment.

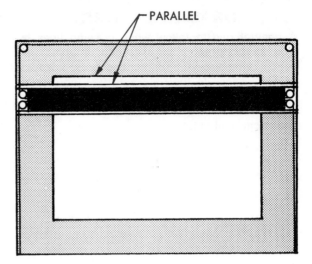

Figure 2.5   Positioning the Paper on the Board

GRADES OF LEAD		
SOFT	**MEDIUM**	**HARD**
7B, 6B, . . 2B, B	HB, F	H, 2H . . 5H, 6H

Pencil Point Shapes

CONICAL   WEDGE   BEVEL

DRAFTING PENCILS

Special graphic lead is used for drafting pencils, and the pencils are graded by number and letter according to their lead hardness. When sharpening wood-bonded pencils, first shape the wood back with a knife or a mechanical sharpener, then point the lead to the shape you prefer—conical, wedge, or bevel—by sanding it on a sanding block or, file or by using a mechanical pointer. Many draftsmen use an ejector type, semi-automatic pencil, which holds a long drawing lead. The lead is ejected to the desired length of projection from the clamping chuck, then pointed in the same manner as the wood-bonded pencil.

Addressograph-Multigraph

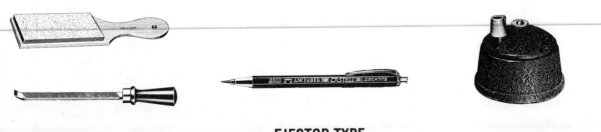

SANDING BLOCK AND FILE   **EJECTOR-TYPE, SEMI-AUTOMATIC PENCIL**   **MECHANICAL POINTER**

DRAWING LINES

A general rule to follow when drawing lines is this: always draw in the direction in which the pencil is leaning. A right-handed person would lean the pencil to the right and draw horizontal lines from left to right. The left-handed person would reverse this procedure and draw horizontal lines from right to left.

Drawing Horizontal Lines

When drawing vertical lines, lean the pencil away from yourself, towards the top of the drafting board, and draw lines from bottom to top.

Drawing Vertical Lines

Lines sloping from the bottom to the top right are drawn from bottom to top; lines sloping from the bottom to the top left are drawn from top to bottom. This procedure for sloping lines would be reversed for a left-handed person.

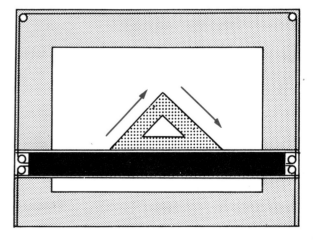

Drawing Sloping Lines

THE COMPASS

This instrument is used to draw circles and arcs. Many styles and sizes are available. The spring-bow compass with center-screw attachment is in widespread use because of its rigidity in maintaining the setting. For large circles and arcs draftsmen use either the beam compass or the bow compass with an extension leg. In many designs the lower part of one leg is detachable, and two attachments are provided, one for lead and one for an inking pen.

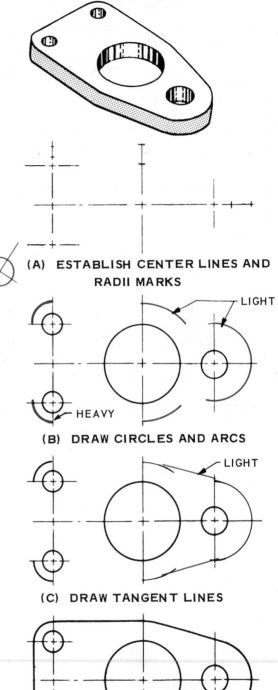

(A) ESTABLISH CENTER LINES AND RADII MARKS

(B) DRAW CIRCLES AND ARCS

(C) DRAW TANGENT LINES

(D) COMPLETE OBJECT LINES

Sequence of Steps for Drawing a View Having Circles and Arcs

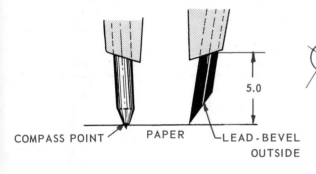

5.0

COMPASS POINT   PAPER   LEAD-BEVEL OUTSIDE

Sharpening and Setting the Compass Lead

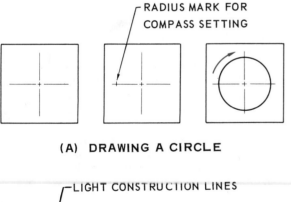

RADIUS MARK FOR COMPASS SETTING

(A) DRAWING A CIRCLE

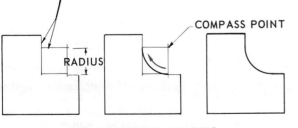

LIGHT CONSTRUCTION LINES

COMPASS POINT

RADIUS

(B) DRAWING AN ARC

Drawing Circles and Arcs

SCALES

Shown are the common scales used by draftsmen to make measurements on their drawings. Scales are used only for measuring and are not to be used for drawing lines. It is important that draftsmen draw accurately to scale. The scale used must be indicated in the title block or strip.

When objects are drawn at their actual size, the drawing is called *full scale* or scale 1:1. Many objects, however, such as buildings, ships, or airplanes, are too large to be drawn full scale, so they must be drawn to a *reduced scale*. An example would be the drawing of a house to a scale of 1:50 (metric) or, in the *inch-pound* scale, 1:48 (¼″ = 1 foot).

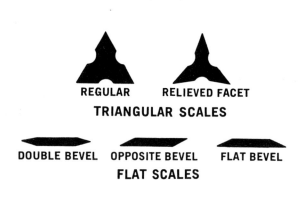

REGULAR   RELIEVED FACET

TRIANGULAR SCALES

DOUBLE BEVEL   OPPOSITE BEVEL   FLAT BEVEL

FLAT SCALES

End View Shapes of Scales

Frequently, objects such as small watch parts are drawn larger than their actual size so that their shape can be seen clearly. Such a drawing has been drawn to an *enlarged scale*. The minute hand of a wrist watch, for example, could be drawn to scale 4:1.

Many mechanical parts are drawn to half scale, 1:2, and fifth scale, 1:5. Notice that the scale of the drawing is expressed as an equation. The left side of the equation represents a unit of the size drawn, and the right side a unit of the actual object. Thus one unit of measurement on the drawing = 5 units of measurement on the actual object.

Scales are made with a variety of combined scales marked on their surfaces. This combination of scales spares the draftsman the necessity of calculating the sizes to be drawn when he is working to a scale other than full size.

SI (METRIC) SCALES

The linear unit of measurement for mechanical drawings is the millimetre. Scale multipliers and divisors of 2 and 5 are recommended, giving the scales shown in the accompanying table. The numbers shown indicate the difference in size between the drawing and the actual part. For example, the ratio 10:1 shown on the drawing means that the drawing is ten times the actual size of the part, whereas a ratio of 1:5 on the drawing means the object is five times as large as it is shown on the drawing.

The units of measurement for architectural drawings are the metre and millimetre. The same scale multipliers and divisors used for mechanical drawings are also used for architectural drawings.

ENLARGED	SIZE AS	REDUCED
1000:1	1:1	
500:1		1:2
200:1		1:5
100:1		1:10
50:1		1:20
20:1		1:50
10:1		1:100
5:1		1:200
2:1		1:500
		1:1000

Recommended Metric Scales

THE INCH SCALES

There are three types of scales which show various values that are equal to one inch. They are the decimal inch scale, the fractional inch scale, and the scale which has divisions of 10, 20, 30, 40, 50, 60 and 80 parts to the inch. This last scale is known as the civil engineer's scale.

On fractional inch scales, multipliers or divisors of 2, 4, 8 and 16 are used, offering such scales as full size, half size, quarter size, etc.

THE FOOT SCALES

These scales are used mostly in architectural work. They differ from the inch scales in that each major division represents a foot, not an inch, and in the fact that the end units are subdivided into inches or parts of an inch. The more common scales are the ⅛ inch = 1 foot, ¼ inch = 1 foot, 1 inch = 1 foot and 3 inches = 1 foot.

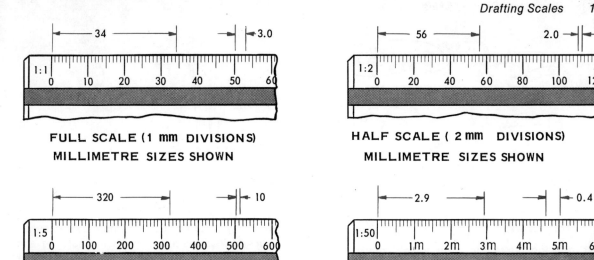

FULL SCALE (1 mm DIVISIONS)
MILLIMETRE SIZES SHOWN

HALF SCALE (2 mm DIVISIONS)
MILLIMETRE SIZES SHOWN

FIFTH SCALE (10 mm DIVISIONS)
MILLIMETRE SIZES SHOWN

FIFTIETH SCALE (100 mm DIVISIONS)
METRE SIZES SHOWN

METRIC SCALES

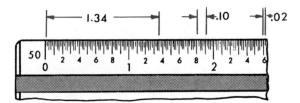

DECIMAL INCH SCALE - FULL SCALE

DECIMAL INCH SCALE - HALF SCALE

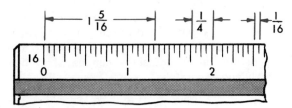

FRACTIONAL INCH SCALE - FULL SCALE

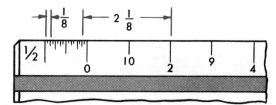

FRACTIONAL INCH SCALE - HALF SCALE

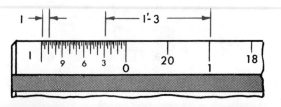

1 INCH = 1 FOOT SCALE - 1/12 SCALE

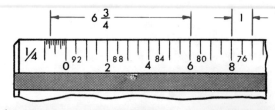

1/4 INCH = 1 FOOT SCALE - 1/48 SCALE

INCH AND FOOT SCALES

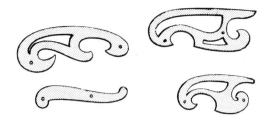

Instruments and accessories illustrated on this page, courtesy Addressograph-Multigraph

IRREGULAR CURVES

For drawing curved lines in which, unlike circular arcs, the radius of curvature is not constant, an instrument known as an irregular curve or French curve is used. The patterns for these curves are based on various combinations of ellipses, spirals, and other mathematical curves. The curves are available in a variety of shapes and sizes. Generally, the draftsman plots a series of points of intersection along the desired path, then uses the French curve to join these points so that a smooth-flowing curve results.

DIVIDERS

Used for laying out or transferring measurements, dividers have a steel pin insert in each leg and come in a variety of sizes and designs, similar to the compass. The compass can be used as a divider by replacing the lead point with a steel pin.

ERASING SHIELDS

These thin pieces of metal have a variety of openings to permit the erasure of fine detail line or note work without disturbing nearby work that is to be left on the drawing. Through the use of this device, erasures can be performed quickly and accurately.

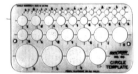

TEMPLATES

To save time, many draftsmen now use templates for drawing small circles and arcs. Templates are also available for drawing standard square, hexagonal, triangular, and elliptical shapes and standard electrical and architectural symbols.

BRUSHES

A light brush is used to keep the drawing area clean. By using a brush to remove eraser particles and any accumulated dirt, the draftsman avoids smudging the drawing.

4.0 TO 6.0 LETTERING USED ON DRAWING TITLES, SUB-TITLES AND DRAWING NUMBERS

3.0 FOR BILLS OF MATERIAL, DIMENSIONS AND GENERAL NOTES

4.0 FOR HEADINGS AND PROMINENT NOTES

Figure 2.7   Vertical and Sloped Lettering Used on Drawings

LETTERS AND FIGURES

It is most important that the lettering used on working drawings can be read and executed easily and quickly. For this reason, single-stroke, commercial Gothic upper case letters, either vertical or inclined, are now used almost exclusively on technical drawings. Figure 2.7 shows the lettering standards for mechanical drafting.

LETTERING AIDS

Lettering sets or guides are used when it is desirable to have more uniform and accurate letters and numerals than can be obtained by the freehand method. Lettering sets contain a number of guide templates that give a variety of letter shapes and sizes, as well as different slope angles.

Instant lettering is a new method of dry transfer lettering that offers a wide variety of lettering at good quality and speed.

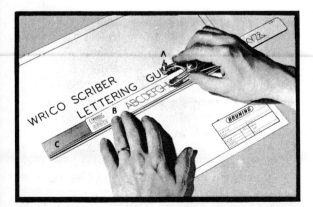

Lettering Aids   Addressograph-Multigraph

Letraset

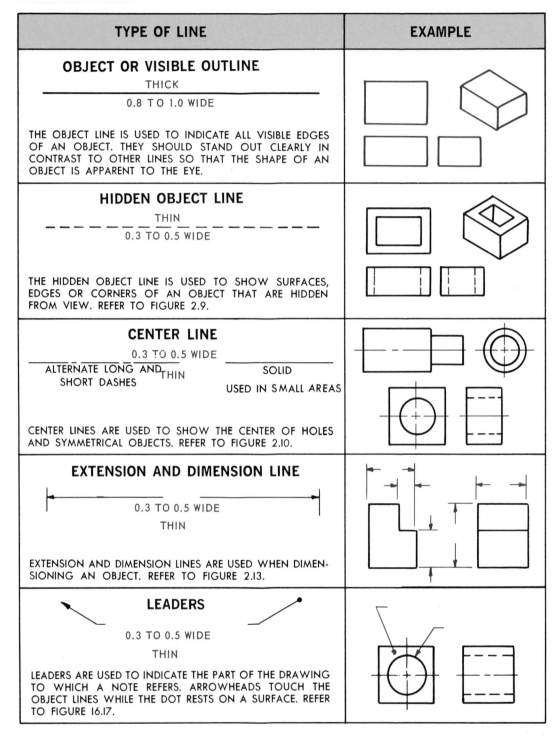

TYPE OF LINE	EXAMPLE
OBJECT OR VISIBLE OUTLINE THICK 0.8 TO 1.0 WIDE THE OBJECT LINE IS USED TO INDICATE ALL VISIBLE EDGES OF AN OBJECT. THEY SHOULD STAND OUT CLEARLY IN CONTRAST TO OTHER LINES SO THAT THE SHAPE OF AN OBJECT IS APPARENT TO THE EYE.	
HIDDEN OBJECT LINE THIN 0.3 TO 0.5 WIDE THE HIDDEN OBJECT LINE IS USED TO SHOW SURFACES, EDGES OR CORNERS OF AN OBJECT THAT ARE HIDDEN FROM VIEW. REFER TO FIGURE 2.9.	
CENTER LINE 0.3 TO 0.5 WIDE ALTERNATE LONG AND SHORT DASHES THIN SOLID USED IN SMALL AREAS CENTER LINES ARE USED TO SHOW THE CENTER OF HOLES AND SYMMETRICAL OBJECTS. REFER TO FIGURE 2.10.	
EXTENSION AND DIMENSION LINE 0.3 TO 0.5 WIDE THIN EXTENSION AND DIMENSION LINES ARE USED WHEN DIMENSIONING AN OBJECT. REFER TO FIGURE 2.13.	
LEADERS 0.3 TO 0.5 WIDE THIN LEADERS ARE USED TO INDICATE THE PART OF THE DRAWING TO WHICH A NOTE REFERS. ARROWHEADS TOUCH THE OBJECT LINES WHILE THE DOT RESTS ON A SURFACE. REFER TO FIGURE 16.17.	

Figure 2.8   Line Symbols

LINE WORK

The various lines used in drawing form the "alphabet" of the drafting language; like letters of the alphabet, they differ in appearance. The distinctive features of all lines that form a permanent part of the drawing are the differences in thickness and construction. Lines must be clearly visible and stand out in sharp contrast to each other. This line contrast is necessary for a clear and easily understood drawing.

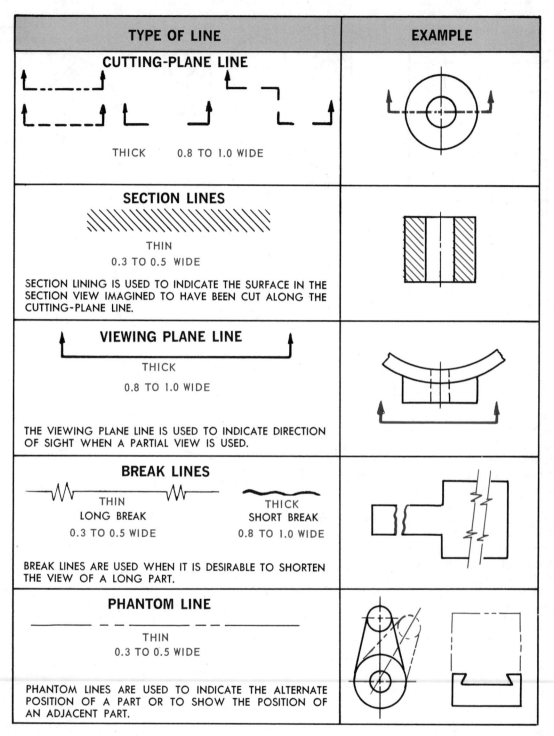

TYPE OF LINE	EXAMPLE

Figure 2.8 (Cont'd) Line Symbols

LINE WIDTHS

Two widths of lines, thick and thin, are recommended for use on drawings. The actual width of each line is governed by the size and style of the drawing, and the smallest size to which it is to be reduced. Spacing between parallel lines should be such that there is no fill-in when reproduced by photographic methods. Spacing of no less than 2.0 mm normally meets reproduction requirements.

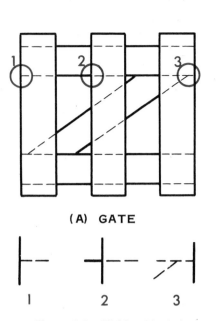

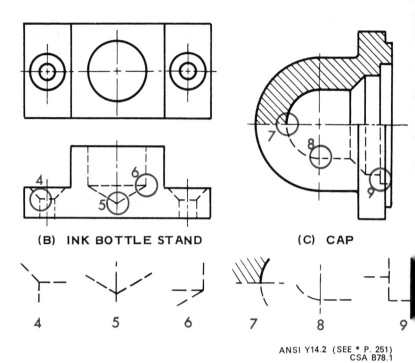

(A) GATE   **(B) INK BOTTLE STAND**   **(C) CAP**

| 1 | 2 | 3 | 4 | 5 | 6 | 7 | 8 | 9 |

Figure 2.9   Hidden Lines

ANSI Y14.2 (SEE * P. 251)
CSA B78.1

HIDDEN LINES

Hidden lines consist of short, evenly-spaced dashes, and are used to show the hidden features of an object. They should be omitted when not required to preserve the clarity of the drawing. The length of dashes may vary slightly in relation to the size of the drawing.

Lines depicting hidden features and phantom details should always begin and end with a dash in contact with the line at which they start and end, except when such a dash would form a continuation of a visible detail line. Dashes should join at corners. Arcs should start with dashes at the tangent points.

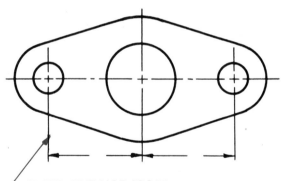

CENTER LINE NOT BROKEN WHEN EXTENDED BEYOND OBJECT

CENTER LINES

Center lines are used to indicate center points, axes of cylindrical parts, and axes of symmetry. Solid center lines are often used as a simplified drafting practice; however, the interrupted line is preferred. Center lines should project for a short distance beyond the outline of the part or

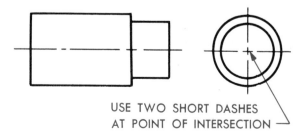

USE TWO SHORT DASHES AT POINT OF INTERSECTION

Figure 2.10   Center Line Technique   CSA B78.1

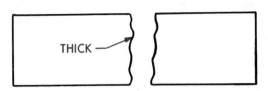

DRAWN FREEHAND OR WITH INSTRUMENTS

(A) SHORT BREAKS - ALL SHAPES

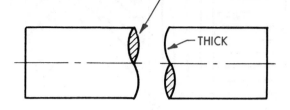

THICK

(C) SOLID CYLINDERS

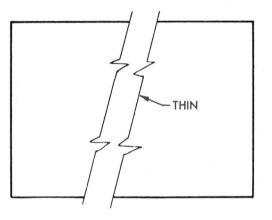

THIN

(B) LONG BREAKS - ALL SHAPES

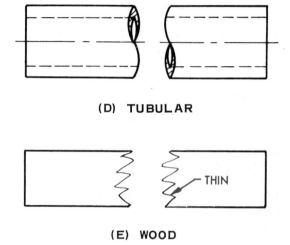

(D) TUBULAR

THIN

(E) WOOD

Figure 2.11   Conventional Break Lines

CSA B78.1

feature to which they refer. They may be extended to show relationship of symmetrical features, or for use as extension lines for dimensioning purposes, but in this case the extended portion shall not be broken.

In end views of circular features, the point of intersection of two center lines should be shown by two intersecting short dashes.

BREAK LINES

Break lines as shown in figure 2-11 are used to shorten the view of long uniform sections or when only a partial view is required. Such lines are used on both detail and assembly drawings. The thin line with freehand zig-zags is recommended for long breaks, the thick freehand line for short breaks, and the jagged line for wood parts.

The special breaks shown for cylindrical and tubular parts are useful when an end view is not shown; otherwise, the thick break line is adequate.

CONSTRUCTION AND GUIDE LINES

The draftsman first draws very light *construction lines,* setting out the main shape of the object in various views. Since these first lines are very light, they can be erased easily should changes or corrections be necessary. When the draftsman is satisfied that his layout is accurate, the construction lines are then changed to their proper type, according to the "alphabet" of lines. *Guide lines,* used to ensure uniform lettering, are also drawn very lightly.

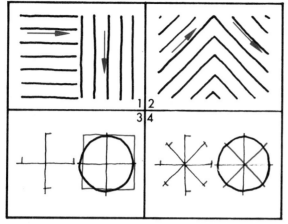

Sketching Lines and Circles

SKETCHING

Freehand sketching is a necessary part of drafting, because the draftsman in industry frequently sketches his ideas and designs prior to making instrumental drawings. He may also use sketches to explain thoughts and ideas to other people in discussions of mechanical parts and mechanisms.

Sketching, therefore, is an important method of communication. Practice in sketching helps the student to develop a good sense of proportion and accuracy of observation. It can be used to advantage when you are learning the fundamentals of drafting practice and procedures.

A fairly soft (HB, F, or H) pencil should be used for sketching. Plain paper can be used for preliminary practice. Many types of graph or ordinate paper are available and can be used to advantage when close accuracy to scale or proportion is desirable. The directions in which horizontal, vertical, and oblique lines are sketched are illustrated.

Since the shapes of objects are made up of flat and curved surfaces, the lines forming views of objects will be both straight and curved. Do not attempt to draw long lines with one continuous stroke. First plot points along the desired line path, then connect these points with a series of light strokes.

When sketching a view (or views), first lightly sketch the overall size as a rectangular or square shape, estimating its proportions carefully. Then add lines for the details of the shape, and thicken all lines forming a part of the view.

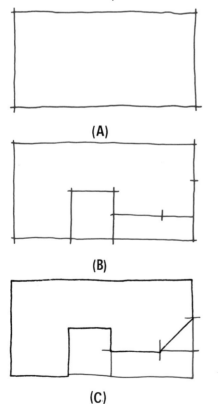

Sketching a Figure Having Straight Lines

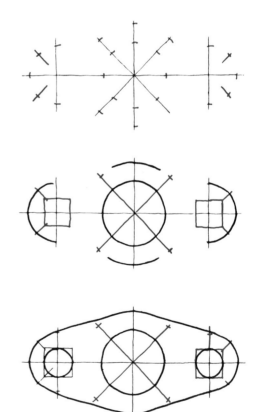

Sketching a Figure Having Circles and Arcs

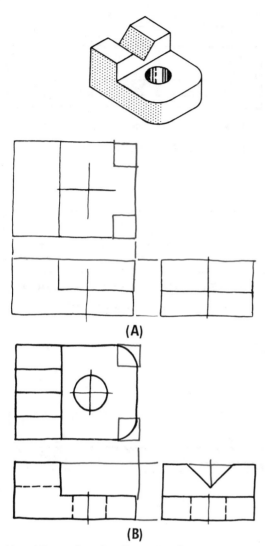

(A)

(B)

Usual Procedure for Sketching Three Views

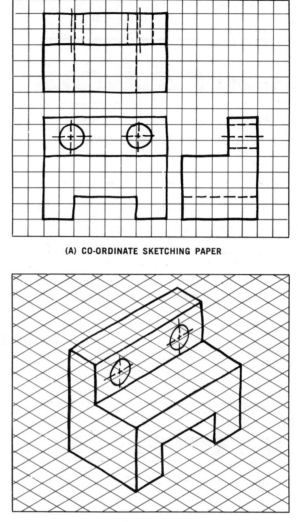

(A) CO-ORDINATE SKETCHING PAPER

(B) ISOMETRIC SKETCHING PAPER

Sketching Paper

References

CSA B78.1
ANSI Y14.2
Addressograph-Multigraph of Canada Ltd. (Bruning Division) for photographs of drawing instruments.

Review Questions

1. What instrument replaces the two common set squares and the protractor?
2. What regular instruments are replaced by a drafting machine?
3. Name two common types of reproduction that are made from tracings.
4. Give the dimensions for standard drawing sheet sizes A1 to A4 inclusive.
5. What is a basic rule of technique in drawing lines?
6. Explain: Scale 1:2. Is this an enlarged or reduced scale?
7. Give the two most important requirements for lettering.
8. What style of lettering is considered "standard" for mechanical drawing?
9. What is meant by "line contrast"?
10. What is the recommended technique for sketching long, continuous lines?

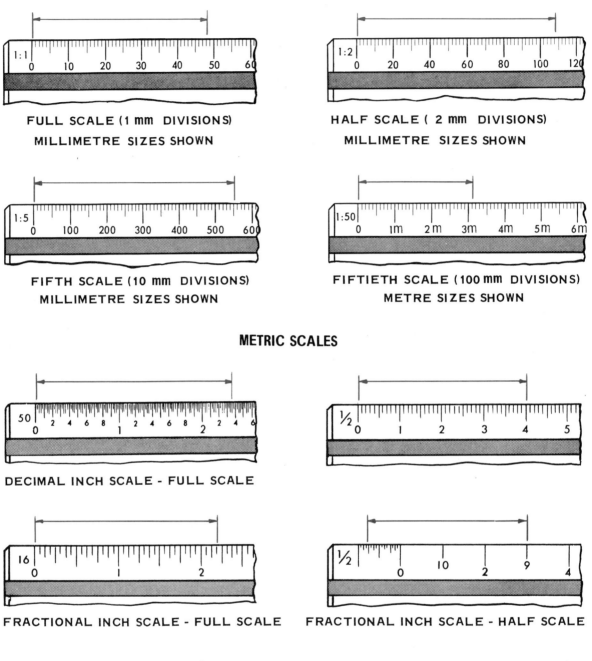

FULL SCALE (1 mm DIVISIONS)
MILLIMETRE SIZES SHOWN

HALF SCALE (2 mm DIVISIONS)
MILLIMETRE SIZES SHOWN

FIFTH SCALE (10 mm DIVISIONS)
MILLIMETRE SIZES SHOWN

FIFTIETH SCALE (100 mm DIVISIONS)
METRE SIZES SHOWN

METRIC SCALES

DECIMAL INCH SCALE - FULL SCALE

FRACTIONAL INCH SCALE - FULL SCALE

FRACTIONAL INCH SCALE - HALF SCALE

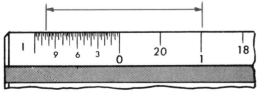

1 INCH = 1 FOOT SCALE - 1/ 12 SCALE

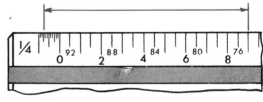

1/ 4 INCH= 1 FOOT SCALE - 1/ 48 SCALE

INCH AND FOOT SCALES

Figure 2.12   Test in Reading Drafting Scales

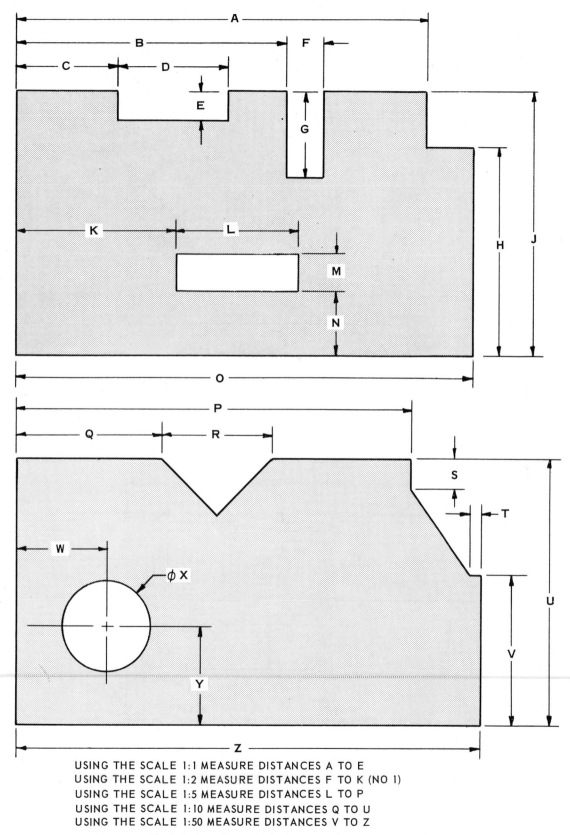

USING THE SCALE 1:1 MEASURE DISTANCES A TO E
USING THE SCALE 1:2 MEASURE DISTANCES F TO K (NO 1)
USING THE SCALE 1:5 MEASURE DISTANCES L TO P
USING THE SCALE 1:10 MEASURE DISTANCES Q TO U
USING THE SCALE 1:50 MEASURE DISTANCES V TO Z

Figure 2.13   Scale Measurement Test

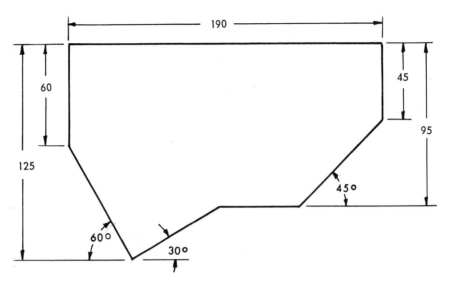

Figure 2.14   Template #1

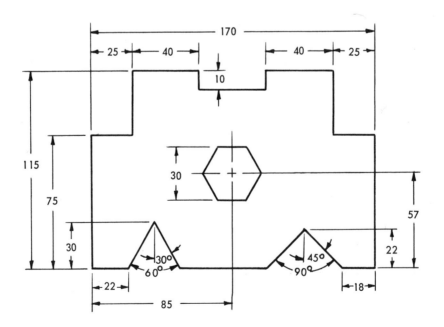

Figure 2.15   Template #2

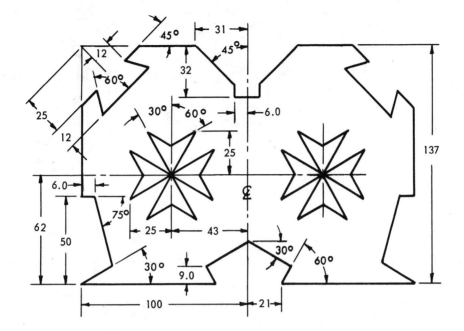

Figure 2.16   Template #3

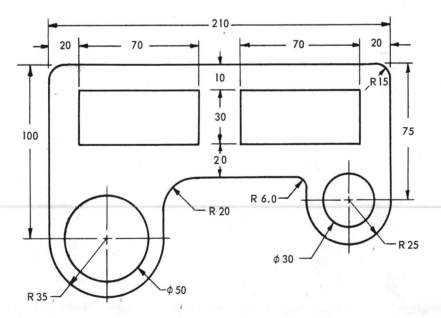

Figure 2.17   Template #4

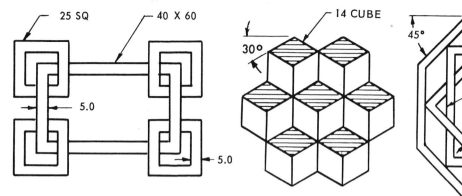

A

B

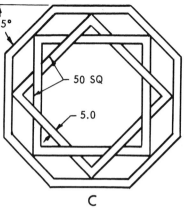

C

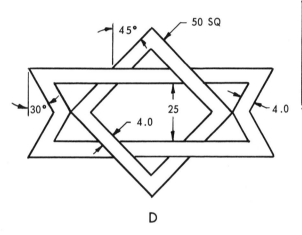

D

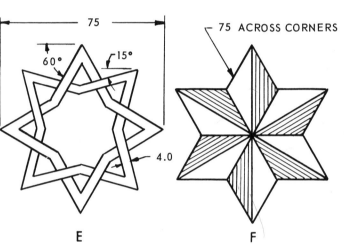

E

F

Figure 2.18   Inlay Designs

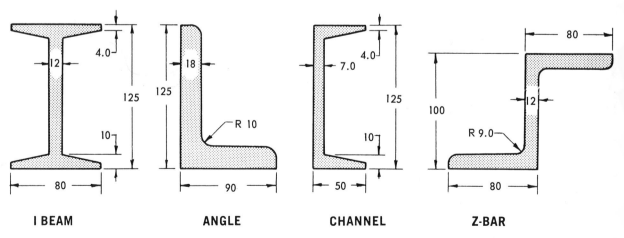

I BEAM   **ANGLE**   **CHANNEL**   **Z-BAR**

Figure 2.19   Structural Steel Shapes

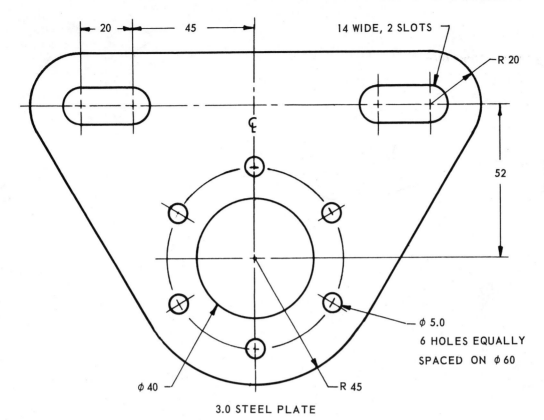

20   45   14 WIDE, 2 SLOTS

R 20

52

φ 5.0

6 HOLES EQUALLY
SPACED ON φ 60

φ 40   R 45

3.0 STEEL PLATE

Figure 2.20   Shaft Support (.12 Steel Plate)

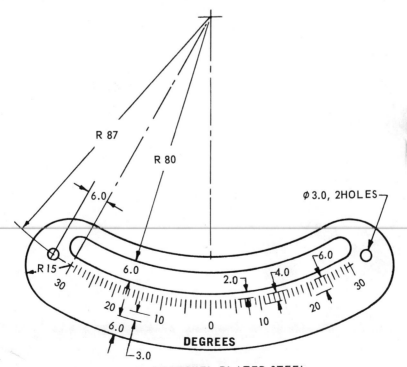

R 87   R 80

6.0   φ 3.0, 2HOLES

R 15   6.0   6.0

30   6.0   2.0   4.0   30

20   10   0   10   20

6.0   DEGREES

3.0

1.5 NICKEL PLATED STEEL

Figure 2.21   Dial Indicator (.06 Nickel Plated Steel)

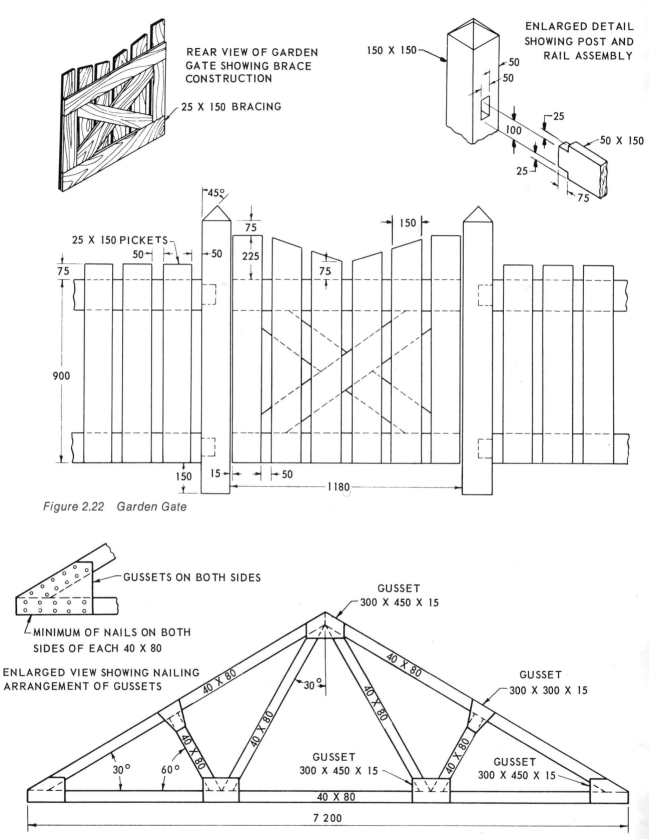

REAR VIEW OF GARDEN
GATE SHOWING BRACE
CONSTRUCTION

25 X 150 BRACING

ENLARGED DETAIL
SHOWING POST AND
RAIL ASSEMBLY

150 X 150

50
50
100
25
25
75
50 X 150

45°

25 X 150 PICKETS
50
50
75
75
225
75
150
900
150
15
50
1180

Figure 2.22   Garden Gate

GUSSETS ON BOTH SIDES

MINIMUM OF NAILS ON BOTH
SIDES OF EACH 40 X 80

ENLARGED VIEW SHOWING NAILING
ARRANGEMENT OF GUSSETS

GUSSET
300 X 450 X 15

40 X 80

GUSSET
300 X 300 X 15

30°

40 X 80

40 X 80

40 X 80

40 X 80

40 X 80

30°   60°

GUSSET
300 X 450 X 15

GUSSET
300 X 450 X 15

40 X 80

7 200

Figure 2.23   Roof Truss

CHAPTER THREE

THEORY
OF
SHAPE
DESCRIPTION

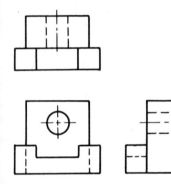

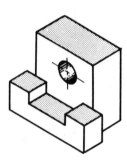

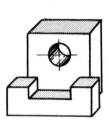

ISOMETRIC   **OBLIQUE**   **PERSPECTIVE**

ORTHOGRAPHIC PROJECTION   **PICTORIAL DRAWINGS**

Figure 3.1   Types of Projections Used in Drafting

Pictorial drawings are similar to photographs in that they show objects as they would appear to the eye of the observer. Such drawings, however, are not satisfactory for technical designs; the drawings used in industry must show clearly the exact shape of objects, and this cannot usually be accomplished in just one pictorial view, in which many details of the object may be hidden.

REPRESENTING OBJECTS BY VIEWS

Objects must be represented on flat paper in such a manner that the exact shape can be understood easily. This representation is done by drawing a number of separate views of the object as seen from different positions, then arranging those views in a systematic manner, projected one from the other. This type of draw-

ing is called *orthographic projection.* The word "orthographic" is derived from two Greek words: *orthos,* meaning straight, correct, at right angles to; and *graphikos,* to write or describe by drawing lines.

THIRD ANGLE PROJECTION

The principles of orthographic projection can be applied in four different "angles" or systems: 1st, 2nd, 3rd, and 4th angle projection. 3rd angle orthographic projection is used in North America and in many European countries; 1st angle is used primarily in the British Isles. The rule of 3rd angle projection is this: Each view is a picture of the surface nearest to it in an adjacent view.

Usually three views are sufficient to explain the shape of the object being drawn. The commonest views are Front, Top, and Right Side.

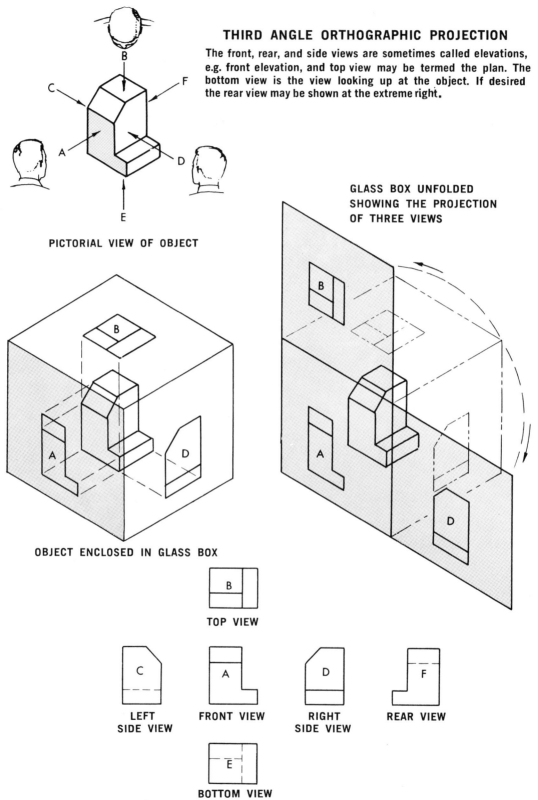

THIRD ANGLE ORTHOGRAPHIC PROJECTION

The front, rear, and side views are sometimes called elevations, e.g. front elevation, and top view may be termed the plan. The bottom view is the view looking up at the object. If desired the rear view may be shown at the extreme right.

PICTORIAL VIEW OF OBJECT

GLASS BOX UNFOLDED SHOWING THE PROJECTION OF THREE VIEWS

OBJECT ENCLOSED IN GLASS BOX

TOP VIEW

LEFT SIDE VIEW   FRONT VIEW   RIGHT SIDE VIEW   REAR VIEW

BOTTOM VIEW

ORTHOGRAPHIC DRAWING SHOWING THE SIX PRINCIPAL VIEWS

Figure 3.2   Third Angle Orthographic Projection

CSA B78.1

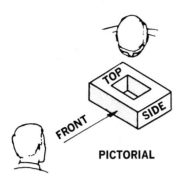

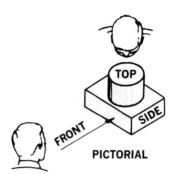

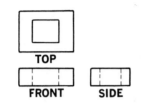

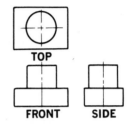

Figure 3.3   Graphical Representation of Objects

ANSI Y14.3
CSA B78.1

VIEWS
SELECTION OF VIEWS

Views should be chosen that will best describe the object to be shown. Only the minimum number of views that will completely portray the size and shape of the part should be used. They should also be chosen to avoid hidden feature lines whenever possible.

ONE-VIEW DRAWINGS

In one-view drawings, the third dimension, such as thickness, may be expressed by a note or by descriptive words or abbreviations, such as "diameter", or "hexagon across flats". Square sections may be indicated by light crossed diagonal lines. This applies whether the face is parallel or inclined to the drawing plane.

THIS END VIEW
AVOIDED

THIS END VIEW
PREFERRED

Figure 3.4   Avoidance of Hidden Line Features

ANSI Y14.3
CSA B78.1

NUMBER OF VIEWS

Except for complex objects of irregular shape, it is seldom necessary to draw more than three views. For representing simple parts, one- or two-view drawings will often be adequate.

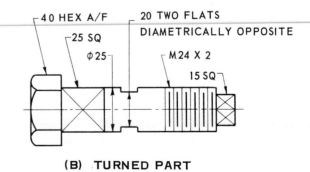

(A) FLAT PART

(B) TURNED PART

Two-View Drawings   CSA B78.1

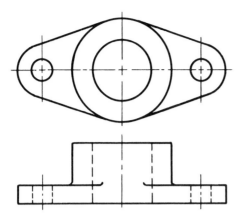 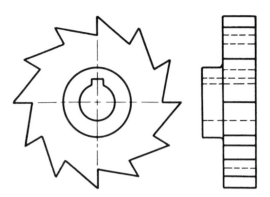

(A) SIDE VIEW NOT REQUIRED   **(B) TOP VIEW NOT REQUIRED**

One-View Drawings

TWO-VIEW DRAWINGS

Frequently the draftsman will decide that only two views are necessary to explain fully the shape of an object. For this reason, some drawings consist of top and front views only, or front and right side views only. Two views are usually sufficient to explain fully the shape of cylindrical objects; if three views were used, two of them would be identical, or almost identical, depending on the detail structure of the part.

THREE-VIEW DRAWINGS

The need for three-view drawings, to fully explain the shape of an object, is shown in the drawing below. Each of the three views, top, front and side, clearly shows features that are not seen in the other views.

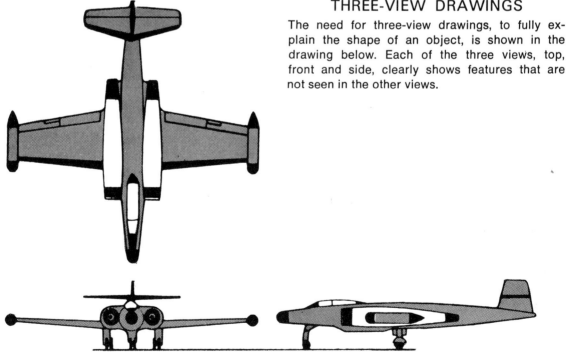

Three-View Drawing

USE OF A MITER LINE

The use of a miter line provides a convenient method of constructing the third view once two views are established.

USING A MITER LINE TO CONSTRUCT THE RIGHT SIDE VIEW

1. Given the top and front views, project lines to the right of the top view.
2. Establish how far from the front view the side view is to be drawn. (Distance "D")
3. Construct the miter line at 45° to the horizon.
4. Where the horizontal projection lines of the top view intersect the miter line, drop vertical projection lines.

5. Project horizontal lines to the right of the front view and complete the side view.

USING A MITER LINE TO CONSTRUCT THE TOP VIEW

1. Given the front and side views, project vertical lines up from the side view.
2. Establish how far away from the front view the top view is to be drawn. (Distance "D").
3. Construct the miter line at 45° to the horizon.
4. Where the vertical projection lines of the side view intersect the miter lines, project horizontal projection lines to the left.
5. Project vertical lines up from the front view and complete the top view.

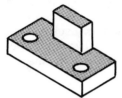

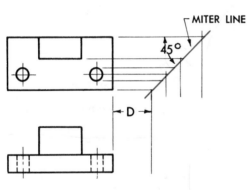

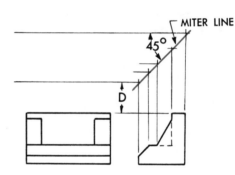

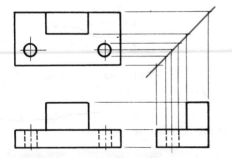

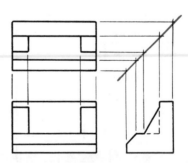

ESTABLISHING WIDTH LINES ON SIDE VIEW

ESTABLISHING WIDTH LINES ON TOP VIEW

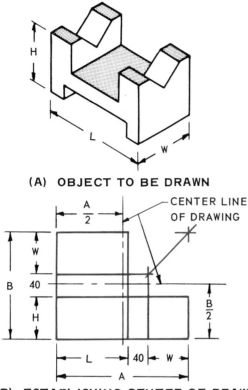

(A) OBJECT TO BE DRAWN

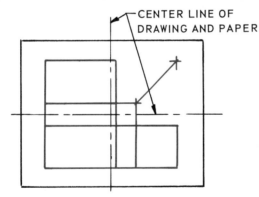

(B) ESTABLISHING CENTER OF DRAWING

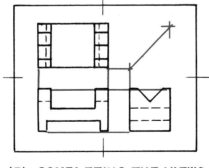

(C) ROUGHING IN DRAWING ON PAPER

(D) COMPLETING THE VIEWS

Figure 3.5 Balancing the Drawing on the Paper

SPACING THE VIEWS

It is important for clarity and good appearance that the views be well balanced on the drawing paper, whether the drawing shows one view, two views, three views, or more. The draftsman must anticipate the space required for the number of views to be drawn. He must then block them out on the drawing sheet to leave a margin that is reasonably equal all around the drawing.

Once the size of paper, scale, and number of views are established, the balancing of the three views is relatively simple. A popular method of doing so is shown. In this example, a distance of 40 mm is left between views. Remember that the spacing suitable between parallel dimension lines on most drawings is 10 mm. Between the outline of the object and the nearest dimension line the space is usually about 10 mm. For the beginner draftsman, between 30 and 40 mm is recommended as the distance between views.

References

CSA B78.1
ANSI Y14.3

Review Questions

1. What is meant by orthographic projection?

2. Name the different angles or systems of orthographic projection.

3. What angle of projection is used in North America?

4. What is the rule for this angle of projection?

5. Name the three most common views for an orthographic projection drawing.

6. Which view is seldom omitted?

7. What factor determines the choice and number of views to be drawn?

8. When only one view is drawn, how may the third dimension be expressed?

9. How many views are usually necessary for cylindrically shaped objects?

10. What procedure should be followed to balance the views on a drawing?

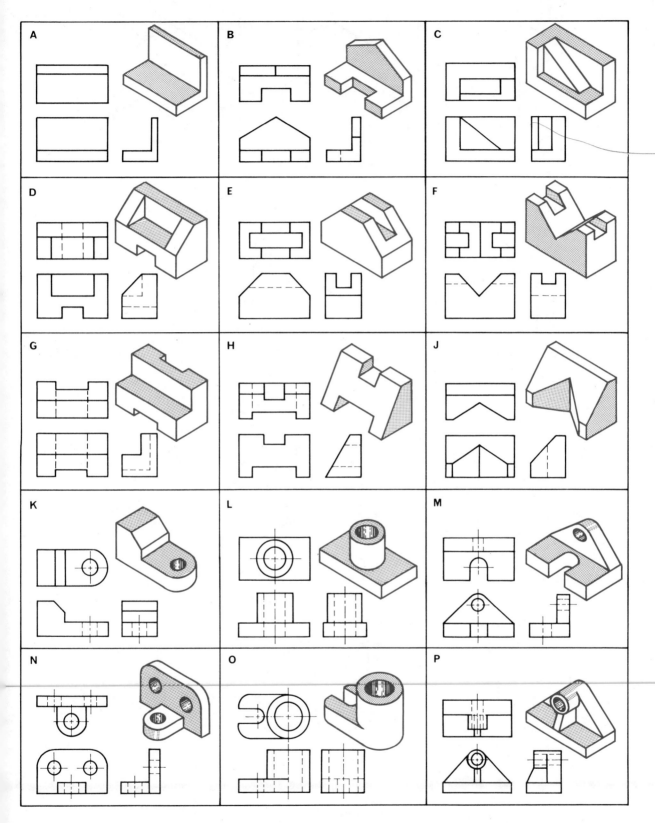

Figure 3.6   Illustrations of Orthographic Projection

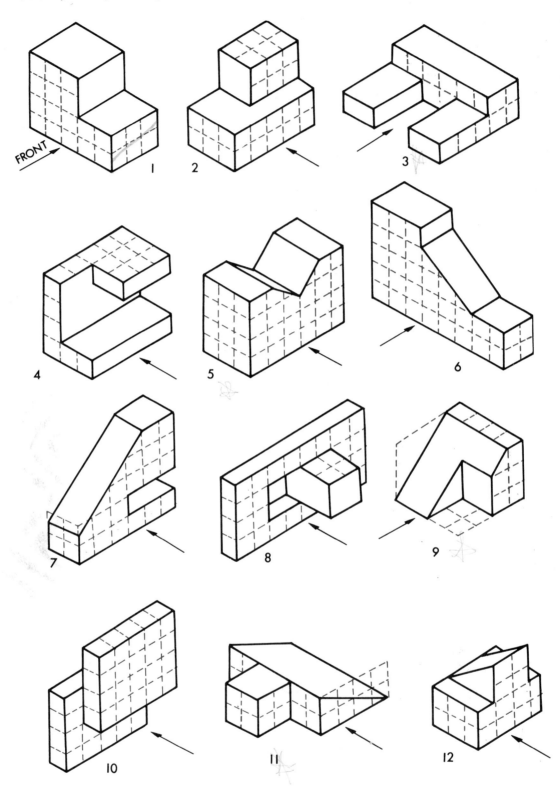

FRONT

Figure 3.7   Freehand Sketching Assignments 1 to 12

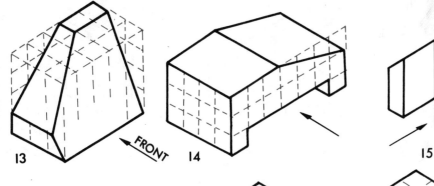

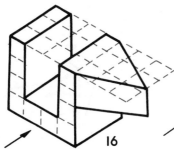

FRONT

13   14   15

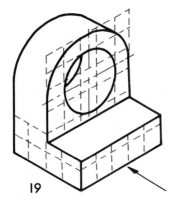

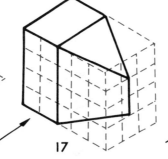

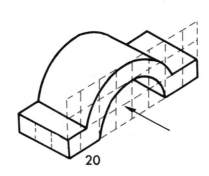

16   17   18

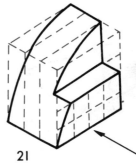

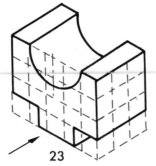

19   20   21

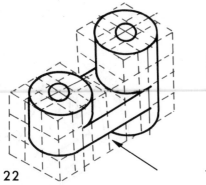

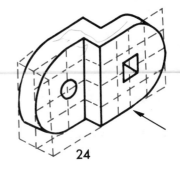

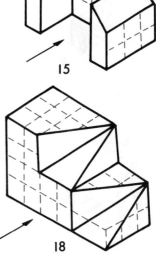

22   23   24

Figure 3.8   Freehand Sketching Assignments 13 to 24

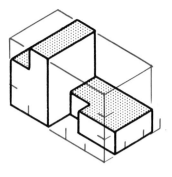

25

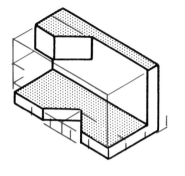

26

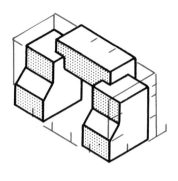

27

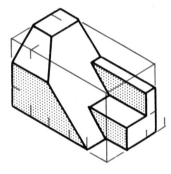

28

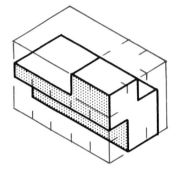

29

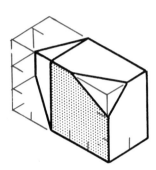

30

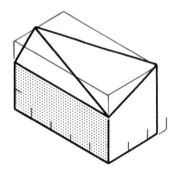

31

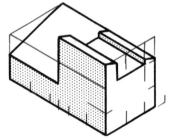

32

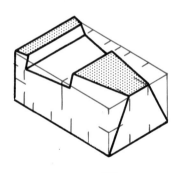

33

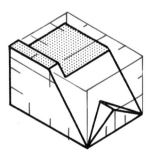

34

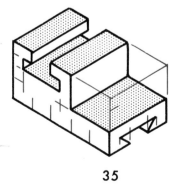

35

36

Figure 3.9   Freehand Sketching Assignments 25 to 36

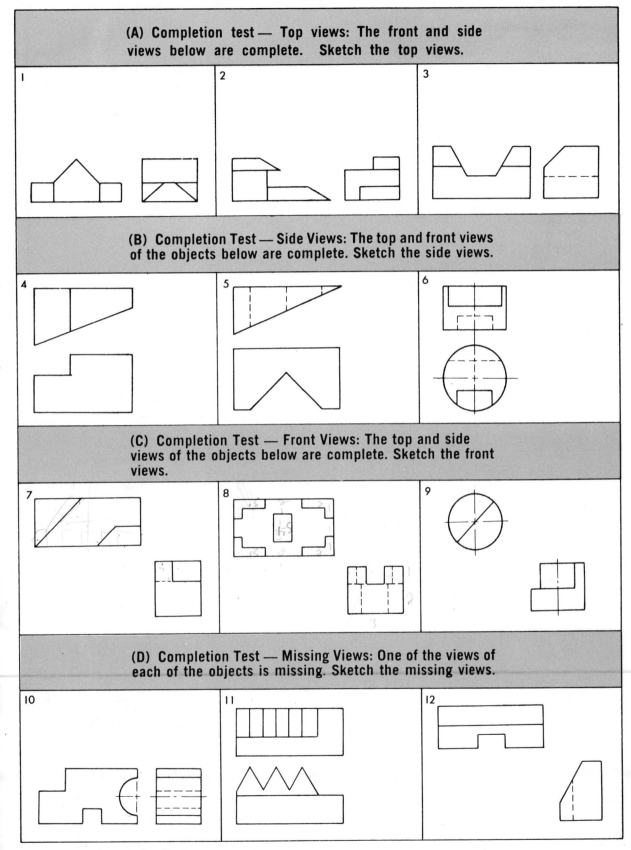

(A) Completion test — Top views: The front and side views below are complete. Sketch the top views.

1

2

3

(B) Completion Test — Side Views: The top and front views of the objects below are complete. Sketch the side views.

4

5

6

(C) Completion Test — Front Views: The top and side views of the objects below are complete. Sketch the front views.

7

8

9

(D) Completion Test — Missing Views: One of the views of each of the objects is missing. Sketch the missing views.

10

11

12

Figure 3.10   Completion Tests

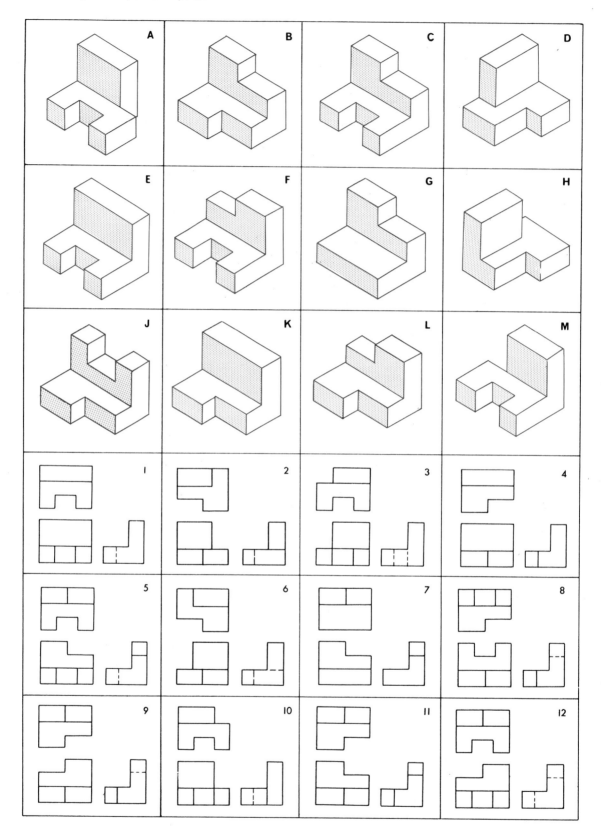

Figure 3.11   Match Pictorial Drawings A to M with Orthographic Drawings

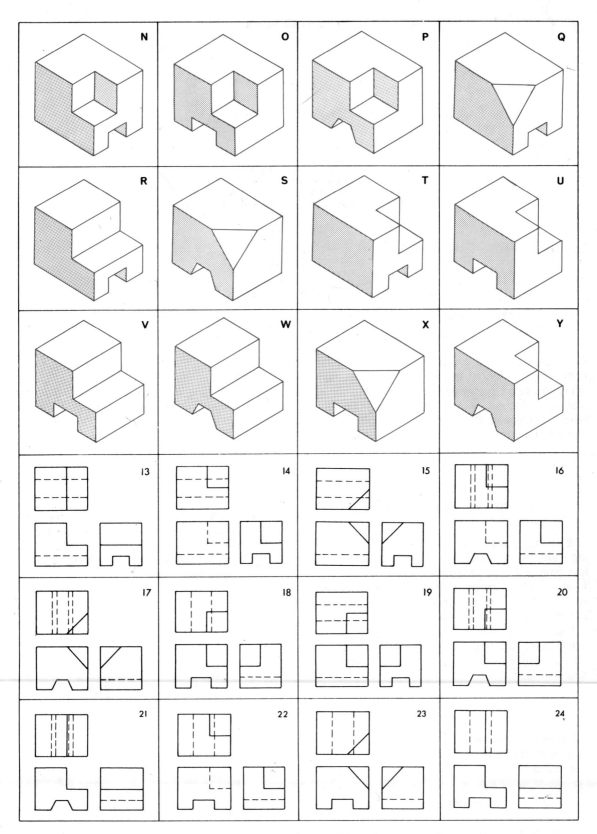

Figure 3.12   Match Pictorial Drawings N to Y with Drawings 13 to 24

CHAPTER FOUR

BASIC DIMENSIONING

UNITS OF MEASUREMENT [3, 4]

Although the metric system of dimensioning has become the official standard of measurement, many drawings presently in use are still dimensioned in inches or feet and inches. For this reason draftsmen should be familiar with all the dimensioning systems which they may encounter.

THE SI (METRIC) SYSTEM

The standard metric units on engineering drawings are the millimetre for linear measure, and micrometre for surface roughness. For architectural drawings metre and millimetre units are used. Unless otherwise specified the figures in this book are dimensioned in millimetres.

Metric dimensioning is based on the use of a minimum two figures. Whole dimensions from one to nine will show a zero to the right of the decimal point, not to the left.

2.0 not 0.2

Whole dimensions containing two or more figures do not require the zero to the right of the decimal point.

10 not 10.0

A millimetre value of less than one is shown with a zero to the left of the decimal point.

0.2 not .2 or .20

0.26 not .26

Commas should not be used to separate groups of three numbers in either inch or metric values. A space should be used in place of the comma.

32 541, not 32,541

2.562 827 6, not 2.5628276

Identification A metric drawing should include a general note, such as UNLESS OTHERWISE SPECIFIED DIMENSIONS ARE IN MILLIMETRES and be identified by the word METRIC prominently displayed near the title block.

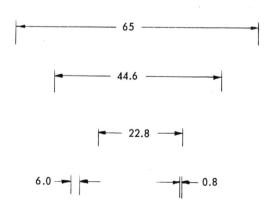

Metric Dimensioning

THE DECIMAL INCH SYSTEM

Parts are designed in basic decimal increments, preferably .02 inches, and are expressed as two place decimal numbers. Using the .02 module, the second decimal place (Hundredths) is an even number or zero. Sizes other than these, such as .25, are used when essential to meet design requirements. When greater accuracy is required, sizes are expressed as three or four place decimal numbers e.g. 1.875.

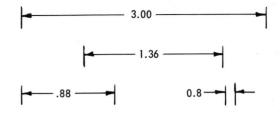

Decimal Dimensioning

DUAL DIMENSIONING

With a great exchange of drawings taking place between North America and the rest of the world it became advantageous, at one point in time, to show drawings in both inches and millimetres. As a result many companies adopted a dual system of dimensioning. Today, however, this type of dimensioning should be avoided if possible. When dimensions in both inches and millimetres are given on the same drawing, the following guidelines should be observed.

Show the millimetre dimension above the inch dimension separated by a horizontal line, or to the left of the inch dimension separated by a slash (oblique) line, or by enclosing the millimetre or inch dimension in brackets.

Only one method should be used on a drawing. A note or illustration should be located near the title block or strip to identify the inch and millimetre dimensions.

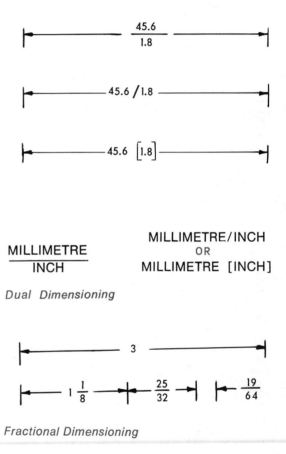

Dual Dimensioning

THE FRACTIONAL INCH SYSTEM

Sizes are expressed in common fractions, the smallest division being 64ths. Sizes other than common fractions are expressed as decimals.

Fractional Dimensioning

THE FEET AND INCHES SYSTEM

This system is used in architectural drawing and for large structural and installation drawings. Dimensions greater than 12 inches are expressed in feet and inches, with parts of an inch given as common fractions. Inch marks are not used, and a zero is added to indicate no full inches. A dash mark is placed between the foot and inch values.

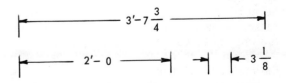

Feet and Inch Dimensioning

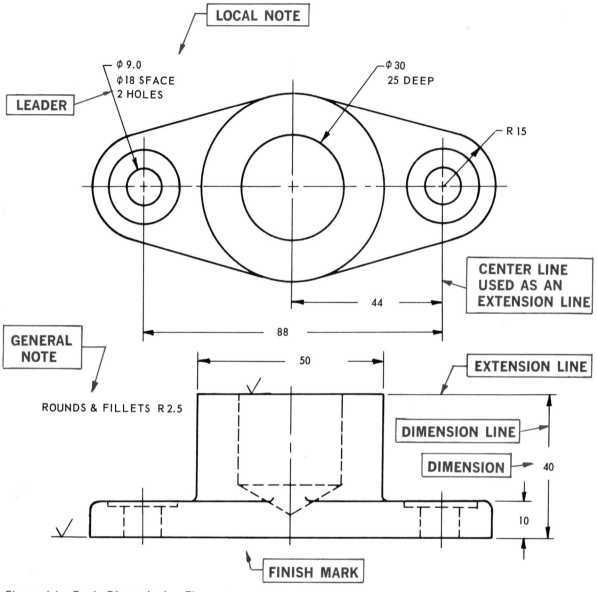

Figure 4.1   Basic Dimensioning Elements

WORKING DRAWINGS

A working drawing is one from which a craftsman can produce a part. The drawing must be a complete set of instructions, so that it will not be necessary to give further information to the person or persons making the object. A working drawing, then, consists of the views necessary to explain the shape, the dimensions needed by the craftsman, and required specifications, such as material and quantity required. The latter information may be found in the notes on the drawing, or it may be located in the title block.

DIMENSIONING

Dimensions are indicated on drawings by means of extension lines, dimension lines, leaders, arrowheads, figures, notes and symbols, to define geometrical characteristics such as lengths, diameters, angles and locations. The lines used in dimensioning are *THIN* in contrast to the outline of the object. The dimension must be clear and concise, and permit only one interpretation. In general, each surface, line or point is located by only one set of dimensions. An exception to these rules is for arrowless and tabular dimensioning which is discussed in chapter 6.

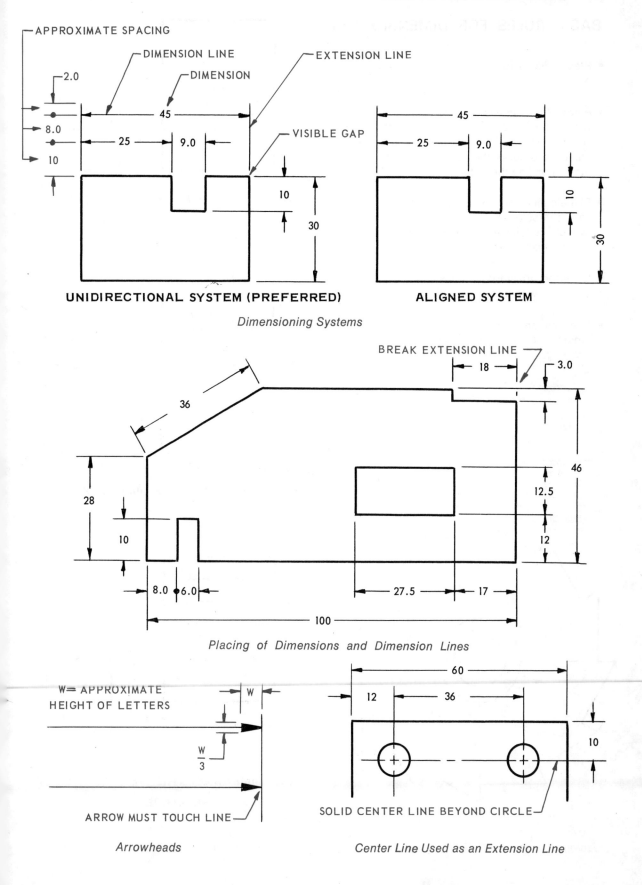

UNIDIRECTIONAL SYSTEM (PREFERRED)   ALIGNED SYSTEM

Dimensioning Systems

Placing of Dimensions and Dimension Lines

W = APPROXIMATE HEIGHT OF LETTERS

ARROW MUST TOUCH LINE

SOLID CENTER LINE BEYOND CIRCLE

Arrowheads

Center Line Used as an Extension Line

BASIC RULES FOR DIMENSIONING

- Place dimensions between the views when possible.

- Place the dimension line for the shortest length, width or height, nearest the outline of the object. Parallel dimension lines are placed in order of their size, making the longest dimension line the outermost.

- Place dimensions near the view that best shows the characteristic contour or shape of the object. In following this rule, dimensions will not always be between views.

- On large drawings, dimensions can be placed on the view to improve clarity.

- Use only one system of dimensions, either the Unidirectional or the Aligned, on any one drawing.

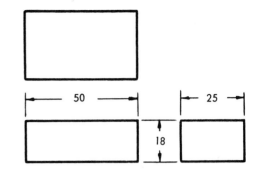

(A) PLACE DIMENSIONS BETWEEN VIEWS

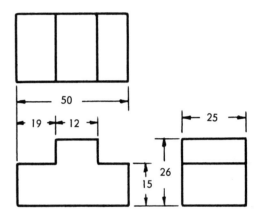

(B) PLACE SMALLEST DIMENSION NEAREST THE VIEW BEING DIMENSIONED

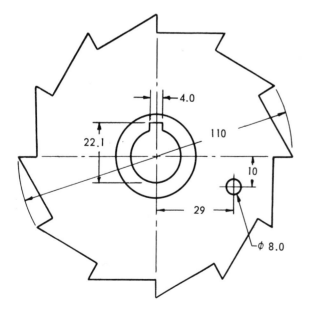

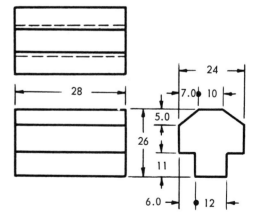

(C) DIMENSION THE VIEW THAT BEST SHOWS THE SHAPE

Placing Dimensions on Views   *Basic Dimensioning Rules*

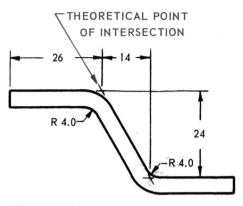

DIMENSIONING FORMED PARTS

Dimensioning to Theoretical Point of Inter-section

DIMENSIONING FORMED PARTS

In dimensioning formed parts, the inside radius should be specified, rather than the outside radius; but where possible, all forming dimensions should be shown on the same side.

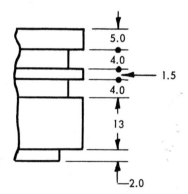

A SMALL CIRCLE MAY BE USED IN LIEU OF ARROWHEADS WHERE SPACE IS RESTRICTED

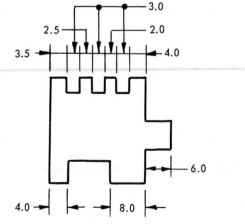

Methods of Dimensioning Limited Spaces

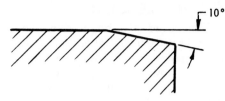

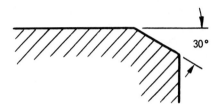

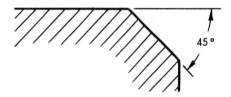

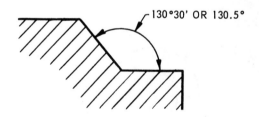

Dimensioning Angles

ANGULAR UNITS

Angles are expressed in units of degrees (°) with divisions of minutes (′) and seconds (″). No dash line is used between degrees, minutes or seconds.

The dimension lines of angles are arcs drawn with the apex of the angle as the center, wherever practicable. The position of the dimension varies according to the size of the angle and appears in a horizontal position. Recommended arrangements are shown above.

LEADERS

Leaders composed of straight ruled lines are used to indicate exactly where dimensions or explanatory notes are to be applied. Leaders terminate in arrowheads or large dots. The arrowhead points at a feature, while the dot rests on it. The note end of the leader runs to either the beginning or the end of the note, never to the middle. It terminates in a short horizontal bar at the mid-height of the lettering of the note.

The arrow end of the leader is a straight inclined line pointing to the surface or point to which the note applies.

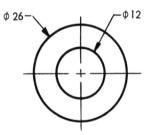

(A) DOT RESTS ON SURFACE

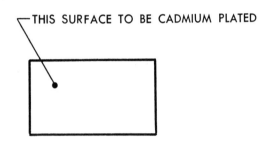

ARROWS POINT TO CENTER

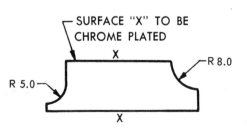

(B) ARROWHEADS POINT TO FEATURE

Leaders

CHAMFERS

Chamfers are normally dimensioned by giving the angle and length of the chamfer. When the chamfer is 45° it may be specified as a note.

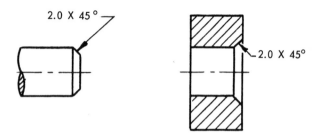

(A) FOR 45° CHAMFERS ONLY

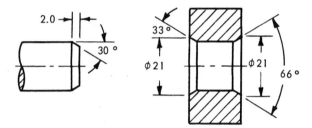

(B) FOR ALL CHAMFERS

Dimensioning Chamfers

NOTES

Notes are used to simplify or complement dimensioning by indicating information on a drawing in a condensed and systematic manner. They may be general or local notes, and should be in the present or future tense.

General notes refer to the part or drawing as a whole. They should be shown in a central position below the view to which they apply or in a general note column. Typical examples of this type of note are:
(a) FINISH ALL OVER
(b) ROUNDS AND FILLETS R 2.0
(c) REMOVE ALL SHARP EDGES

Local notes apply to local requirements only, and are connected by a leader to the point to which the note applies. Typical examples are:
(a) ϕ6.0, 4 HOLES
(b) 2.0 x 45°
(c) ϕ3.0, ϕ11.5 x 86° CSK
(d) M12 x 1.25

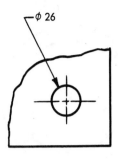

φ 26

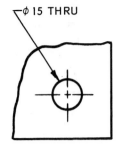

φ 15 THRU

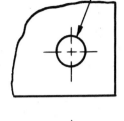

φ 28, 26 DEEP

**DIMENSIONING
ONE HOLE**

**DIMENSIONING A THROUGH
HOLE WHICH IS NOT SHOWN
IN A LONGITUDINAL VIEW**

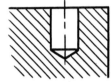

**DIMENSIONING
A BLIND HOLE**

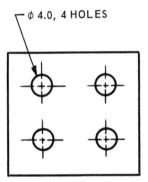

φ 4.0, 4 HOLES

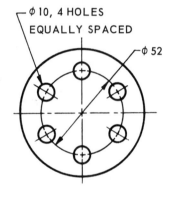

φ 10, 4 HOLES
EQUALLY SPACED

φ 52

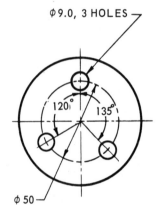

φ9.0, 3 HOLES

120°   135°

φ 50

DIMENSIONING A GROUP OF HOLES

Figure 4.2 Dimensioning Small Holes

OPERATIONAL NAMES

The use of operational names on dimensions, such as *turn, bore, grind, ream, tap, thread,* should be avoided. While the draftsman should be aware of the methods by which a part can be produced, the method of manufacture is better left to the producer. If the completed part is adequately dimensioned, and has finish marks showing finish quality desired, it remains a shop problem to meet the drawing specifications.

ABBREVIATIONS

Abbreviations and symbols are used on drawings to conserve space and time but only where the meaning is quite clear. Therefore, only commonly accepted abbreviations, such as those shown in the Appendix, should be used on drawings.

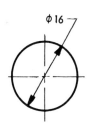
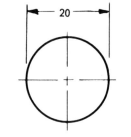
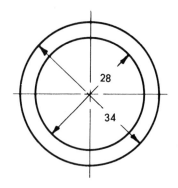

ABBREVIATION "DIA"
OR ∅ SYMBOL
USED WITH LEADER

(A) DIMENSIONING CIRCULAR VIEWS

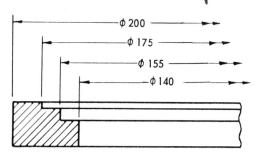
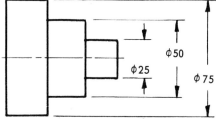
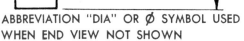

ABBREVIATION "DIA" OR ∅ SYMBOL USED
WHEN END VIEW NOT SHOWN

WITHOUT END VIEW

WITH END VIEW

(B) DIMENSIONING CYLINDRICAL VIEWS

DOUBLE ARROWHEADS USED WHEN
DIMENSION LINE INCOMPLETE

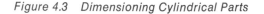
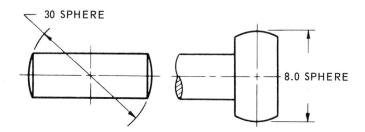

(D) SPHERICAL DIAMETERS

(C) PARTIAL VIEWS

Figure 4.3   Dimensioning Cylindrical Parts

DIAMETERS

When using a leader to specify diameter sizes, as with small holes, the dimension is identified as a diameter by preceding the numerical value with the diameter symbol ∅ or by adding the abbreviation DIA after the numerical value. When

dimensioning countersink, counterbore, and spot-face holes use the methods recommended on page 52.

Where a diameter is dimensioned by means of a dimension line on a circular view, or on a longitudinal view which has a reciprocal circular view, the diameter symbol or the abbreviation DIA may be omitted. Where the diameters of a number of concentric cylindrical features are specified, dimension them on the longitudinal view.

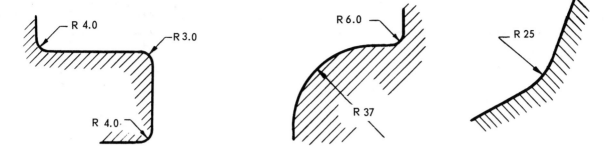

(A) DIMENSIONING RADII WHICH NEED NOT HAVE THEIR CENTERS LOCATED

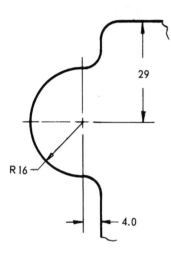

(B) RADII WITH LOCATED CENTERS

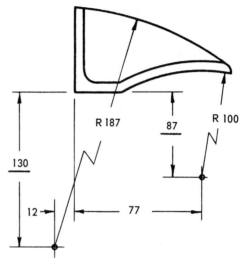

**(C) LOCATING INCONVENIENTLY
PLACED CENTERS OF RADII**

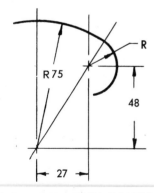

**(D) RADII WITH COMMON
TANGENT POINTS**

Figure 4.4 Dimensioning Radii

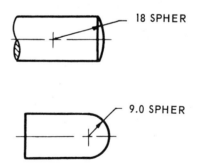

(E) SPHERICAL RADII

RADII

Radii are dimensioned by a dimension line that passes through or is in line with the center of the radius. The dimension line has one arrowhead only, which touches the arc. The letter R must always precede the dimension.

Where a large number of fillet or rounded edges of the same size are shown, they may be specified in the form of a note. The following notes may be used, where appropriate, and may be combined:

ALL EDGES R 3.0 UNLESS OTHERWISE
  SPECIFIED

BREAK SHARP EDGES

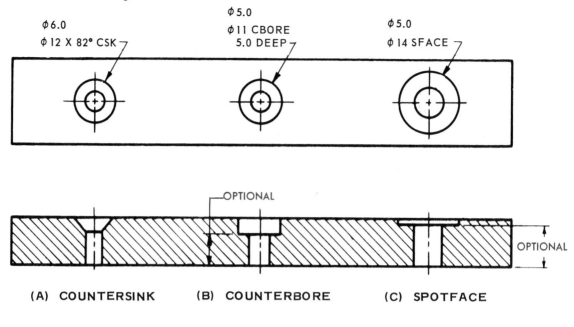

Dimensioning Countersink, Counterbore and Spotface Holes

COUNTERSINKS, COUNTERBORES AND SPOTFACES

The abbreviations CSK, CBORE and SFACE for countersink, counterbore, and spotface, respectively, indicate the form of the surface only and do not restrict the methods used to produce that form. The dimensions for them are usually given as a note, preceded by the size of the through hole.

A countersink is an angular-sided recess to accommodate the head of flat head screws, rivets and similar items. The diameter at the surface and the included angle are given. When the depth of the tapered section of the counter-

sink is critical, this depth is specified in the note or by dimension.

A counterbore is a flat-bottomed cylindrical recess which permits the head of a fastening device, such as a bolt, to lie recessed into the part. The diameter and depth are specified in the note. In some cases the thickness of the remaining stock may be dimensioned rather than the depth of the counterbore.

A spotface is an area where the surface is machined just enough to provide smooth, level seating for a bolthead, nut or washer. Only the diameter is specified. The minimum remaining thickness may be given if required.

SLOTTED HOLES

Elongated holes and slots are used to compensate for inaccuracies in manufacturing and to provide for adjustment. The method selected to locate the slot would depend on how the slot was made, i.e. punched or machined.

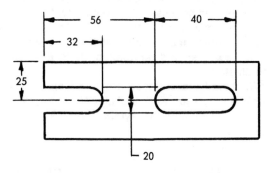

(A) LOCATING END OF HOLE

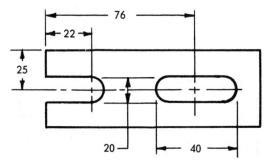

(B) LOCATING CENTER OF HOLE

Dimensioning Slotted Holes

EXTERNAL SURFACES WITH ROUNDED ENDS

External surfaces with rounded ends should be dimensioned by specifying the overall length and width of the piece and the radius of the ends. Holes or other features are dimensioned as shown.

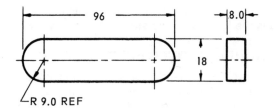

(A) WITHOUT HOLES

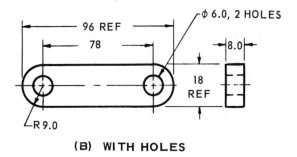

(B) WITH HOLES

Dimensioning External Surfaces with Rounded Ends

Review Questions

1. Name and give the main essentials of the measurement systems used on drawings.
2. What are the three basic requirements for a working drawing?
3. Name and illustrate the two common systems for dimensioning mechanical drawings.
4. Give the three basic rules to follow in dimensioning regular solids.
5. How are dimension lines for angles drawn?
6. What information should be given concerning holes and on which view should it appear?
7. Where are the diameter dimensions usually placed on drawings of solid cylindrical shapes?
8. What is the purpose of a countersink?
9. What is the difference between a counterbore and a spotface?
10. Why are slotted or elongated holes used?

SURFACE SYMBOLS[1,2,]

On many working drawings it may be necessary to indicate that a surface is to be machined without defining either the surface texture or the process to be used. Parts to be cast, molded or forged are some examples where surfaces require machining or finishing. The symbol shown identifies those surfaces to be produced by machining operations.

The machining symbol should not be taken as giving any indication of the surface finish quality. This is the function of the surface texture symbol.

SURFACE TEXTURE SYMBOLS

For a part to withstand severe operating conditions such as friction and wear, a particular surface finish is often essential. All surface finish control starts in the drafting room. In selecting the required surface finish for any particular part, the draftsman must consider factors such as size and function of the part, loading, speeds, operating conditions, and materials.

To meet the requirements for proper surface texture designation and control, a system for accurately describing the desired surface is necessary. Only the height and width of surface irregularities will be covered in this book.

Where it is necessary to indicate that a surface is to be machined without defining either the grade of roughness or the process to be used, the symbol √ should be applied, as in the following illustration.

Where all the surfaces are to be machined, a general note such as " √ ALL OVER" or "FAO" may be used and the symbols on the drawing omitted.

PLACING OF SURFACE SYMBOL

Surface symbols, like dimensions, are not normally duplicated. They should be placed on the same view as the dimensions that give the size or location of the surfaces concerned.

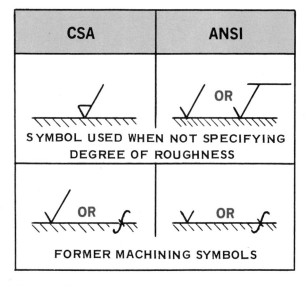

CSA	ANSI
SYMBOL USED WHEN NOT SPECIFYING DEGREE OF ROUGHNESS	
FORMER MACHINING SYMBOLS	

Surface Symbols

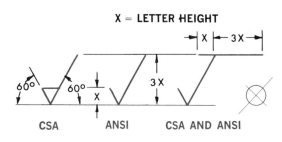

X = LETTER HEIGHT

CSA   ANSI   CSA AND ANSI

Surface Symbol Proportion

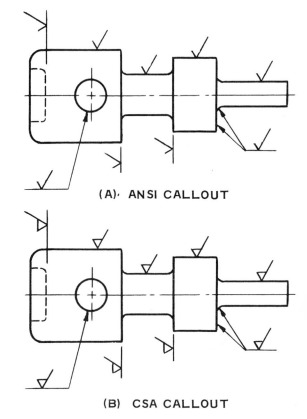

(A) ANSI CALLOUT

(B) CSA CALLOUT

Application of Surface Symbols

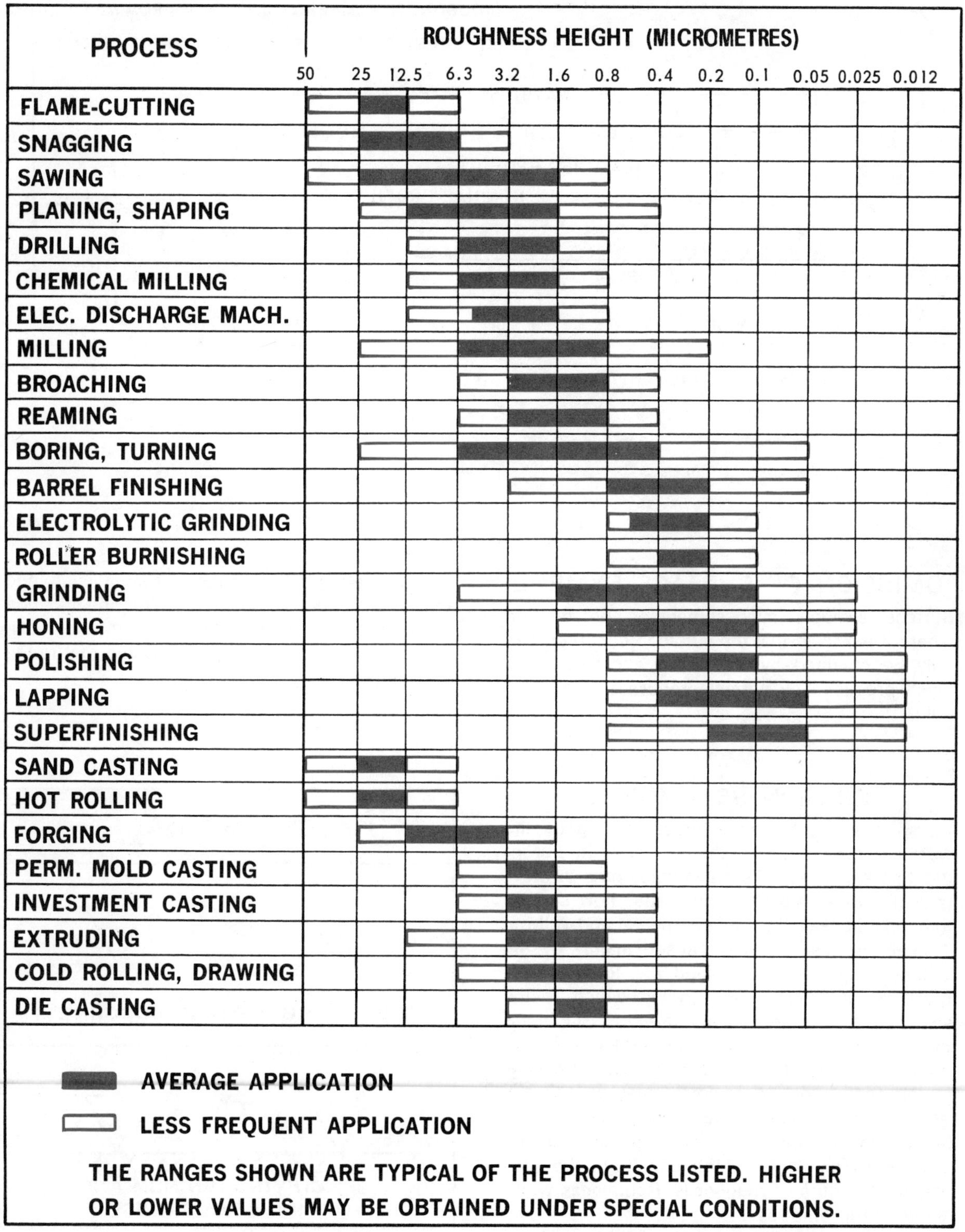

PROCESS
ROUGHNESS HEIGHT (MICROMETRES)
50 25 12.5 6.3 3.2 1.6 0.8 0.4 0.2 0.1 0.05 0.025 0.012
FLAME-CUTTING
SNAGGING
SAWING
PLANING, SHAPING
DRILLING
CHEMICAL MILLING
ELEC. DISCHARGE MACH.
MILLING
BROACHING
REAMING
BORING, TURNING
BARREL FINISHING
ELECTROLYTIC GRINDING
ROLLER BURNISHING
GRINDING
HONING
POLISHING
LAPPING
SUPERFINISHING
SAND CASTING
HOT ROLLING
FORGING
PERM. MOLD CASTING
INVESTMENT CASTING
EXTRUDING
COLD ROLLING, DRAWING
DIE CASTING
AVERAGE APPLICATION
LESS FREQUENT APPLICATION
THE RANGES SHOWN ARE TYPICAL OF THE PROCESS LISTED. HIGHER
OR LOWER VALUES MAY BE OBTAINED UNDER SPECIAL CONDITIONS.

EXTRACTED FROM AMERICAN NATIONAL STANDARD SURFACE TEXTURE B.46.1-1962 (R1971) WITH THE PERMISSION OF THE PUBLISHER, THE AMERICAN SOCIETY OF MECHANICAL ENGINEERS (SEE P. 252).

Figure 4.5 Surface Roughness Range for Common Production Methods

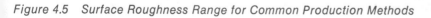

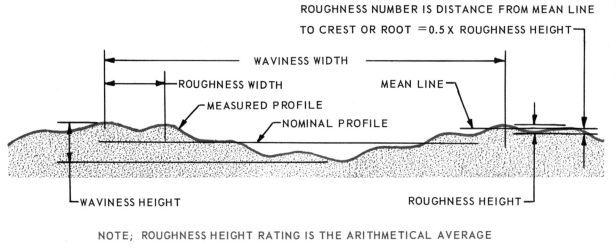

ROUGHNESS NUMBER IS DISTANCE FROM MEAN LINE
TO CREST OR ROOT =0.5 X ROUGHNESS HEIGHT

WAVINESS WIDTH

ROUGHNESS WIDTH

MEAN LINE

MEASURED PROFILE

NOMINAL PROFILE

WAVINESS HEIGHT

ROUGHNESS HEIGHT

NOTE;   ROUGHNESS HEIGHT RATING IS THE ARITHMETICAL AVERAGE
DEVIATION FROM THE ROUGHNESS CENTER LINE

Surface Finish Characteristics

OMISSION OF SURFACE SYMBOL

Surface symbols may sometimes be omitted where it is known that the surface concerned can only be obtained by machining and where the finish produced by normal processes is acceptable.

ROUGHNESS NUMBERS

As surface quality has a direct bearing on the wear and the function of the part, a method of indicating the quality of surface finish on a drawing is required. All surfaces, no matter how smooth they may appear, have minute peaks and valleys. This roughness, which is caused mainly by the cutting edge of the tool and the tool feed, is given a roughness height rating which is the arithmetical average deviation from the roughness center line expressed in micrometres (1 micrometre $= 0.000\,001$ metre) as measured normal to the center line. Micrometres may be abbreviated as μm. Roughness width means the distance parallel to the nominal surface between successive peaks or ridges which constitute the predominant pattern of roughness. Roughness width is rated in millimetres.

When it is necessary to indicate the grade of roughness, a roughness height rating is placed at the left of the long leg. The long leg and extension is always on the right. The specification of

only one rating indicates the maximum value, and any lesser value is acceptable. The specification of two ratings indicates the minimum and maximum values, and anything lying within that range is acceptable.

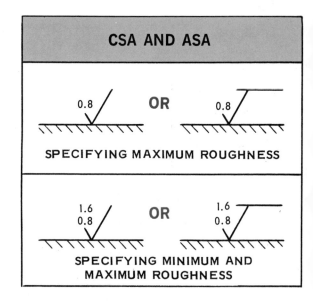

Location of Roughness Numbers on Machining Symbols

WAVINESS NUMBERS

The minute peaks and valleys (roughness) are superimposed on larger peaks and valleys called *waves*. Waviness results from such factors as machine or work deflection, vibration, chatter, heat treatment, and working strains.

Waviness height is rated in millimetres as the peak-to-valley distance. Waviness width is rated in millimetres as the spacing of successive wave peaks or successive wave valleys. Maximum waviness height rating is placed above the horizontal extension, and any lesser rating is acceptable.

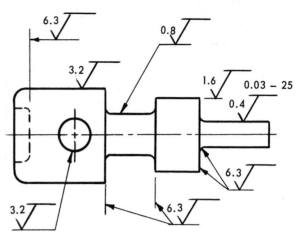

Application of Roughness and Waviness Numbers

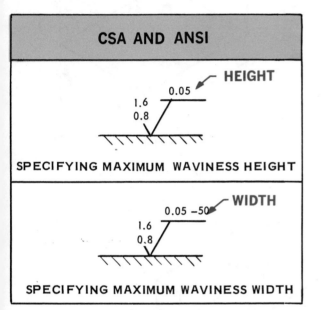

Location of Waviness Numbers on Machining Symbols

Maximum waviness width rating is placed above the horizontal extension and to the right of the waviness height rating. Any lesser rating is acceptable.

Review Questions

1. What is the purpose of machining symbols?

2. Where should the machining symbols be placed?

3. How is the roughness height rating expressed?

4. What factors may cause waviness?

5. How are waviness height and width rated, and where are the ratings placed on the machining symbol?

References

1. ANSI — B46.1
2. CSA — B95
3. CSA — B78.2
4. ANSI — Y14.5

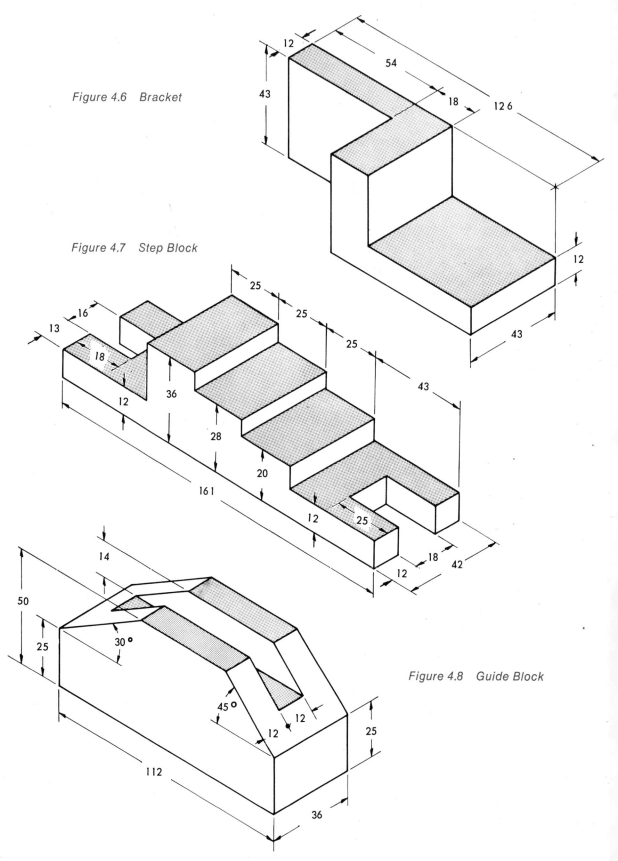

Figure 4.6   Bracket

Figure 4.7   Step Block

Figure 4.8   Guide Block

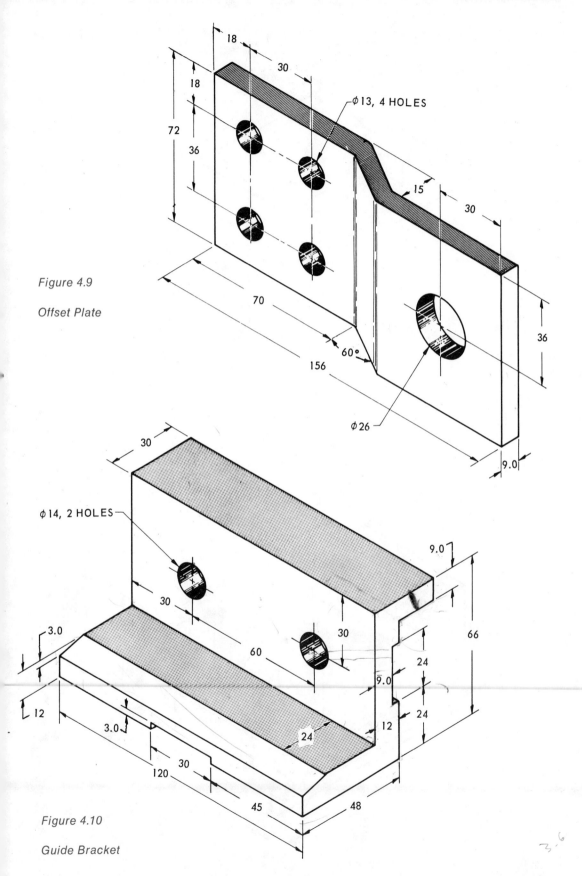

Figure 4.9

Offset Plate

Figure 4.10

Guide Bracket

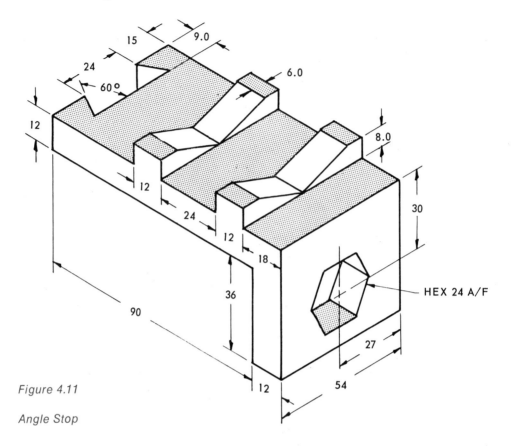

Figure 4.11

Angle Stop

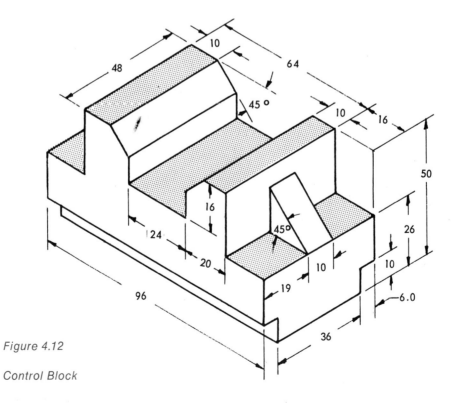

Figure 4.12

Control Block

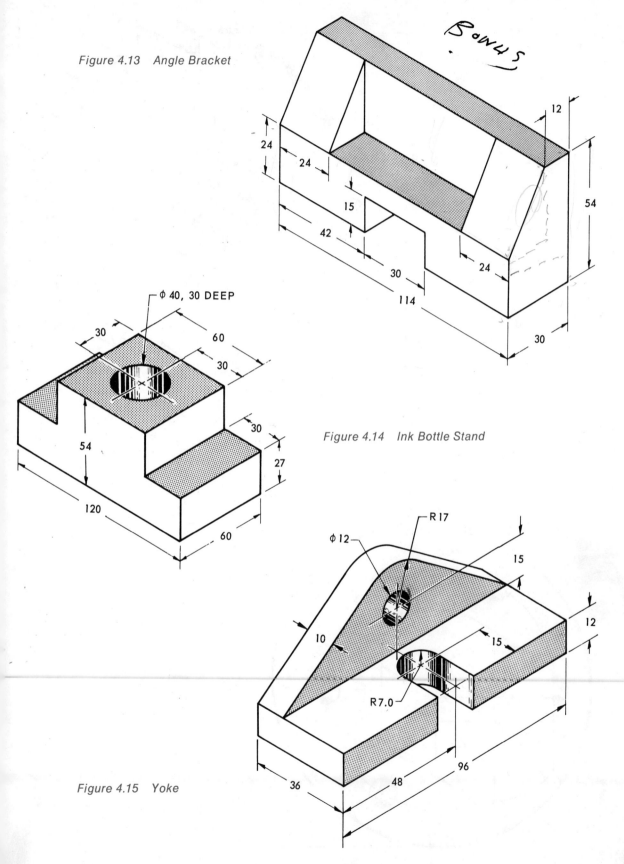

Figure 4.13   Angle Bracket

Figure 4.14   Ink Bottle Stand

Figure 4.15   Yoke

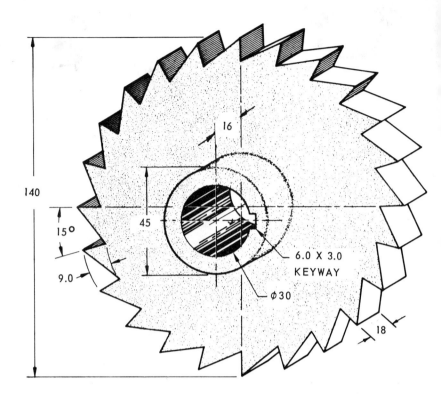

140

15°

45

16

9.0

6.0 X 3.0
KEYWAY

φ30

18

Figure 4.16   Ratchet Wheel

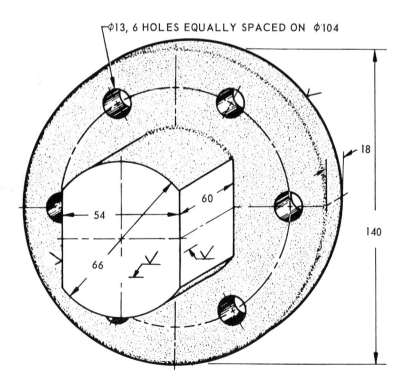

φ13, 6 HOLES EQUALLY SPACED ON φ104

18

54

60

140

66

Figure 4.17   Axle Cap

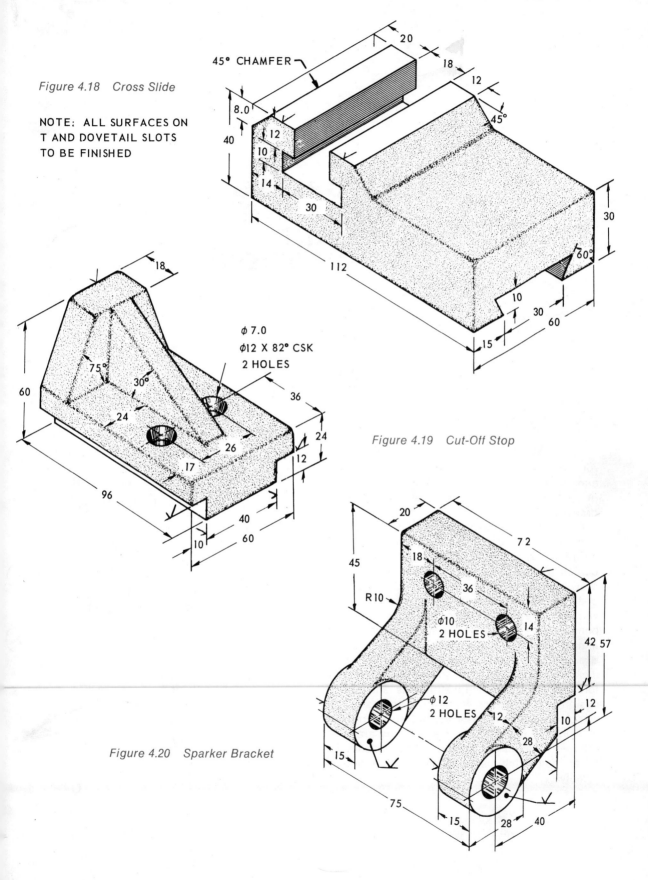

45° CHAMFER

Figure 4.18   Cross Slide

NOTE: ALL SURFACES ON T AND DOVETAIL SLOTS TO BE FINISHED

20
18
12
8.0
12
45°
40
10
14
30
112
30
30
60°
10
15
60

18
φ 7.0
φ12 X 82° CSK
2 HOLES
75°
30°
24
26
17
60
36
24
12
96
40
10
60

Figure 4.19   Cut-Off Stop

20
72
45
18
36
R 10
φ10
2 HOLES
14
42 57
φ12
2 HOLES
12
12
10
28
15
15
28
40
75

Figure 4.20   Sparker Bracket

CHAPTER FIVE

WORKING DRAWINGS AND CONVENTIONS

ASSEMBLY AND DETAIL DRAWINGS

ASSEMBLY DRAWINGS

All machines and mechanisms are made up of numerous parts. A drawing showing the product in its completed state is called an *assembly drawing.*

Assembly drawings vary greatly in the amount and type of information they give, depending on the nature of the machine or mechanism they depict. The primary functions of the assembly drawings are to show the product in its completed shape, to indicate the relationship of its various components, and to designate those components by a part or detail number. Other information that might be given includes: overall dimensions, capacity dimensions, relationship dimensions between parts (necessary information for assembly), operating instructions, and data on design characteristics. Some mechanisms are assembled units in themselves, but also form part of a total machine. Such mechanisms are often referred to as *sub-assemblies.* The transmission of an automobile is an example of a sub-assembly.

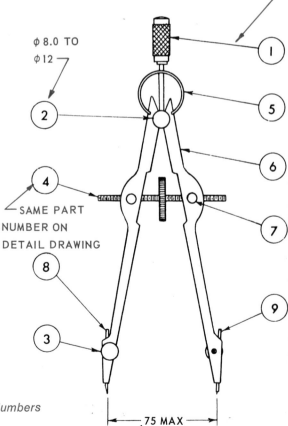

Figure 5.1   *The Use of Identification Numbers on Assembly Drawings*

DETAIL DRAWINGS

The working drawings of each of the parts are called *detail drawings,* since each part is a "detail" of the complete machine or mechanism. Very often the working drawing for each detail is made on a separate drawing sheet. When a number of the details are to be made of the same material and will be manufactured similarly, they can be grouped on a large common sheet.

Several drawings may be made of the same part, each one giving only the information neces- sary for a particular step in the manufacture of the part. A part made from cast iron, for ex- ample, may have one detail drawing for the patternmaker and one detail drawing for the machinist, each drawing having only the di- mensions and specifications necessary for that particular step in its manufacture.

The nature of the parts, the manufacturing techniques to be employed, and the drafting practices of the individual engineering office will determine the procedures for making detail draw- ings.

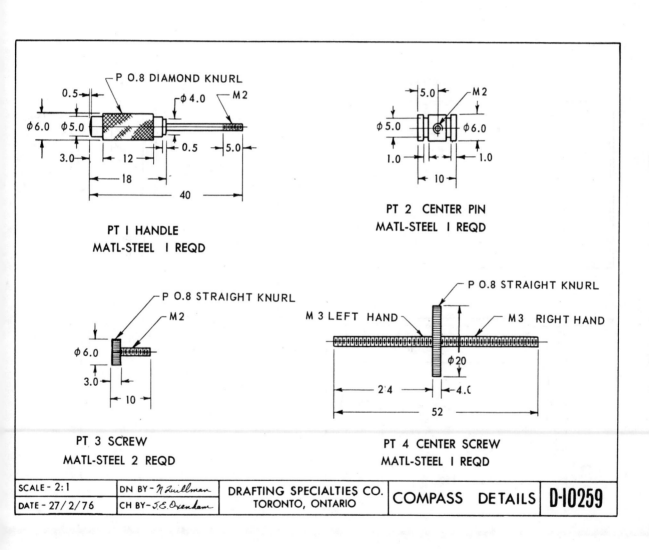

Figure 5.2   Detail Drawing Showing Many Details on One Drawing

DETAIL ASSEMBLY DRAWINGS

Detail assembly drawings are often made for fairly simple objects, such as pieces of furniture, when the parts are few in number and not intricate in shape. All the dimensions and information necessary for the construction of each part and for the assembly of the parts are given directly on the assembly drawing. Separate views of specific parts, or enlargements showing the fitting together of parts, may also be drawn in addition to the regular drawing. Note that the enlarged views are drawn in picture form and not as regular orthographic views. This method is peculiar to the cabinet-making trade and is not normally used in mechanical drawing.

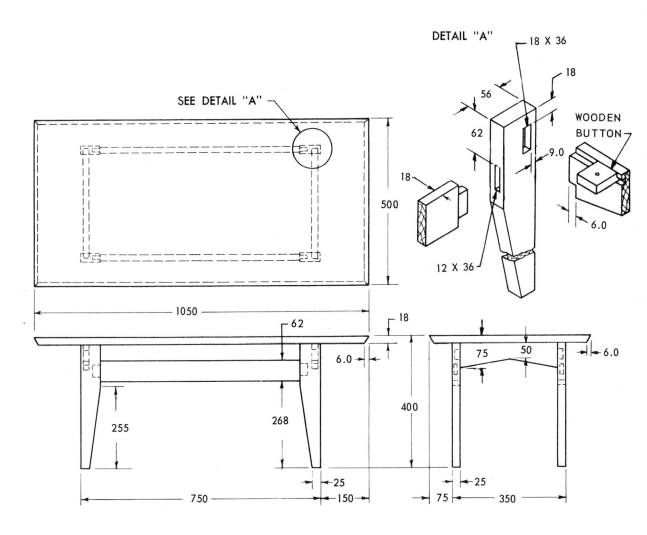

Figure 5.3   *Combined Detail and Assembly Drawing*

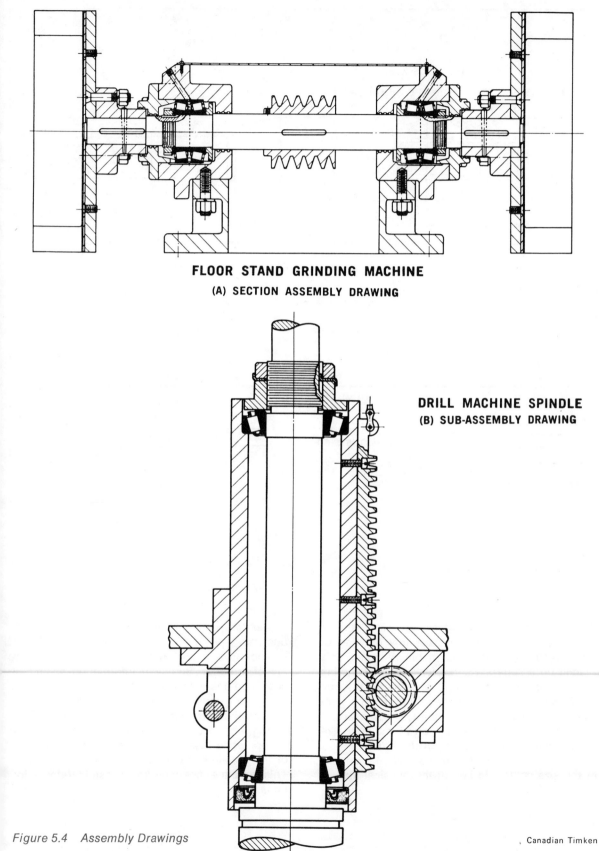

FLOOR STAND GRINDING MACHINE
(A) SECTION ASSEMBLY DRAWING

DRILL MACHINE SPINDLE
(B) SUB-ASSEMBLY DRAWING

Figure 5.4   Assembly Drawings

Canadian Timken

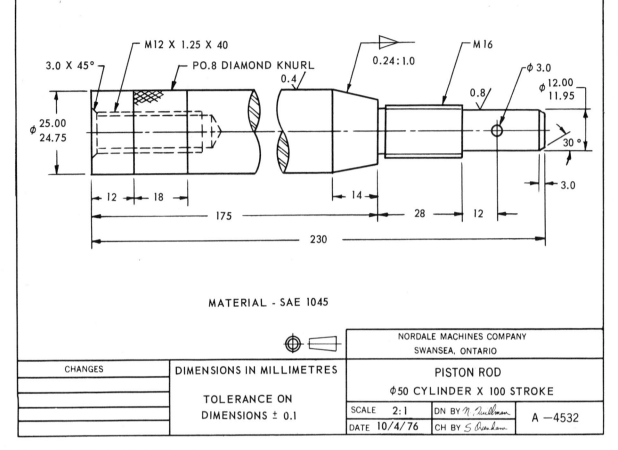

Figure 5.5   Typical Detail Drawing

BILLS OF MATERIALS

A bill of material is an itemized list of all the components shown on an assembly drawing or on a detail drawing. Often a bill of material is placed on a separate sheet for ease of handling and duplicating. As the bill of material is used by the purchasing department to order the necessary material for the design, it is necessary to show in the bill of material the raw material size rather than the finished size of the part.

For castings, a pattern number should appear in the size column in lieu of the physical size of the part.

Standard components, such as bolts, nuts and bearings, which are purchased ready-made, should have a part number and appear in the bill of material. Sufficient information should be shown in the descriptive column to enable the purchasing agent to order correct parts.

Parts lists for bills of materials placed on the bottom of the drawing should read from bottom to top, while bills of materials placed on the top of the drawings should read from top to bottom. This practice provides for possible later additions.

QTY	ITEM	MATL	DESCRIPTION	PT NO
1	BASE	CI	PATTERN # A3154	1
1	CAP	CI	PATTERN # B87156	2
1	SUPPORT	MS	10 X 50 X 112	3
1	BRACE	MS	6.0 X 25 X 48	4
1	COVER	ST	3.42 (10 USS GA) X 150	5
1	SHAFT	CRS	ϕ 25 X 160	6
2	BEARINGS	SKF	RADIAL BALL 62002	7
2	RETAINING RING	TRUARC	N5000 - 725	8
1	KEY	ST	WOODRUFF 608	9
1	SET SCREW CUP		HEX SOCKET M6 X 10 LG	10
4	BOLT - HEX HD - REG	SEMI - FIN	M10 X 40 LG	11
4	NUT - REG - HEX	ST	M10	12
4	LOCKWASHER	ST	10.2 ID X 17.2 OD X 2.2	13
				14

(A) TYPICAL BILL OF MATERIAL

PTS 7 TO 13 ARE PURCHASED ITEMS

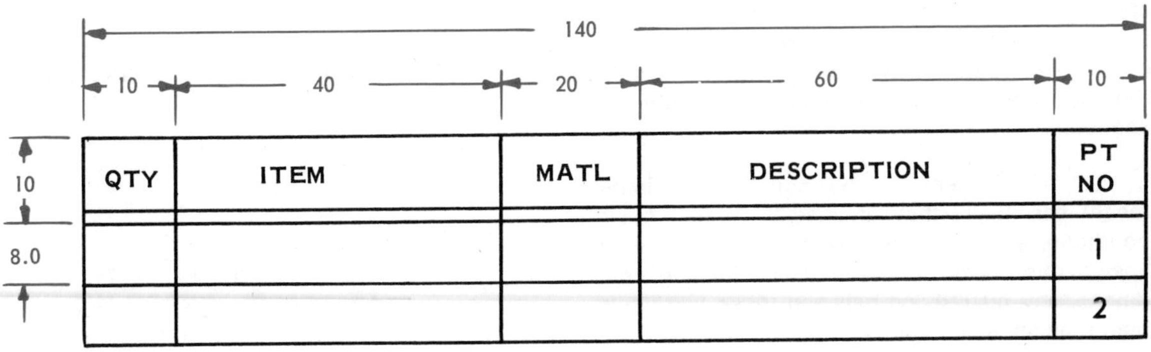

QTY	ITEM	MATL	DESCRIPTION	PT NO
				1
				2

(B) SAMPLE SIZES

Figure 5.6   Bill of Material

TOLERANCES AND ALLOWANCES[1]

In the 6,000 years of the history of engineering drawing as a means for the communication of engineering information, it seems inconceivable that such an elementary practice as the tolerancing of dimensions, which we take so much for granted today, was introduced for the first time only about 60 years ago.

Apparently, engineers and workmen came only very gradually to the realization that *exact* dimensions and shapes could not be attained in the shaping of physical objects, such as the manufacture of materials and products. The skilled handicraftsman of old prided himself on being able to work to exact dimensions. What he really meant was that he dimensioned objects with a degree of accuracy greater than that with which he could measure them. The use of modern measuring instruments would have shown the deviations from the sizes which he deemed exact.

As soon as it was realized that variations in the sizes of parts had always been present, that such variations could be restricted but not avoided, and also that slight variation in the size which a part was originally intended to have could be tolerated without its correct functioning being impaired, it became evident that interchangeable parts need not be identical parts. It was seen to be sufficient if the significant sizes which controlled their fits lay between definite limits. Accordingly, the problem of interchangeable manufacture developed from the making of parts to a supposedly exact size to the holding of part sizes between two limits lying so closely together that any intermediate size would be acceptable.

The development of the concept of limits meant essentially that an exactly defined *basic* condition, expressed by one numerical value or specification, was replaced by two limiting conditions, any result lying between these two limits being acceptable. One standard level was replaced by two limiting levels enclosing a zone of acceptability, or tolerance, and a workable scheme of interchangeable manufacture, indispensable to mass production methods, thus became established.

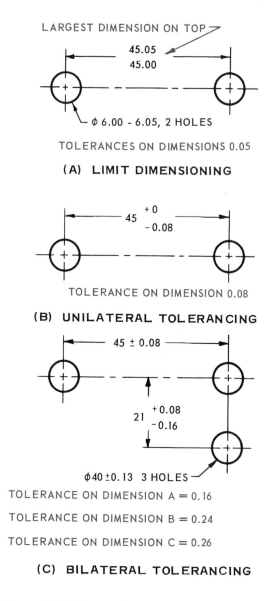

Figure 5.7   Tolerancing Methods

LIMITS AND FITS[2,4,]

As mentioned previously, the workman cannot be expected to produce the exact size of part as indicated by the dimensions on a drawing, so a certain amount of variation on each dimension must be tolerated. For example, a dimension given as 37 $\pm$ 0.1 mm means that the manufactured part can be anywhere in size between

36.9 mm and 37.1 mm and that the *tolerance* permitted on this dimension is 0.2 mm. The largest and smallest permissible sizes (37.1 mm and 36.9 mm respectively) are known as the *limits*.

In order to calculate limit dimensions and fits, the following definitions should be clearly understood.

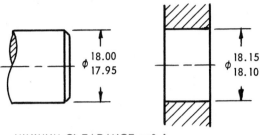

MINIMUM CLEARANCE = 0.1

MAXIMUM CLEARANCE = 0.2

(A) CLEARANCE FIT

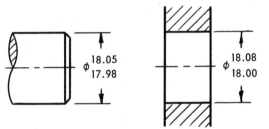

MAXIMUM CLEARANCE = 0.1

MAXIMUM INTERFERENCE=0.05

(B) TRANSITION FIT

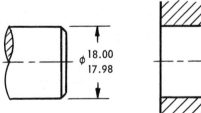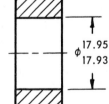

MINIMUM INTERFERENCE = 0.03

MAXIMUM INTERFERENCE = 0.07

(C) INTERFERENCE FIT

Figure 5.8   Types of Fits

Tolerances: The tolerance on a dimension is the total permissible variation in its size, which is the difference between the limits of size. A tolerance need not be expressed to the same number of figures to the right of the decimal point as the dimension.

Limits of Size: The limits are the maximum and minimum sizes permitted for a specific dimension.

Allowance: An allowance is the intentional difference in correlated dimensions of mating parts. It is the minimum clearance (positive allowance) or maximum interference (negative allowance) between such parts.

All dimensions on a drawing have tolerances. Some dimensions must be more exact than others, and hence have smaller tolerances. General practice is to allow a deviation in size such as ± 0.2 for all dimensions shown to one decimal place, and ± 0.02 for all dimensions shown to two decimal places. These tolerances are usually decimal places. These tolerances are usually shown in the form of a general note on the drawings. For example:

> EXCEPT WHERE STATED OTHERWISE, TOLERANCES ON DIMENSIONS ± 0.2

Where dimensions require a greater accuracy than that provided by the general note, then individual tolerances or limits will be shown for that dimension. For example:

$$0.9 \pm 0.1$$

Tolerancing Methods: Dimensional tolerances are expressed in either of two ways: limit dimensioning or plus and minus tolerancing.

Limit Dimensioning: In the limiting dimension method, only the maximum and minimum dimensions are specified.

Plus and Minus Tolerancing: For this method the dimension of the specified size is given first, followed by a plus and minus expression of tolerance.

DIMENSIONING OF SPECIAL FEATURES[2, 3]

REFERENCE AND NOT-TO-SCALE DIMENSIONS

When a reference dimension is shown on a drawing for information only, and is not necessary for the manufacture of that part, it must be clearly labelled REF.

When a dimension on a drawing is altered, making it not to scale, either the letters NTS appear beside the dimension or a straight line is drawn below the dimension to indicate that the dimension is not drawn to scale.

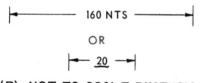

(A) REFERENCE DIMENSION

(B) NOT TO SCALE DIMENSION

Reference and Not-to-Scale Dimensions

SPECIFYING SIZE AND LOCATION

Size and location are specified by means of two systems, based on *rectangular co-ordinates* or *polar co-ordinates*. Both systems may be used on the same drawing. The choice of system is usually governed by manufacturing methods. But any given point or surface should be located by one system only.

The *rectangular dimensioning system* is a method for indicating distance, location, and size by means of linear dimensions measured parallel or perpendicular to reference axes or planes that are perpendicular to each other.

The *polar dimensioning system* is a method of indicating the position of a point, line, or surface by means of a linear dimension and an angle, other than 90°, implied by the vertical and horizontal centerlines.

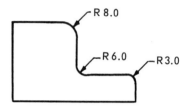

(A) BY DIMENSION

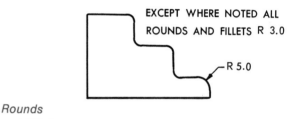

Rounds and Fillets

(B) BY NOTE

FILLETS AND ROUNDS

A *round*, or radius, is put on the outside of a piece to improve its appearance and to avoid forming a sharp edge that might injure anyone handling it. A *fillet* is additional metal allowed in the inner intersection of two surfaces for casting practices and to improve the strength of the part.

The dimensioning of fillets and rounds normally takes the form of a note. Where fillets and rounds vary in size, the individual dimensions must be shown.

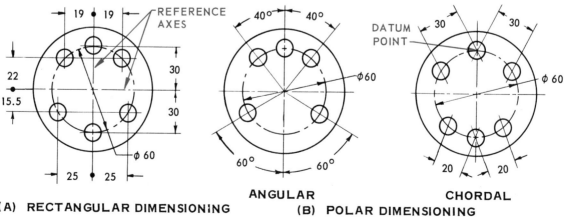

(A) RECTANGULAR DIMENSIONING

ANGULAR

CHORDAL

(B) POLAR DIMENSIONING

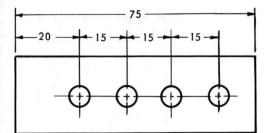

(A) POINT-TO-POINT DIMENSIONING

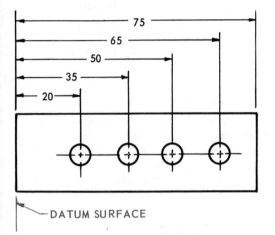

—DATUM SURFACE

(B) DATUM DIMENSIONING

Figure 5.9 Comparison Between Point-to-Point and Datum Dimensioning

POINT-TO-POINT DIMENSIONING

Point-to-point dimensions are applied direct from one feature to another and are intended to locate surfaces or features directly between the points indicated.

DATUM DIMENSIONING

When a number of dimensions start from a common data point or points on a line or surface, the system is referred to as datum dimensioning.

WIRE, SHEET METAL, AND DRILL ROD

Wire, sheet metal, and drill rod which are manufactured to gauge or code sizes, should be shown by their decimal dimensions, but gauge numbers, drill letters, etc., may be shown in parentheses following those dimensions.
Examples:
Sheet — 3.42 (No. 10 USS GA)
— 2.05 (No. 12 B & S GA)
Drill — ϕ 4.85 (No. 11 DRILL)
— ϕ6.53 (F DRILL)

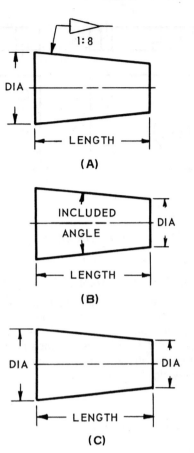

TAPERS

The following dimensions may be used, in suitable combinations, to define the size and form of tapered features:
The diameter (or width) at each end of the tapered feature;
The length of the tapered feature;
The rate of taper, or the included angle.

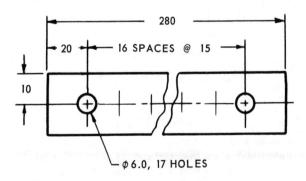

REPETITIVE PARTS

One method of showing distances between repetitive holes or parts is illustrated above.

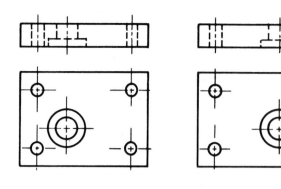

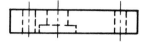

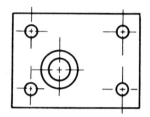

PT 1   PT 2

TWO DRAWINGS

PT 1 - AS SHOWN
PT 2 - OPPOSITE HAND

ONE DRAWING

Figure 5.10   Opposite Hand Views

OPPOSITE HANDED VIEWS

Where parts are symmetrically opposite, such as for right and left hand usage, one part is drawn in detail and the other is indicated by a note such as *Part 1 same except opposite hand.* It is preferable to show both part numbers on the same drawing.

ENLARGED VIEWS

To eliminate the crowding of details or dimensions, an enlarged removed view may be used. The enlarged view should be oriented in the same manner as the main view, the scale of enlargement must be shown, and both views should be identified by one of the methods shown.

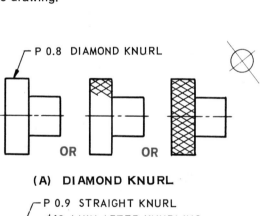

(A) DIAMOND KNURL

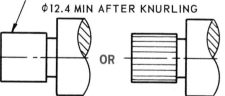

(B) STRAIGHT KNURL

Knurls

KNURLING

Knurling is an operation which puts patterned indentations in the surface of a metal part to provide a good finger grip. Knurls are specified by a note calling for the type and pitch. The length and diameter of the knurl are shown as dimensions on the drawing. Showing the knurled area by hatching lines is optional.

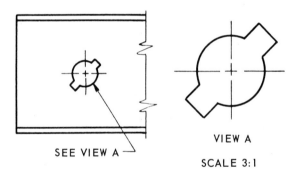

SEE VIEW A

VIEW A

SCALE 3:1

(A) ENLARGED VIEW OF FEATURE

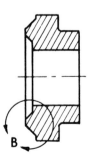

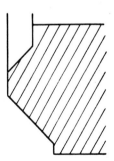

VIEW B

SCALE 4:1

(B) ENLARGED REMOVED VIEW

Figure 5.11   Enlarged Views

CSA B78.1

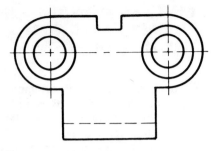

LEFT SIDE ONLY

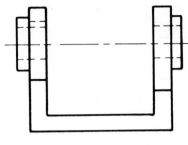

PARTIAL SIDE VIEWS

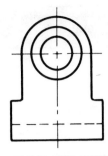

RIGHT SIDE ONLY

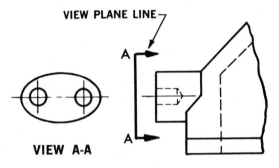

VIEW A-A

**VIEW PLANE LINE USED TO INDICATE
DIRECTION AND WEIGHT OF PARTIAL VIEW**

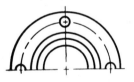

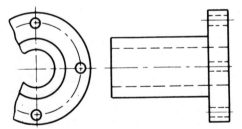

PARTIAL VIEW AND FULL VIEW

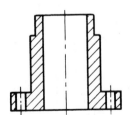

**FULL SECTION VIEW
HALF VIEW AND**

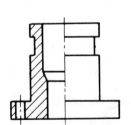

**HALF VIEW AND
HALF SECTION VIEW**

ANSI Y14.3-1957 (SEE * P. 251)
CSA B78.1

Figure 5.12   Partial Views

PARTIAL VIEWS

Symmetrical objects may often be adequately portrayed by half views.

Partial views, which show only a limited portion of the object with remote details omitted, should be used, when necessary, to clarify the meaning of the drawing. Such views are used to avoid having to draw many hidden features.

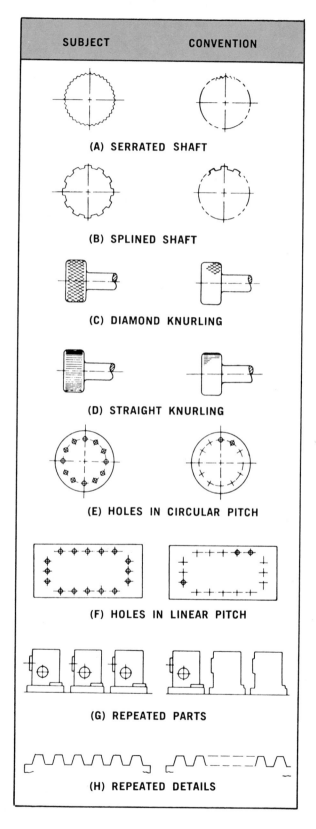

SUBJECT	CONVENTION

(A) SERRATED SHAFT

(B) SPLINED SHAFT

(C) DIAMOND KNURLING

(D) STRAIGHT KNURLING

(E) HOLES IN CIRCULAR PITCH

(F) HOLES IN LINEAR PITCH

(G) REPEATED PARTS

(H) REPEATED DETAILS

Figure 5.13 Conventional Representation of Common Features

CONVENTIONAL REPRESENTATION OF COMMON FEATURES [5, 6]

To simplify the representation of common features a number of conventional drawing practices are used. Many conventions are deviations from "true" projection for the purpose of clarity; others are used for the purpose of saving time. These conventions must be executed carefully, for clarity is even more important than speed.

REPETITIVE DETAILS

Repetitive features, such as gear and spline teeth, are shown by drawing a partial view, showing two or three of the features, with a phantom line or lines to indicate the extent of the remaining features.

HOLES

A series of similar holes is indicated by drawing one hole, and showing the centerlines only for the others.

REPETITIVE PARTS

Repetitive parts, or intricate features, are shown by drawing one in detail, and the others in simple outline only. A covering note is added to the drawing.

INTERSECTION OF UNFINISHED SURFACES

The intersection of unfinished surfaces that are rounded or filleted at the point of theoretical intersection may be indicated conventionally by a line coinciding with the theoretical point of intersection. The need for this convention is shown by the examples shown in figure 5.15 where the upper top views are shown in true projection. Note that in each example the true projection would be misleading. In the case of the large radius such as shown in figure 5.15 (D) no line is drawn.

Members such as ribs and arms that blend into other features end in curves called *runouts*. Small runouts are usually drawn freehand. Large runouts are drawn with an irregular curve, template, or compass.

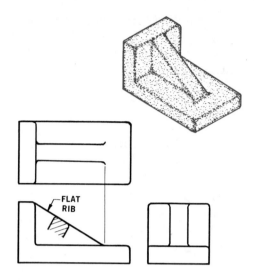

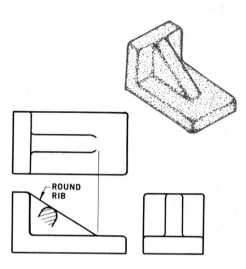

FLAT
RIB

ROUND
RIB

(A)

(B)

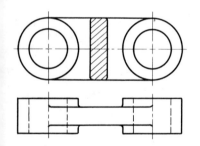

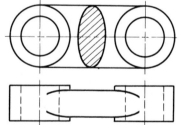

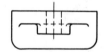

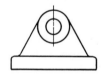

(C)

(D)

(E)

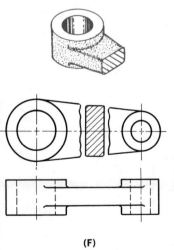

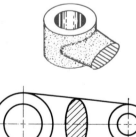

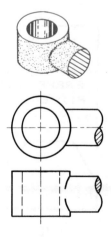

(F)

(G)

(H)

Figure 5.14   Conventional Representation of Runouts

ANSI Y14.3-1957 (SEE * P. 251)

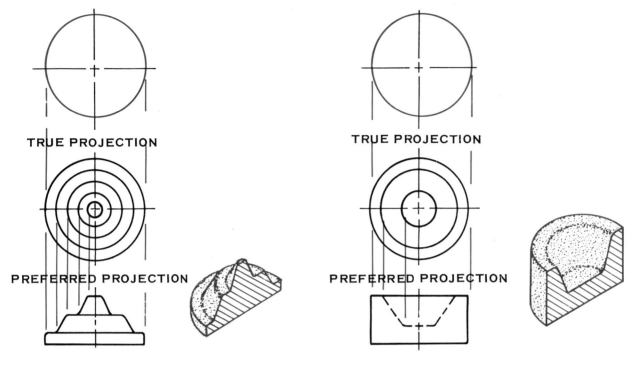

TRUE PROJECTION

PREFERRED PROJECTION

(A)

TRUE PROJECTION

PREFERRED PROJECTION

(B)

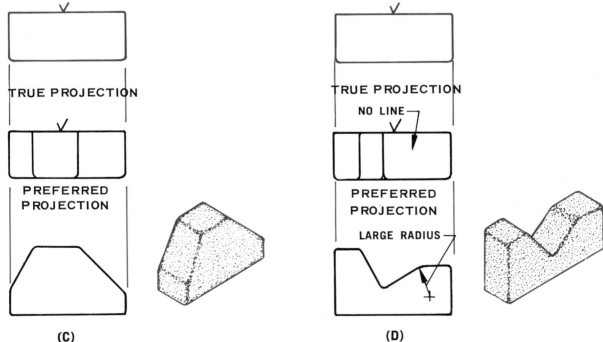

TRUE PROJECTION

PREFERRED PROJECTION

(C)

TRUE PROJECTION

NO LINE

PREFERRED PROJECTION

LARGE RADIUS

(D)

Figure 5.15   Conventional Representation of Rounds and Fillets

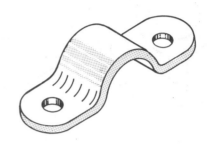

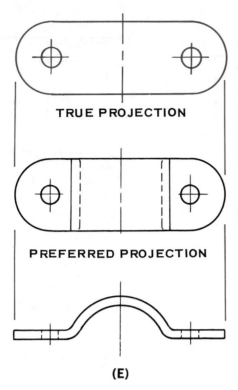

TRUE PROJECTION

PREFERRED PROJECTION

(E)

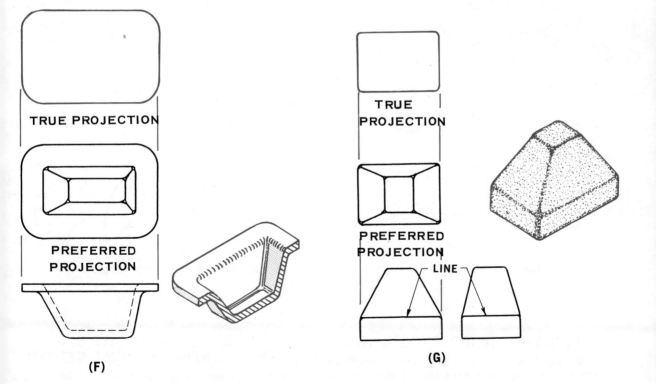

TRUE PROJECTION

PREFERRED PROJECTION

(F)

TRUE PROJECTION

PREFERRED PROJECTION

LINE

(G)

Figure 5.15 (Cont'd) Conventional Representation of Rounds and Fillets

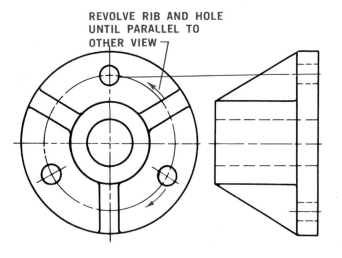

(A) ALIGNMENT OF RIB AND HOLES

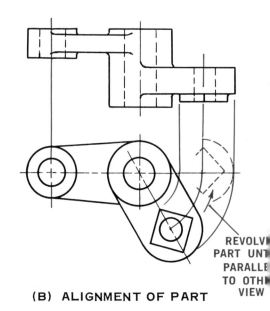

(B) ALIGNMENT OF PART

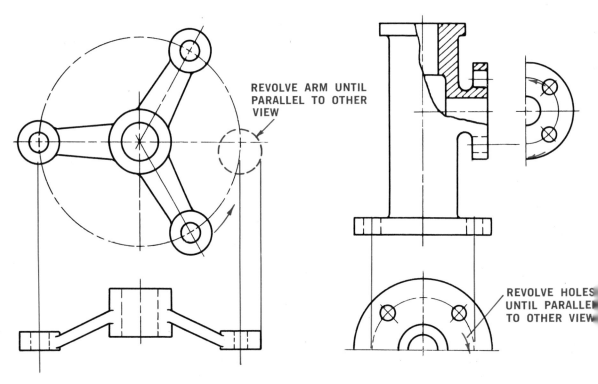

(C) ALIGNMENT OF ARM

(D) ALIGNMENT OF HOLES

Figure 5.16   Alignment of Parts and Holes

FORESHORTENED PROJECTION

When the true projection of a piece would result in confusing foreshortening, parts such as ribs or arms should be rotated until they are parallel to the line of the section or projection.

HOLES REVOLVED TO SHOW TRUE DISTANCE FROM CENTER

Drilled flanges in elevation or section should show the holes at their true distance from the center, rather than the true projection.

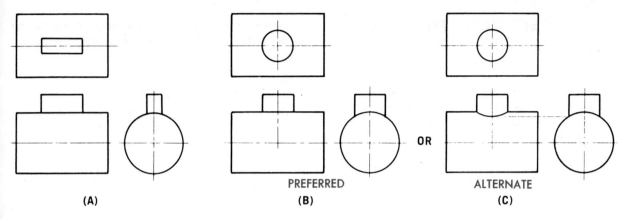

(A)   PREFERRED (B)   ALTERNATE (C)

Figure 5.17   *Conventional Representation of External Intersections*

CSA B78.1

CYLINDRICAL INTERSECTIONS

The intersection of rectangular and circular contours, unless they are very large, is shown conventionally as in figures 5.17 and 5.19. The same convention may be used to show the intersection of two cylindrical contours; or the curve of intersection may be shown as a circular arc.

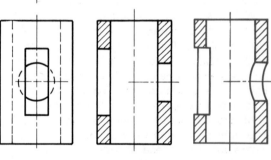

PREFERRED   TRUE

Figure 5.19   *Conventional Representation of Cylindrical Intersections*

CSA B78.1

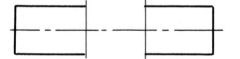

STEP 1   DRAW 2 PERPENDICULAR LINES

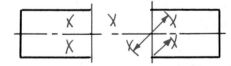

STEP 2   SWING ARCS AS SHOWN TO LOCATE CENTERS FOR COMPASS POINTS

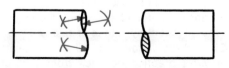

STEP 3   DRAW ARCS AND SECTIONS

Figure 5.18 *Steps for Drawing the "S" Break for Circular Parts*

CONVENTIONAL BREAKS

Long simple parts such as shafts, bars, tubes, and arms need not be drawn their entire length. Conventional breaks may be used, conveniently located, with the true length indicated by a dimension.

Often a part can be drawn to a larger scale to produce a clearer drawing if a conventional break is used. The breaks used on circular objects, known as S breaks, may be drawn either freehand or with instruments. The procedure for drawing an S break using a compass is shown. Freehand drawing of S breaks is not recommended on shafts 20 mm or larger in diameter. The suggested radius used for the break varies between the diameter of the shaft to 0.7 times the size of the shaft diameter.

REPRODUCTION OF DRAWINGS

The purpose of the engineering drawing is to communicate to others the specific data to be used in the construction and assembly of a product. The drawing fails in purpose unless it is reproduced accurately and disseminated to those who need it.

For many years, the most popular reproduction process was blueprinting. Although durable and waterproof, blueprints had to be washed and dried, and duplicates could only be made as negatives of the originals.

The demand for a faster and more versatile type of reproduction during World War II was responsible for the introduction of the diazo process (white prints) of duplicating drawings. The diazo process was faster than blueprinting and produced copies which were direct duplicates of the originals. It was reliable, inexpensive and, as a result, enjoyed rapid acceptance.

With this type of duplicating process the drawing is made on a translucent material . . . paper, cloth or plastic. The drawing, which is referred to as the tracing, is placed on sensitized print paper and, while being held still, is exposed to a strong light for a predetermined length of time. The length of time depends on the strength of the light and the printing speed of the print paper. The light penetrates through the tracing, except where the ink or lead shields the chemicals on the print paper from the light, and dissolves the chemical on the print paper, creating a latent image on the copy paper. There are several methods for developing the latent image . . . (1) by conveying the copy paper across ammonia vapor (dry process), (2) by passing the copy through developer rollers (moist process) where a chemical solution is applied to the emulsion, or (3) by pressure diazo.

The demands for more economical and versatile methods of reproducing drawings and the expense of filing has brought about the introduction of new methods of reproducing drawings.

Microfilm has been gaining wide use in recent years offering a 35 mm image set into an aperture card. Here the drawing is reduced to 35 mm and inserted into a rectangle cut in a tab card. Additional data may be keypunched on the card. The drawing may also be stored on a roll of 35 mm film.

Microfilm enables the drawing to be stored in a fraction of the floor space needed for filing the full-size paper originals. It can be referenced on the screen of a reader, or, if a print is required, it can be blown back on an enlarger-printer.

Photo-reproduction has proven to be another of the newest and most versatile methods for reproducing engineering drawings. One such printer offers, in addition to 1:1 printing, five reduction settings by which a drawing, or part of a drawing, can be physically reduced in size. Drawing reductions allow such advantages as less paper use, lower handling and mailing costs, and smaller filing space requirements.

Another advantage is that the draftsman can draw on practically any type of paper since the drawing is photographed and prints or tracings can be made from the original work.

Such photo-copying equipment is excellent for scissors and paste-up drafting.

References

1. F. L. Spalding, *The Development of Standards for Dimensioning and Tolerancing,* Graphic Science, 8 No. 2, (1966)
2. ANSI Y14.5
3. CSA B78.2
4. CSA B97.1
5. CSA B78.1
6. ANSI Y14.2

Review Questions

1. What is the primary function of an assembly drawing?
2. What are detail drawings?
3. When are detailed assembly drawings used?
4. What is meant by "limits of size"?
5. Give three examples where conventional drawing practice deviates from theoretically true projection.
6. Outline the printing procedure to reproduce drawings using the facilities in your drafting classroom.

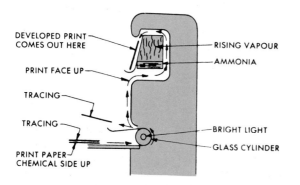

DEVELOPED PRINT COMES OUT HERE
RISING VAPOUR
AMMONIA
PRINT FACE UP
TRACING
TRACING
BRIGHT LIGHT
GLASS CYLINDER
PRINT PAPER CHEMICAL SIDE UP

ROLLERS MOVE THE TRACING AND PRINT AROUND THE LIGHT, AND MOVE THE PRINT PAST THE RISING AMMONIA VAPOUR.

Figure 5.20   The Printing Process

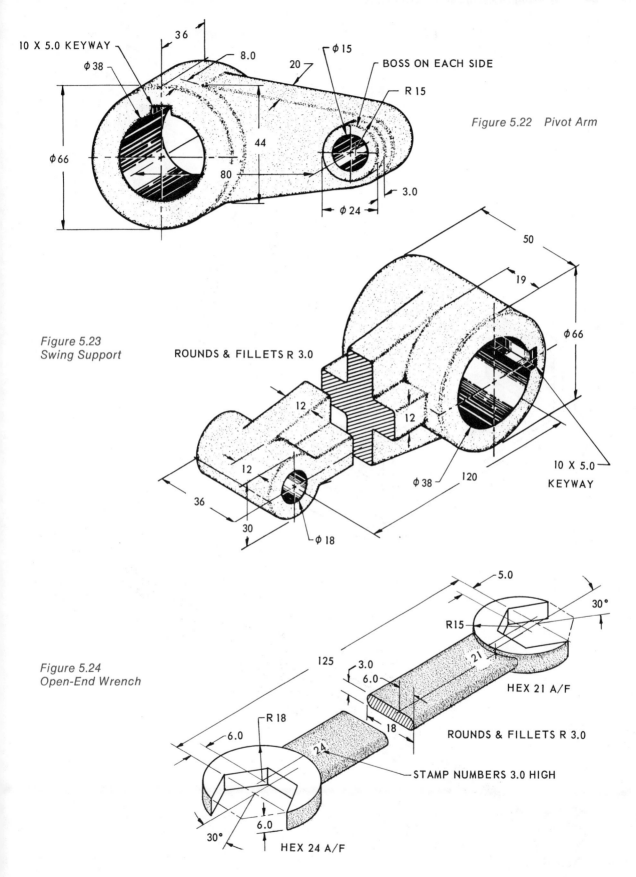

10 X 5.0 KEYWAY
φ 38
φ 66
36
8.0
20
φ 15
BOSS ON EACH SIDE
R 15
44
80
3.0
φ 24

Figure 5.22   Pivot Arm

Figure 5.23
Swing Support

ROUNDS & FILLETS R 3.0

50
19
φ 66
12
12
12
36
30
φ 18
φ 38
120
10 X 5.0
KEYWAY

Figure 5.24
Open-End Wrench

5.0
30°
R15
21
HEX 21 A/F
125
3.0
6.0
18
ROUNDS & FILLETS R 3.0
6.0
R 18
24
STAMP NUMBERS 3.0 HIGH
6.0
30°
HEX 24 A/F

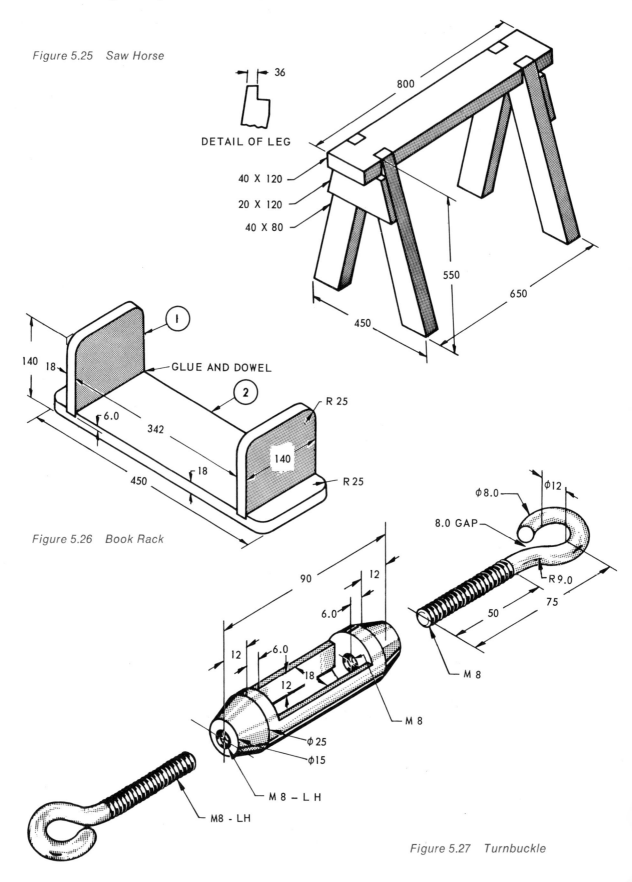

Figure 5.25   Saw Horse

DETAIL OF LEG

36

40 X 120
20 X 120
40 X 80

800
550
650
450

Figure 5.26   Book Rack

140
18
6.0
342
450
18
140
R 25
R 25
GLUE AND DOWEL
1
2

Figure 5.27   Turnbuckle

90
12
6.0
6.0
12
18
12
M 8
ϕ 25
ϕ 15
M 8 – L H
M8 - LH

ϕ8.0
ϕ12
8.0 GAP
R 9.0
50
75
M 8

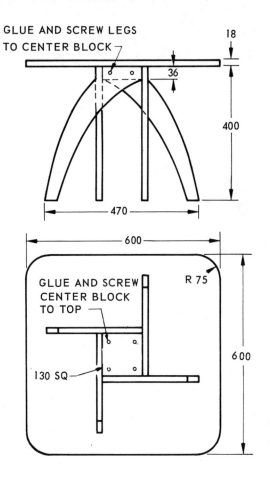

GLUE AND SCREW LEGS
TO CENTER BLOCK

18

36

400

470

600

R 75

GLUE AND SCREW
CENTER BLOCK
TO TOP

130 SQ

600

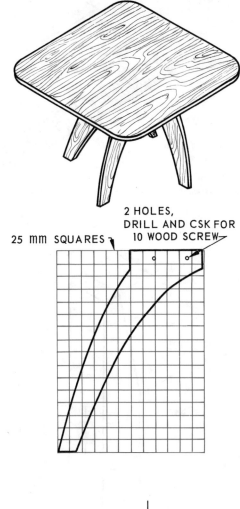

2 HOLES,
DRILL AND CSK FOR
10 WOOD SCREW

25 mm SQUARES

Figure 5.28   Garden Table

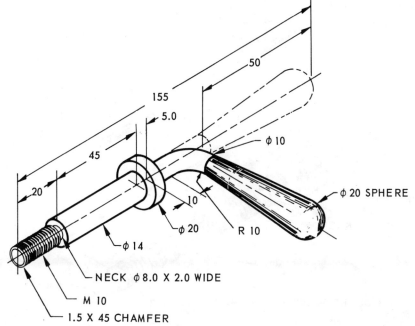

155

50

5.0

45

φ 10

20

φ 20 SPHERE

10

φ 20

R 10

φ 14

NECK φ8.0 X 2.0 WIDE

M 10

1.5 X 45 CHAMFER

Figure 5.29   Handle

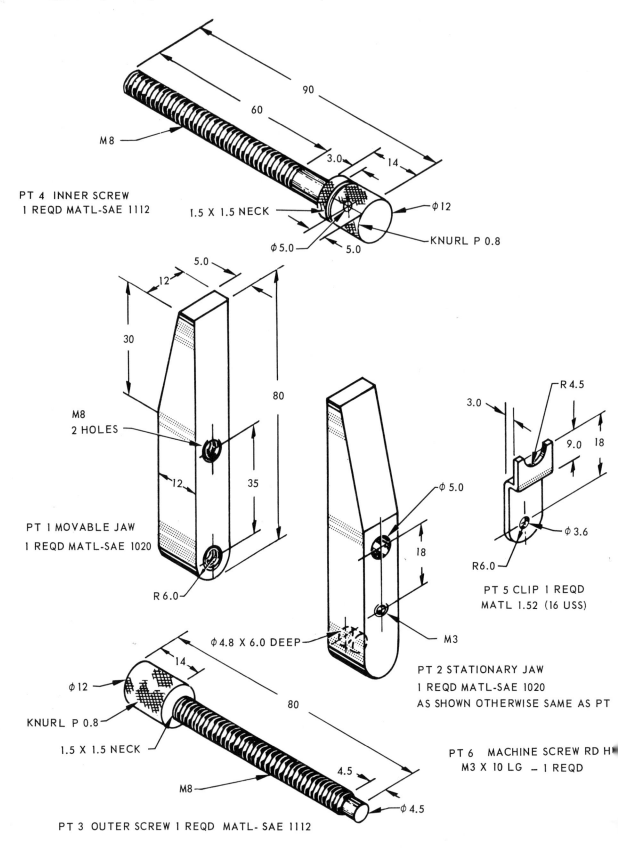

90

60

M8

PT 4 INNER SCREW
1 REQD MATL-SAE 1112

3.0

14

1.5 X 1.5 NECK

φ12

KNURL P 0.8

φ5.0

5.0

5.0

12

30

80

M8
2 HOLES

12

35

PT 1 MOVABLE JAW
1 REQD MATL-SAE 1020

R 6.0

φ 5.0

18

φ4.8 X 6.0 DEEP

M3

PT 2 STATIONARY JAW
1 REQD MATL-SAE 1020
AS SHOWN OTHERWISE SAME AS PT

3.0

R 4.5

9.0 18

φ 3.6

R6.0

PT 5 CLIP 1 REQD
MATL 1.52 (16 USS)

PT 6   MACHINE SCREW RD H
M3 X 10 LG — 1 REQD

φ12

14

KNURL P 0.8

1.5 X 1.5 NECK

M8

80

4.5

φ 4.5

PT 3 OUTER SCREW 1 REQD MATL- SAE 1112

Figure 5.30   Parallel Clamps

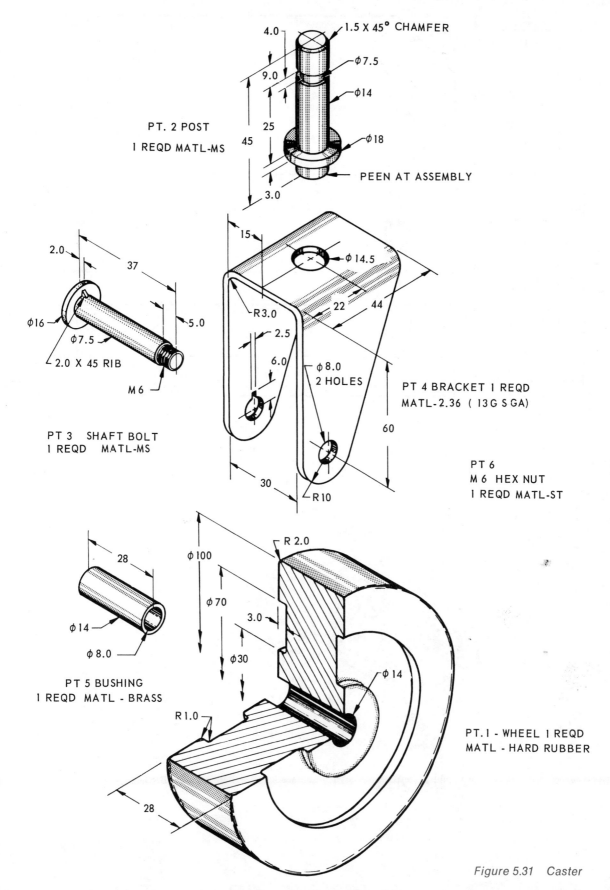

Figure 5.31   Caster

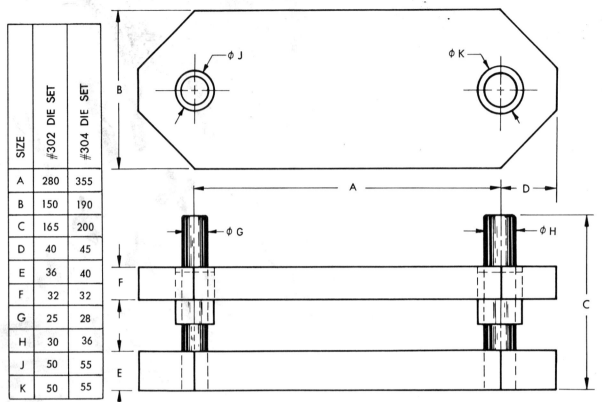

SIZE	#302 DIE SET	#304 DIE SET
A	280	355
B	150	190
C	165	200
D	40	45
E	36	40
F	32	32
G	25	28
H	30	36
J	50	55
K	50	55

Figure 5.32   Two-Post Die Set

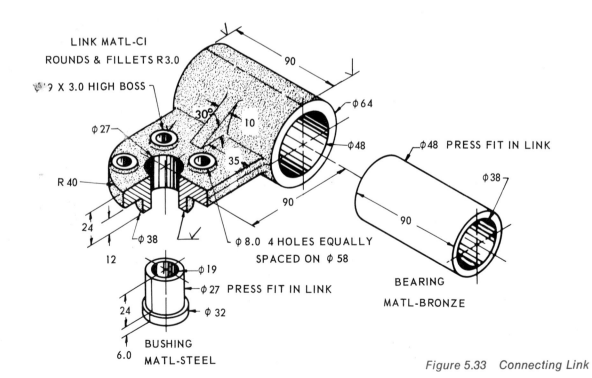

LINK MATL-CI
ROUNDS & FILLETS R3.0
2 X 3.0 HIGH BOSS
φ 27
R 40
24
φ 38
12
30°   10
35
90
φ 64
φ 48
φ 8.0 4 HOLES EQUALLY
SPACED ON φ 58
90
φ 48 PRESS FIT IN LINK
φ 38
90
BEARING
MATL-BRONZE
φ 19
φ 27 PRESS FIT IN LINK
24
φ 32
6.0
BUSHING
MATL-STEEL

Figure 5.33   Connecting Link

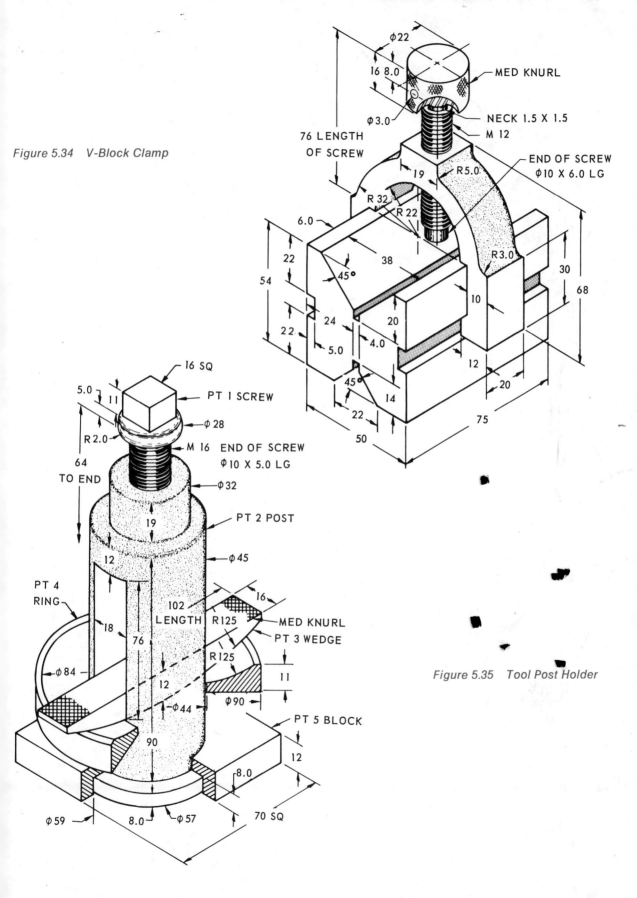

Figure 5.34   V-Block Clamp

φ22

MED KNURL

16 8.0

φ3.0

NECK 1.5 X 1.5
M 12

76 LENGTH
OF SCREW

END OF SCREW
φ10 X 6.0 LG

19   R5.0

R 32
R 22

6.0

22   45°   38

R3.0

54   30   68

24   20   10

2 2   4.0

5.0   45°   12

45°

14

22   20

50   75

16 SQ

PT 1 SCREW

5.0   11

φ 28

R 2.0

M 16   END OF SCREW
φ10 X 5.0 LG

64
TO END

φ32

19

PT 2 POST

12   φ45

PT 4
RING   16

102
LENGTH   R125

MED KNURL

18   PT 3 WEDGE

76   R125

φ84   11

12

φ44   φ90

PT 5 BLOCK

90

12

8.0

φ59   8.0   φ57   70 SQ

Figure 5.35   Tool Post Holder

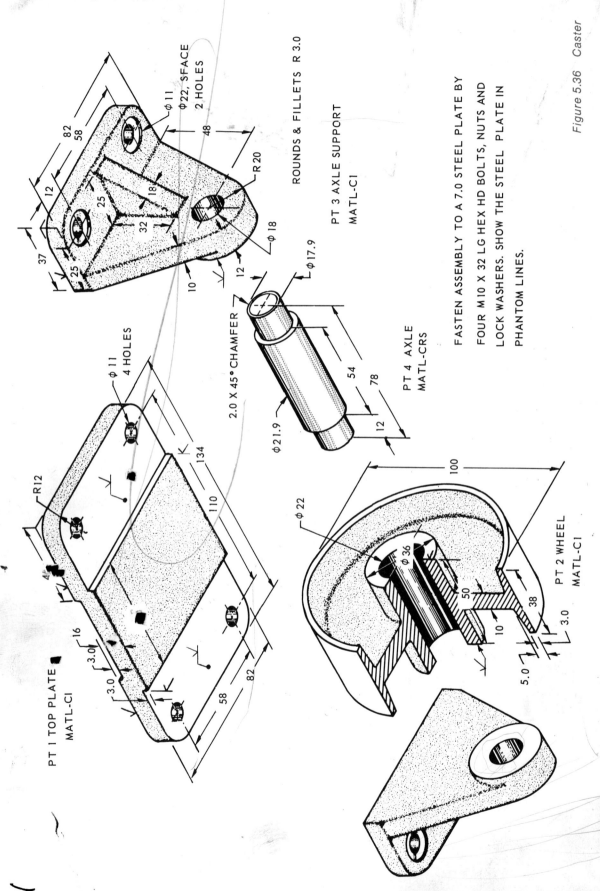

Φ 11
Φ22, SFACE
2 HOLES

82
58
12
25
18
32
37
25
48

R 20

Φ 18

ROUNDS & FILLETS R 3.0

10   12

PT 3 AXLE SUPPORT
MATL-CI

L Φ17.9

2.0 X 45° CHAMFER

54
78
12
Φ 21.9

PT 4 AXLE
MATL-CRS

FASTEN ASSEMBLY TO A 7.0 STEEL PLATE BY
FOUR M10 X 32 LG HEX HD BOLTS, NUTS AND
LOCK WASHERS. SHOW THE STEEL PLATE IN
PHANTOM LINES.

Φ 11
4 HOLES

R12

134
110
16
3.0
3.0
58
82

PT 1 TOP PLATE
MATL-CI

Φ 22

100
Φ 36
50
38
10
3.0
5.0

PT 2 WHEEL
MATL-CI

Figure 5.36   Caster

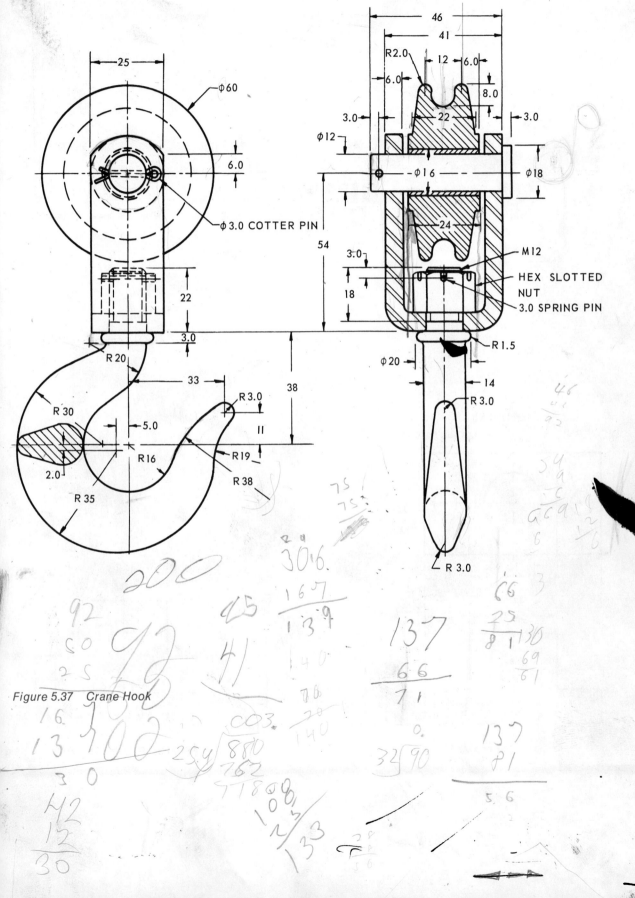

Figure 5.37   Crane Hook

CHAPTER SIX

SIMPLIFIED DRAFTING

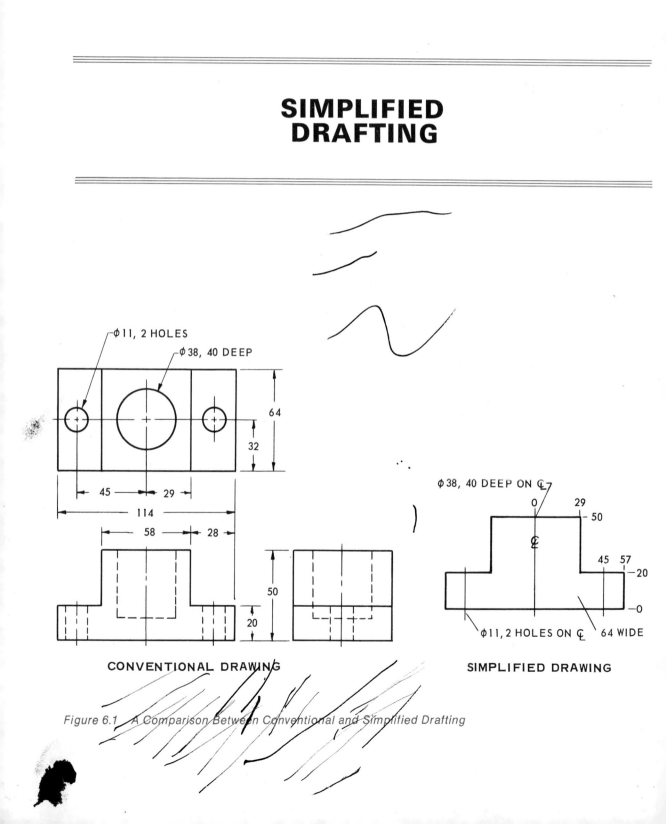

Figure 6.1   A Comparison Between Conventional and Simplified Drafting

SIMPLIFIED DRAFTING

The challenge of modern industry is to produce more and better goods at competitive prices. Drafting, like all other branches of industry, must share in the responsibility for making this increased productivity possible. The old concept of drafting, that of producing an elaborate and beautiful drawing, complete with all the lines, projected views, and sections, must give way to a simplified method. The new simplified method of drafting must embrace many modern economical drafting practices but surrender nothing in either clarity of presentation or accuracy of dimensioning. Drafting stripped of its frills is the new standard.

Three most effective practices used in simplified drafting are:

- Simplification of dimensioning

- Simplification of detail drawing

- Extensive use of freehand sketching.

SIMPLIFICATION OF DIMENSIONING

Simplification of dimensioning not only reduces drafting time but avoids cluttering a drawing with unnecessary lines, thereby making it easier to read.

No other single factor has more influence on the use of drawings than dimensioning. It is not sufficient to have dimensions numerically correct; it is equally important to dimension a drawing properly so that computation of sizes is unnecessary.

Arrowless Dimensioning 1, 2

To avoid having a large number of dimensions extending away from the part, arrowless or ordinate dimensioning may be used. In this system, the "zero" lines represent the vertical and horizontal datum lines, and each of the dimensions without an arrowhead indicates the distance from the zero line. There is never more than one zero line in each direction.

Arrowless dimensioning is particularly useful when the features are produced on a general-purpose machine, such as a jig borer, tape-controlled drill, or turret-type press.

HOLE SYMBOL	HOLE SIZE
A	6.0
B	5.0
C	4.0
D	3.0

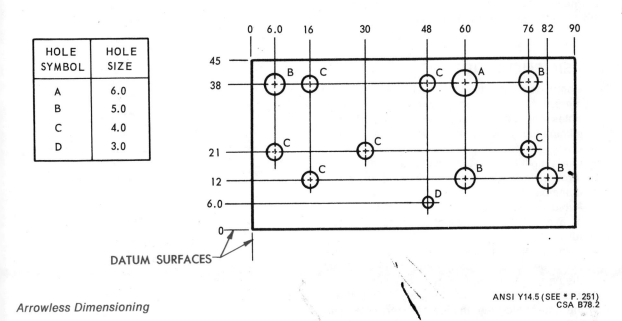

DATUM SURFACES

Arrowless Dimensioning

ANSI Y14.5 (SEE * P. 251)
CSA B78.2

HOLE SYMBOL	HOLE DIA	LOCATION X →	Y ↑
A_1	6.0	58	38
B_1	5.0	6.0	38
B_2	5.0	76	38
B_3	5.0	60	12
B_4	5.0	80	12
C_1	4.0	16	38
C_2	4.0	48	38
C_3	4.0	6.0	20
C_4	4.0	30	20
C_5	4.0	76	20
C_6	4.0	16	12
D_1	3.0	48	6.0

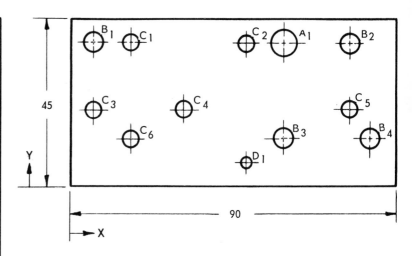

Tabular Dimensioning   ANSI Y14.5 (SEE * P. 251)
CSA B78.2

Tabular Dimensioning 1

When there is a very large number of holes or repetitive features, such as in a chassis or a printed circuit board, and where the multitude of center lines would make a drawing difficult to read, tabular dimensioning is recommended. In this system each hole or feature is assigned a letter, or a letter and numeral subscript. The feature dimensions and the feature location along the X and Y axes are given in a table. The numbering and lettering of the features are normally from left to right and from top to bottom.

SIMPLIFICATION OF DETAILS

1. Complicated parts are best described by means of a drawing. However, explanatory notes can complement the drawing, thereby eliminating views that are time consuming to draw.
2. Use simplified drawing practices as described throughout this text, especially on threads and common features.
3. Avoid unnecessary views. In many cases one or two views are sufficient to explain the part fully.
4. When a large number of holes of similar size are to be made in a part, there is a chance that the person producing the part may misinterpret a conventional drawing. To simplify the drawing and reduce the chance of error, hole symbols such as shown in figure 6.3 are recommended.

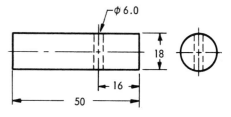

CONVENTIONAL DRAWING

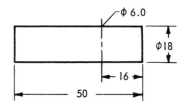

EXAMPLE I

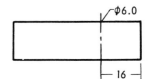

PT. 2 ⌀18 X 50 LG

EXAMPLE 2

NOTE PT. 2 ⌀18 X 50 LG
⌀ 6.0 HOLE - 16 FROM END

PART DESCRIBED BY A NOTE

EXAMPLE 3

Simplified Drafting Practices for Detailed Parts

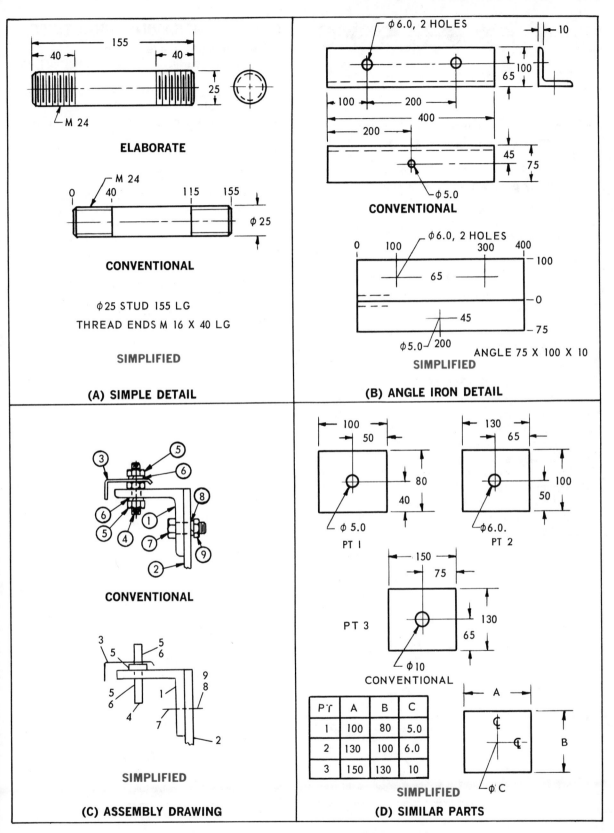

(A) SIMPLE DETAIL

ELABORATE

CONVENTIONAL

φ25 STUD 155 LG
THREAD ENDS M 16 X 40 LG

SIMPLIFIED

(B) ANGLE IRON DETAIL

φ6.0, 2 HOLES

CONVENTIONAL

φ6.0, 2 HOLES

ANGLE 75 X 100 X 10

SIMPLIFIED

(C) ASSEMBLY DRAWING

CONVENTIONAL

SIMPLIFIED

(D) SIMILAR PARTS

φ5.0 PT 1

φ6.0. PT 2

PT 3

φ10

CONVENTIONAL

PT	A	B	C
1	100	80	5.0
2	130	100	6.0
3	150	130	10

SIMPLIFIED

Figure 6.2   Comparison Between Conventional and Simplified Drawings

Figure 6.3 Recommended Hole Symbols in Order of Preference

5. The use of the abbreviation ₵ indicates that all dimensions are symmetrical about the line indicated.
6. A simplified assembly drawing should be for assembly purposes only. Some means of simplification are:

   • Standard parts such as nuts, bolts, and washers need not be drawn;

   • Reference part circles and arrowheads on leaders can be omitted;

   • Small fillets and rounds on cast parts need not be shown;

   • Phantom outline of complicated details can often be used.

Freehand Sketching

Most shops care little whether the drawing is freehand, whether one view is shown or whether the drawing is to scale, so long as the proportions are approximate. They are interested in having the necessary information clearly shown. Freehand sketches and drawings made with instruments can be shown on one sheet. However, it must be clearly understood that the use of freehand sketching does not give the draftsman a license to turn out sloppy work.

OTHER TIMESAVING PRACTICES

• Use templates where possible.
• Show only partial views of symmetrical objects.
• Avoid the use of elaborate pictorial or repetitive detail.
• Avoid the use of unnecessary hidden lines which do not add clarification.
• Use description wherever practical to eliminate drawings.
• Use symbols instead of words.
• Use pre-printed repetitive symbols and notes on drawings where applicable.
• Within limits, a small drawing is made more easily and quickly than a large drawing.
• Eliminate repetitive data by use of general notes or phantom lines.
• Omit center lines except when necessary for processing.
• Eliminate views where the shape or dimension can be given by description; for example, hex, sq., φ, on ₵, thk, etc.

References

1. CSA B78.2
2. ANSI Y14.5

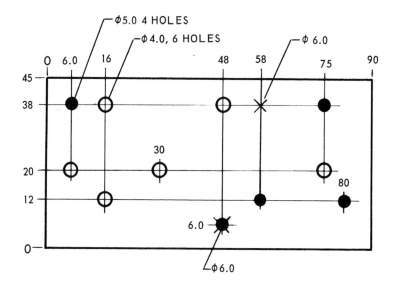

Hole Symbols Used with Arrowless Dimensioning

Review Questions

1. Why is simplified drafting important to modern industry?
2. What are the two methods used in the simplification of dimensioning?
3. When is each of these methods of particular use?
4. Give four techniques used in the simplification of details.
5. Give two important considerations when making freehand sketches.

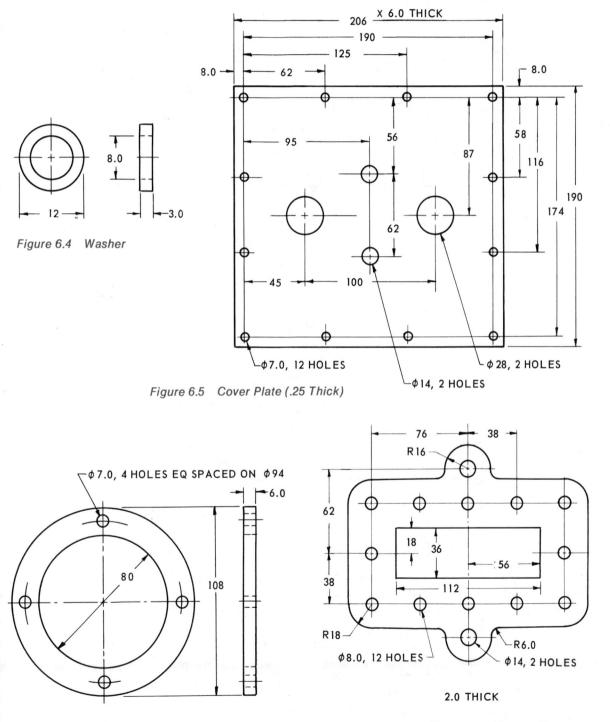

Figure 6.4   Washer

Figure 6.5   Cover Plate (.25 Thick)

Figure 6.6   Spacer

Figure 6.7   Gasket (.06 Thick)

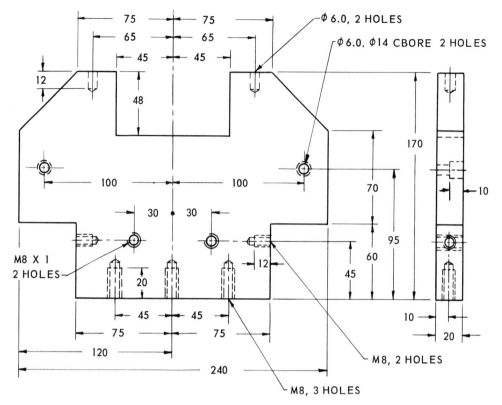

Figure 6.8   Back Plate

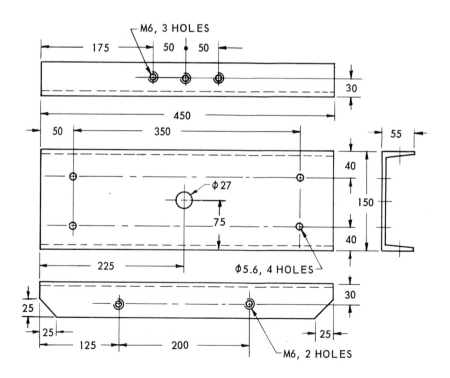

Figure 6.9   Channel Clamp

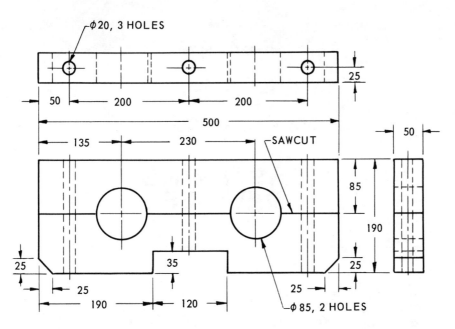

Figure 6.10   Tube Support

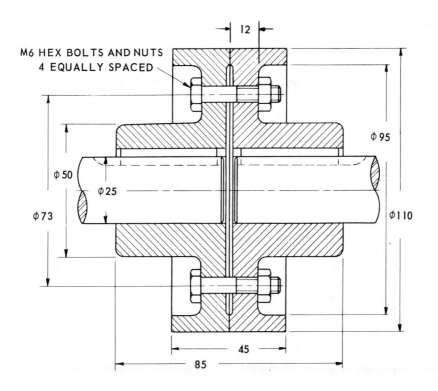

Figure 6.11   Flanged Coupling

CHAPTER SEVEN

FASTENING DEVICES

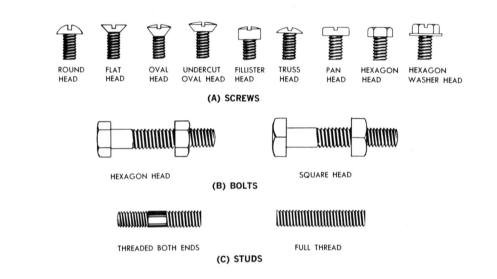

ROUND HEAD   FLAT HEAD   OVAL HEAD   UNDERCUT OVAL HEAD   FILLISTER HEAD   TRUSS HEAD   PAN HEAD   HEXAGON HEAD   HEXAGON WASHER HEAD

(A) SCREWS

HEXAGON HEAD   SQUARE HEAD

(B) BOLTS

THREADED BOTH ENDS   FULL THREAD

(C) STUDS

Threaded Fasteners

Fastening devices are important in the construction of manufactured products, in the machines and devices used in manufacturing processes, and in the construction of all types of buildings. Fastening devices are used in the smallest watch and the largest ocean liner.

There are two basic kinds of fastening. Rivets and welds are *permanent fastenings;* bolts, screws, studs, nuts, pins and keys are *removable fastenings.* As industry progressed, fastening devices became standardized, and they have definite characteristics and names. A thorough knowledge of the design and graphic representation of the commoner fasteners is an essential part of drafting.

SCREW THREADS [1,2]

Threaded fastenings, such as screws, bolts, studs, and nuts, are manufactured in a great variety of forms and sizes. See the charts in the appendix for the dimensions and specifications of standard threaded fasteners. Shown above are some of the common machine screws, cap screws, bolts, nuts, and studs.

A screw thread is a continuous ridge of uniform section in the form of a helix on the external or internal surface of a cylinder. A *helix* (plural, *helices*) is a curve generated by a point moving uniformly about a cylinder and uniformly parallel to the axis of the cylinder. The principle of the helix curve can be demonstrated by winding a piece of string about a transparent glass cylinder, such as a test tube or a straight-sided drinking glass.

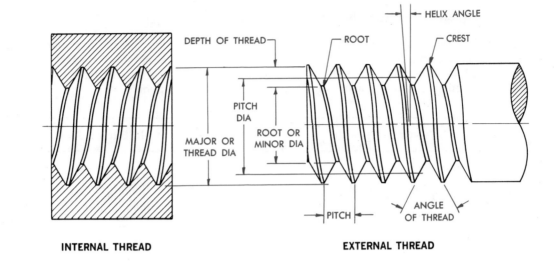

Screw Thread Terms

THREAD FORMS

The ISO metric thread form is now replacing all the present V-shaped metric and inch threads. The Unified National was the standard V-shaped inch thread used before the adoption of the metric thread. Prior to that the American National thread was the standard thread form in use in North America and the Whitworth thread form the British standard.

The sharp V thread form is seldom used for general fastening purposes, but it is sometimes used in precision instruments. The knuckle thread is usually rolled or cast. A familiar example of this form is seen on electric light bulbs and sockets. The square and acme forms are designed to transmit motion or power, as on the lead screw of a lathe. The buttress thread takes pressure in only one direction—against the surface perpendicular to the axis.

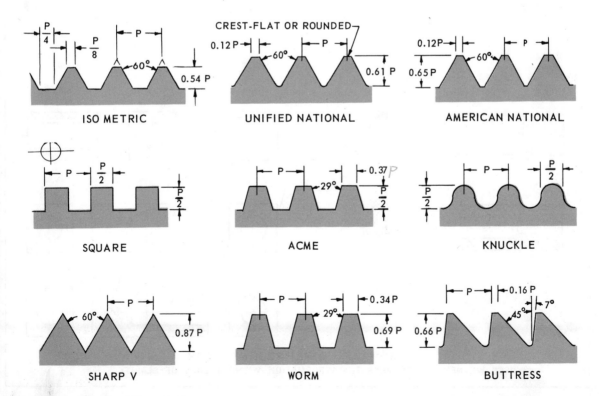

Figure 7.1   Standard Thread Forms

THREAD REPRESENTATION

True representation of a screw thread is seldom provided on working drawings because it would require very laborious and accurate drawing, involving repetitive development of the helix curve of the thread. A symbolic representation of threads is now standard practice. For the schematic external *thread symbol,* lines are drawn perpendicular to the axis, with thin lines

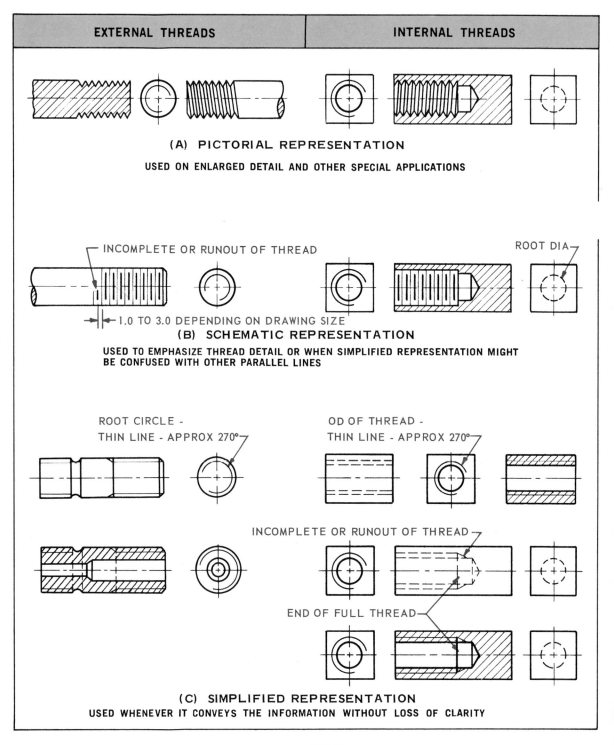

EXTERNAL THREADS   **INTERNAL THREADS**

(A) PICTORIAL REPRESENTATION

USED ON ENLARGED DETAIL AND OTHER SPECIAL APPLICATIONS

INCOMPLETE OR RUNOUT OF THREAD   ROOT DIA

1.0 TO 3.0 DEPENDING ON DRAWING SIZE

(B) SCHEMATIC REPRESENTATION

USED TO EMPHASIZE THREAD DETAIL OR WHEN SIMPLIFIED REPRESENTATION MIGHT BE CONFUSED WITH OTHER PARALLEL LINES

ROOT CIRCLE -
THIN LINE - APPROX 270°

OD OF THREAD -
THIN LINE - APPROX 270°

INCOMPLETE OR RUNOUT OF THREAD

END OF FULL THREAD

(C) SIMPLIFIED REPRESENTATION

USED WHENEVER IT CONVEYS THE INFORMATION WITHOUT LOSS OF CLARITY

Figure 7.1   Canadian Standard Thread Conventions (CSA)   CSA B78.1

representing the crest of the thread and heavy lines representing the root. For a threaded hole that is hidden from view, hidden lines are drawn parallel to the axis to represent the minor and major diameters.

For the *simplified external thread symbol* a solid line (Canadian Standard) or a broken line (American Standard) is drawn parallel to the axis to represent the minor diameter. For a threaded hole that is hidden from view, the simplified symbol is the same as the regular symbol.

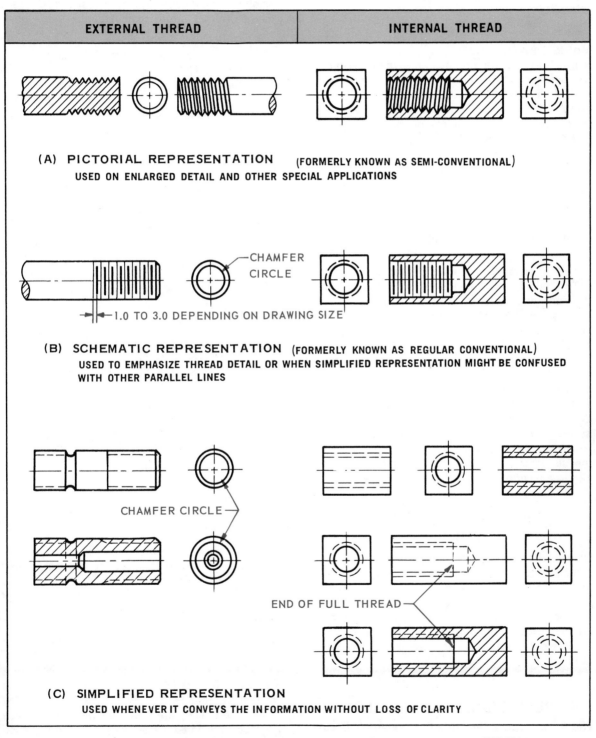

| EXTERNAL THREAD | INTERNAL THREAD |

(A) PICTORIAL REPRESENTATION (FORMERLY KNOWN AS SEMI-CONVENTIONAL)
USED ON ENLARGED DETAIL AND OTHER SPECIAL APPLICATIONS

CHAMFER CIRCLE

1.0 TO 3.0 DEPENDING ON DRAWING SIZE

(B) SCHEMATIC REPRESENTATION (FORMERLY KNOWN AS REGULAR CONVENTIONAL)
USED TO EMPHASIZE THREAD DETAIL OR WHEN SIMPLIFIED REPRESENTATION MIGHT BE CONFUSED WITH OTHER PARALLEL LINES

CHAMFER CIRCLE

END OF FULL THREAD

(C) SIMPLIFIED REPRESENTATION
USED WHENEVER IT CONVEYS THE INFORMATION WITHOUT LOSS OF CLARITY

Figure 7.2 American National Standard Thread Conventions (ANSI)

ANSI Y14.6 (SEE * P. 251)

THREAD STANDARDS

With the progress and growth of industry, a need has grown for uniform, interchangeable threaded fasteners. The factors that influence standards, aside from the threaded forms previously mentioned, are the **pitch** of the thread and the **major diameter**.

Metric Threads

Metric threads are grouped into diameter-pitch combinations distinguished from each other by the pitch applied to specific diameters. The "pitch" for metric threads is the distance between corresponding points on adjacent teeth. In addition to a coarse and fine pitch series, a series of constant pitches is available.

Inch Threads

Up to 1976, practically all threaded assemblies on this continent were designed using inch-sized threads. In this system the pitch is equal to

$$\frac{1}{\text{Number of threads per inch.}}$$

The number of threads per inch is set for different diameters in what is called a thread "series". For the Unified National system there is the coarse thread series and the fine thread series.

In addition, there is an extra fine thread series, UNEF, for use where a small pitch is desirable, such as on thin-walled tubing. For special work and for diameters larger than those specified in the coarse and fine series, the Unified thread system has three series that provide for the same number of threads per inch regardless of the diameter. These are the 8-thread series, the 12-thread series, and the 16-thread series.

RIGHT- AND LEFT-HANDED THREADS

Unless designated otherwise, threads are assumed to be right-hand. A bolt being threaded into a tapped hole would be turned in a right-hand (clockwise) direction. For some special applications, such as turnbuckles, left-hand threads are required. When such a thread is necessary, the letters LH are added after the thread designation.

THREAD GRADES AND CLASSES

The **fit** of a screw thread is the amount of clearance between the screw and the nut when they are assembled together.

Metric Threads

For each of the two main thread elements, pitch diameter and crest diameter, a number of tolerance grades have been established. The number of the tolerance grades reflects the size of the tolerance. For example: Grade 4 tolerances are smaller than Grade 6 tolerances and Grade 8 tolerances are larger than Grade 6 tolerances.

In each case, Grade 6 tolerances should be used for medium quality length of engagement applications. The tolerance grades below Grade 6 are intended for applications involving fine quality and/or short lengths of engagement. Tolerance grades above Grade 6 are intended for coarse quality and/or long lengths of engagement.

In addition to the tolerance grade a positional tolerance is required. This defines the maximum-material limits of the pitch and crest diameters of the external and internal threads and indicates their relationship to the basic profile.

In conformance with current coating (or plating) thickness requirements and the demand for ease of assembly, a series of tolerance positions reflecting the application of varying amounts of allowance has been established as follows:

For external threads:

> Tolerance position "e" (large allowance)
> Tolerance position "g" (small allowance)
> Tolerance position "h" (no allowance)

For internal threads:

> Tolerance position "G" (small allowance)
> Tolerance position "H" (no allowance)

Inch Threads

Three classes of external thread (Classes 1A, 2A, and 3A) and three classes of internal thread (Classes 1B, 2B, and 3B) are provided. These classes differ from each other in the amount of the allowances and tolerances provided in each class.

The general characteristics and uses of the various classes are as follows:

Classes 1A and 1B. These classes produce the loosest fit, that is, the greatest amount of play in assembly. They are useful for work where ease of assembly and disassembly is essential, such as for some ordnance work and for stove bolts and other rough bolts and nuts.

Classes 2A and 2B. These classes are designed for the ordinary good grade of commercial products, such as machine screws and fasteners, and for most interchangeable parts.

Classes 3A and 3B. These classes are intended for exceptionally high-grade commercial products, where a particularly close or snug fit is essential and the high cost of precision tools and machines is warranted.

THREAD DESIGNATION

Metric Threads

ISO metric screw threads are defined by the nominal size (basic major diameter) and pitch, both expressed in millimetres. An "M" specifying an ISO metric screw thread precedes the nominal size and an "x" separates the nominal size from the pitch. For the coarse thread series only, the pitch is not shown unless the dimension for the length of the thread is required. When specifying the length of thread an "x" is used to separate the length of thread from the rest of the designations. For external threads, the length of thread may be given as a dimension on the drawing.

For example, a 10 mm diameter, 1.25 pitch, fine thread series is expressed as M10 x 1.25. A 10 mm diameter, 1.5 pitch, coarse thread series is expressed as M10; the pitch is not shown unless the length of thread is required. If the latter thread was 25 mm long and this information was required on the drawing then the thread callout would be M10 x 1.5 x 25.

A complete designation for an ISO metric screw thread comprises in addition to the basic designation, an identification for the tolerance class. The tolerance class designation is separated from the basic designation by a dash and includes the symbol for the pitch diameter tolerance followed immediately by the symbol for crest diameter tolerance. Each of these symbols consist of first a numeral indicating the grade tolerance followed by a letter indicating the tolerance position (a capital letter for internal threads and a lower case letter for external threads). Where the pitch and crest diameter symbols are identical, the symbol need only be given once and not repeated.

Inch Threads

Thread designation for inch threads, whether external or internal, is expressed in this order: diameter (nominal or major diameter), number of threads per inch, thread form and series, and class of fit.

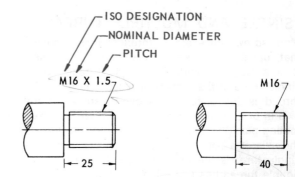

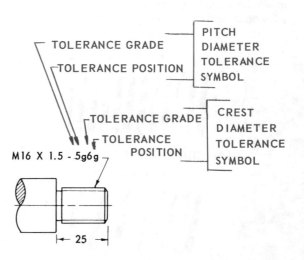

(A) BASIC THREAD CALLOUT

(B) ADDITIONAL THREAD CALLOUT

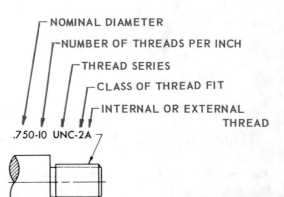

(C) INCH THREAD CALLOUT

Thread Specifications

SINGLE AND MULTIPLE THREADS

Most screws have single threads; it is assumed that, unless the thread is designated otherwise, it is a single thread. The single thread has a single ridge in the form of a helix. The *lead* of a thread is the distance travelled parallel to the axis in one rotation of a part in relation to a fixed mating part (the distance a nut would travel along the axis of a bolt with one rotation of the nut). In single threads the lead is equal to the pitch. A double thread has two ridges, started 180° apart, in the form of helices, and the lead is twice the pitch. A triple thread has three ridges, started 120° apart, in the form of helices, and the lead is three times the pitch. Double and triple threads are used where fast movement is desired with a minimum number of rotations, such as on threaded mechanisms for opening and closing windows.

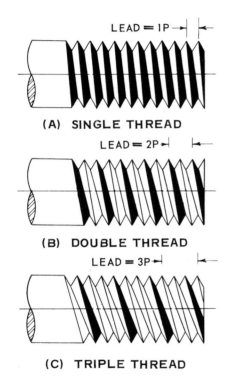

(A) SINGLE THREAD

(B) DOUBLE THREAD

(C) TRIPLE THREAD

Single and Multiple Threads

TERMS RELATED TO THREADED FASTENERS

The *tap drill size* for a threaded (tapped) hole is a diameter equal to the minor diameter of the thread. The *clearance drill size,* which permits the free passage of a bolt, is a diameter slightly greater than the major diameter of the bolt. A *counterbored hole* is a circular, flat-bottomed recess that permits the head of a bolt or cap screw to rest below the surface of the part. A

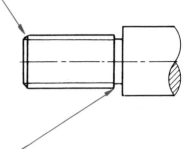

CHAMFER SHOWN AT BEGINNING OF THREAD
CHAMFER SIZE NEED NOT BE SHOWN

RECESS SHOWN AT END OF THREAD
RECESS SIZE NEED NOT BE SHOWN

Omission of Thread Information on Detail Drawings

countersunk hole is an angular-sided recess that accommodates the shape of a flat-head cap screw or machine screw or an oval-head machine screw. *Spotfacing* is a machine operation to provide a smooth, flat surface where a bolt head or nut will rest.

COMMON THREADED FASTENERS

Machine Screws. Machine screws are available in a range of sizes and thread classes, and are available in a variety of heads. They may be used in tapped holes or with nuts.

Cap Screws. A cap screw is a threaded fastener which joins two or more parts together by passing through a clearance hole in one part and screwing into a tapped hole in the other and which is tightened or released by torquing the head.

Cap screws range in size starting from 6.0 mm in diameter and are available in five basic types of head.

Bolts. A bolt is a threaded fastener which passes through clearance holes in assembled parts and threads into a nut. Bolts and nuts are available in a variety of shapes and sizes. The square and hexagon head are the two most popular designs and range in size from 6.0 to 72 mm in diameter.

Studs. Studs are shafts threaded at both ends and are used in assemblies. One end of the stud is threaded into one of the parts being assembled and the other assembly parts, such as washers and covers, are guided over the studs through clearance holes and are held together by means of a nut which is threaded over the exposed end of the stud.

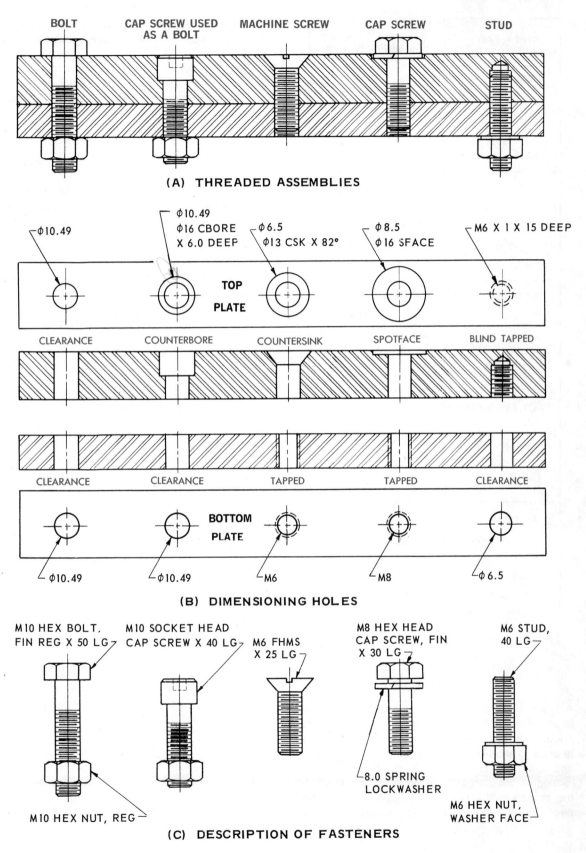

(A) THREADED ASSEMBLIES

(B) DIMENSIONING HOLES

(C) DESCRIPTION OF FASTENERS

Figure 7.3 Common Threaded Fasteners

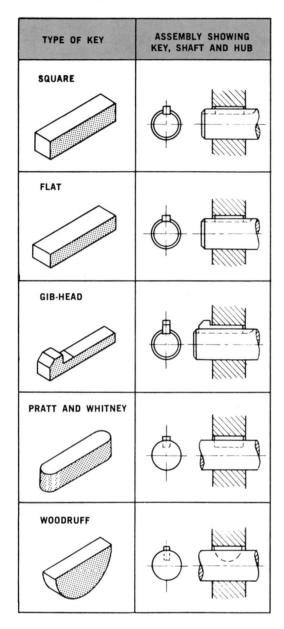

TYPE OF KEY	ASSEMBLY SHOWING KEY, SHAFT AND HUB
SQUARE	
FLAT	
GIB-HEAD	
PRATT AND WHITNEY	
WOODRUFF	

Figure 7.4   Common Keys

KEYS

A key is a piece of steel lying partly in a groove in the shaft, called a *keyseat,* and extending into another groove, called a *keyway,* in the hub. It is used to secure gears, pulleys, cranks, handles, and similar machine parts to shafts, so that the motion of the part is transmitted to the shaft, or the motion of the shaft to the part, without slippage. The key may also act as a safety device: its

size is calculated so that, when overloading takes place, the key will shear or break before the part or shaft breaks.

Common types of key are the square, the flatstock, and the Woodruff. Tables in the appendix give standard square and flat key sizes recommended for various shaft diameters and the necessary dimensions for standard Woodruff keys.

The Woodruff key is semicircular in shape and fits into a semicircular keyseat in the shaft and a rectangular keyway in the hub. Woodruff keys are currently only available in *inch-pound* sizes and are identified by number as follows. Table II in the appendix gives millimetre equivalents of common Woodruff keys. The key number indicates the nominal dimensions of the key. The last two digits of the number give the normal diameter in eighths of an inch, and the digits preceding the last two give the nominal width in thirty-seconds of an inch. For example, a No. 1210 Woodruff key indicates a key 12/32 in. by 10/8 in., or a .38 in. wide by 1.25 in. dia. key.

DIMENSIONING OF KEYWAYS AND KEYSEATS

All dimensions of keyways and keyseats for square and flat keys, with the exception of the length of the flat portion of the keyseat, which is given by a direct dimension on the drawing, are shown on the drawing by a note specifying first the width and then the depth. This type of dimensioning is the standard method used for unit production where the machinist is expected to fit the key into the keyway and keyseat.

For interchangeable assembly and mass production purposes, keyway and keyseat dimensions are given in limit dimensions to assure proper fit and are located from the opposite side of the hole or shaft.

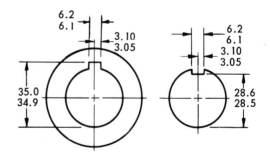

Dimensioning Keyways and Keyseats for Interchangeable Assembly

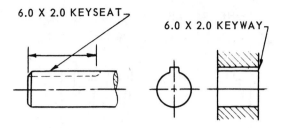

(A) SQUARE AND FLAT KEYS

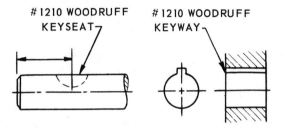

(B) WOODRUFF KEYS

Dimensioning Keyways and Keyseats for Unit Assembly

References

1. CSA B1.1
2. ANSI Y14.6
3. *Manual of Unified Screw Threads for Shop and Drafting Room,* published by CSA.

Review Questions

1. Name and give examples of the two basic kinds of fastening devices used in industry.

2. Give the definition of a screw thread.

3. What is a helix?

4. Name six different thread forms and indicate their general application.

5. What two systems of symbolic representation for threads are now standard practice?

6. What is the "pitch" of a thread?

7. Name two common thread series.

8. When is the lead of a thread not equal to the pitch?

9. Give the information, in the proper order in which it would be expressed, for a typical thread specification.

10. What is meant by a tap drill? a clearance drill?

11. Define the terms "counterbore", "countersink", and "spotface".

12. What is the purpose of keys?

13. What determines the size of key to be used?

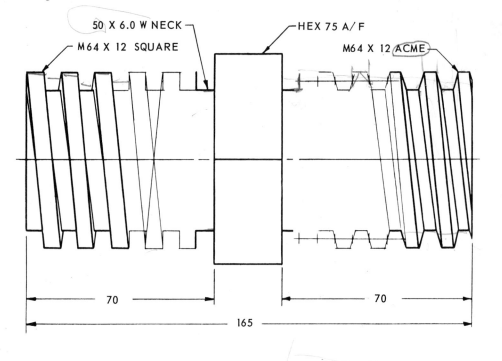

50 X 6.0 W NECK

M64 X 12 SQUARE

HEX 75 A/F

M64 X 12 ACME

70

70

165

Figure 7.5   Connector

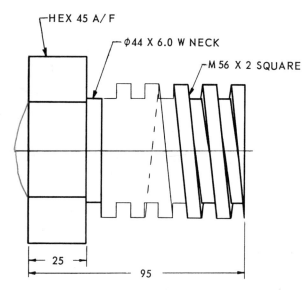

HEX 45 A/F

⌀44 X 6.0 W NECK

M 56 X 2 SQUARE

25

95

Figure 7.6   Plug

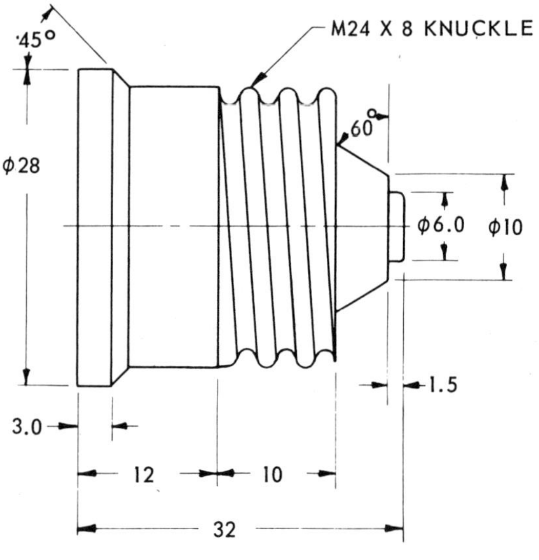

M24 X 8 KNUCKLE

45°

60°

⌀28

⌀6.0   ⌀10

1.5

3.0

12

10

32

Figure 7.7   Fuse

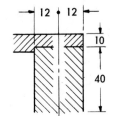
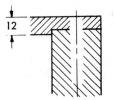

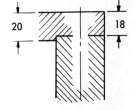

CONNECTION A
M10 X 30 LG
FIN HEX HD CAP SCREW

CONNECTION B
M10 X 40 LG STUD
THREAD EACH END 20 LG
REG HEX NUT AND LOCKWASHER

CONNECTION C
M10 X 30 LG
FL HD CAP SCREW

CONNECTION D
M10 X 1.25 X 25 LG
SOCKET HEAD CAP SCREW
AND LOCKWASHER

USING SIMPLIFIED THREAD SYMBOLS, DRAW TO FULL SIZE THE CONNECTIONS
SHOWN. DIMENSION BOTH THE CLEARANCE AND THE THREADED HOLES. REFER TO
THE APPENDIX FOR SIZES. IF DESIRED, A TOP VIEW OF THE FASTENERS MAY BE DRAWN.

Figure 7.8   Standard Fasteners

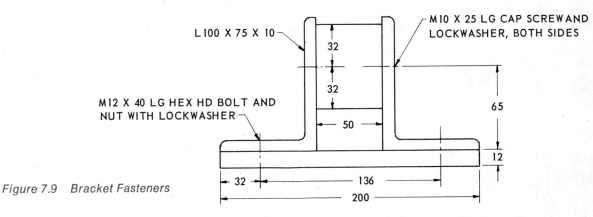

Figure 7.9   Bracket Fasteners

USING SIMPLIFIED THREAD SYMBOLS DRAW THE ABOVE
ASSEMBLY SHOWING THE FASTENERS IN POSITION.

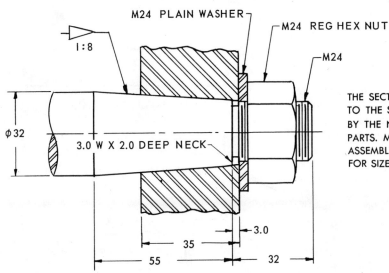

THE SECTIONED COLLAR IS SECURELY HELD
TO THE SHAFT BY THE PRESSURE PRODUCED
BY THE NUT AGAINST THE TWO TAPERED
PARTS. MAKE A DRAWING SIMILAR TO THE
ASSEMBLY SHOWN. REFER TO THE APPENDIX
FOR SIZES

Figure 7.10   Collar Assembly

CHAPTER EIGHT

SECTION VIEWS

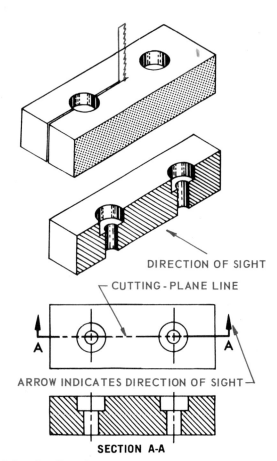

A Section Drawing

Sectional views, commonly called "sections", are used to show interior detail that is too compli-cated to be shown clearly by outside views and the use of hidden lines. In assembly drawings they also serve to indicate a difference in ma-terials.

A section view is obtained by supposing the nearest part of the object to be cut or broken away on an imaginary cutting-plane. The ex-posed or cut surfaces are identified by section lining or cross-hatching. Hidden lines and de-tails behind the cutting-plane line are usually omitted unless they are required for clarity or dimensioning. It should be understood that only

in the section view is any part of the object shown as being removed.

A section view frequently replaces one of the regular views. For example, a regular front view is replaced by a front view "in section", as shown in the illustration.

THE CUTTING-PLANE LINE

A cutting-plane line is used to indicate where the imaginary cutting takes place. The position of the cutting-plane should be indicated on a view of the object or assembly by extra thick lines, terminated by arrowheads showing the viewing direction. Cutting-planes are not shown on sec-tion views.

If two or more sections appear on the same drawing, then the cutting-plane lines are ident-ified by two identical large letters, one at each end of the line and placed behind the arrow-head so that the arrow points away from the letter. The identification letters should not in-clude either I, O, Q or Z.

Section view sub-titles are given when identi-fication letters are used and appear directly be-low the view, incorporating the letters at each end of the cutting-plane line. When the scale is different from the main view it is stated below the sub-title.

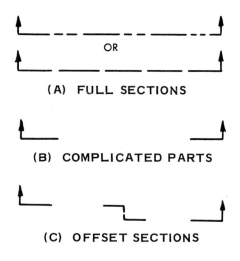

Cutting-Plane Lines

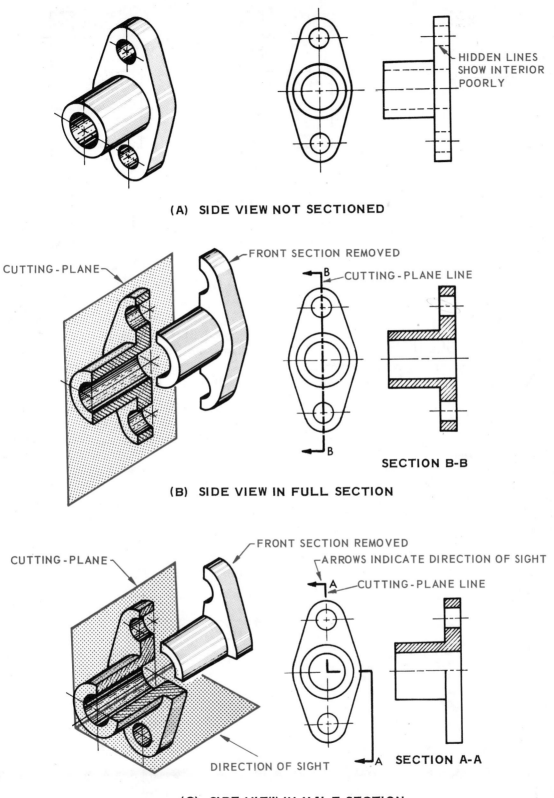

(A) SIDE VIEW NOT SECTIONED

HIDDEN LINES
SHOW INTERIOR
POORLY

CUTTING - PLANE

FRONT SECTION REMOVED

CUTTING - PLANE LINE

SECTION B-B

(B) SIDE VIEW IN FULL SECTION

CUTTING - PLANE

FRONT SECTION REMOVED

ARROWS INDICATE DIRECTION OF SIGHT

CUTTING - PLANE LINE

DIRECTION OF SIGHT

SECTION A-A

(C) SIDE VIEW IN HALF SECTION

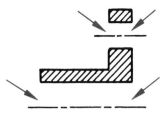
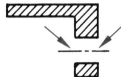

(A) INCOMPLETE - LINES BEHIND CUTTING - PLANE NOT SHOWN

(B) POOR PRACTICE - HIDDEN LINES NOT NECESSARY

(C) GOOD PRACTICE - HIDDEN LINES OMITTED, VISIBLE LINES SHOWN

Visible and Hidden Lines in Section View

TYPES OF SECTIONS

FULL SECTION

When the cutting plane line passes throughout the length or breadth of the object in a straight line, it indicates a *full section*.

HALF SECTION

A symmetrical object or assembly may be drawn as a *half section* showing one half up to the center line in section and the other half in full view. A normal center line is used on the section view in lieu of the cutting-plane line.

The half section drawing is not used when the dimensioning of internal diameters is required, in order to avoid adding hidden lines to the portion showing the external features. This type of section is used mostly for assembly drawings where internal and external features are clearly shown and where only overall and center-to-center dimensions are required.

OFFSET SECTION

An *offset section* is similar to a full section in that the cutting-plane line extends through the object from one side to the other. The cutting-plane is offset or bent to include features that are not in a straight line.

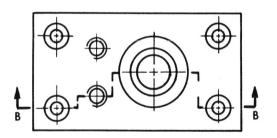

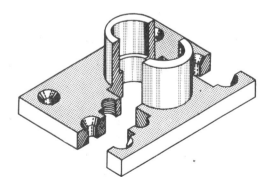

An Offset Section

NOTE - CHANGE IN CUTTING - PLANE LINE NOT SHOWN IN SECTION VIEW

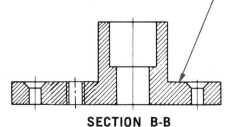

SECTION B-B

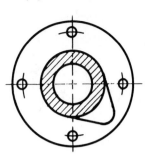

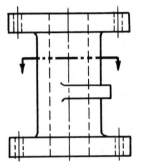

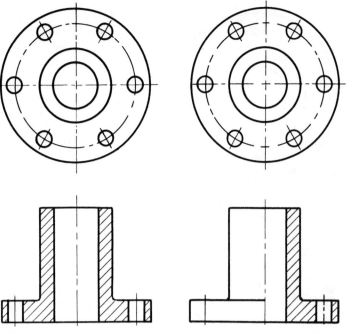

(A) LETTERS AND SUBTITLES MAY BE OMITTED IF ONLY ONE SECTION VIEW IS DRAWN

(B) CUTTING-PLANE LINE FOR FULL AND HALF SECTIONS MAY BE OMITTED WHEN IT CORRESPONDS TO THE CENTER OF THE PART

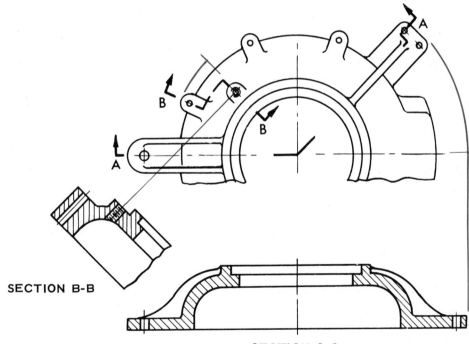

SECTION B-B

SECTION A-A

(C) ALIGNED SECTIONS, WHEREVER PRACTICAL, THE SECTION VIEW WOULD BE PROJECTED PERPENDICULAR TO THE CUTTING-PLANE

ANSI Y14.2 (SEE * P. 251)
CSA B78.1

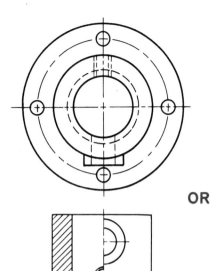

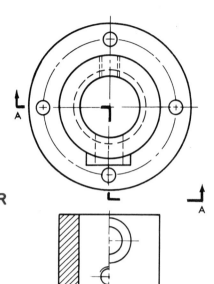

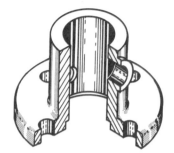

OR

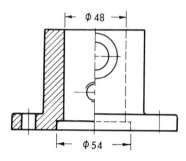

SECTION A-A

Half Section Detail Drawings

φ 48

φ 54

HIDDEN LINES ADDED
FOR DIMENSIONING

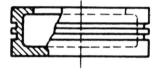

Broken-Out or Partial Section

BROKEN-OUT OR PARTIAL SECTION

Where a sectional view of a portion of the object is needed, *partial* sections may be used. An irregular break line is used to show the extent of the section.

PHANTOM OR HIDDEN SECTION

A *phantom* section is used to show the typical interior shape of an object in one view when the part is not truly symmetrical in shape, and to show mating parts in an assembly drawing. It is a section view superimposed on the regular view without removing the front portion of the object. The section-lining used for phantom sections is light broken lines evenly spaced.

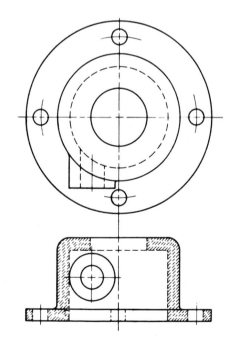

Phantom or Hidden Section

REVOLVED AND REMOVED SECTIONS

Revolved and removed sections are used to show the cross-sectional shape of ribs, spokes, or arms when the shape is not obvious in the regular views. End views are often not needed when a revolved section is used. For a revolved section, draw a center line through the shape on the plane to be described, imagine the part to be rotated 90° and superimpose on the view the shape that would be seen when rotated. If the revolved section does not interfere with the view on which it is revolved, then the view is not broken unless it would provide for clearer dimensioning. When the revolved section interferes or passes through lines on the view on which it is revolved then the general practice is to break the view. Often the break is used to shorten the length of the object. In no circumstances should the lines on the view pass through the section. When superimposed on the view, the outline of the revolved section is a thin continuous line.

The removed section differs in that the section, instead of being drawn right on the view, is removed to an open area on the drawing. Frequently the removed section is drawn to an enlarged scale for clarification and easier dimensioning. Removed sections of symmetrical parts should, where possible, be placed on the extension of the center line.

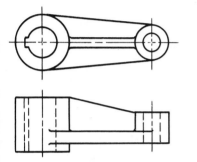

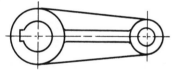

(A) END VIEW NOT CLEAR

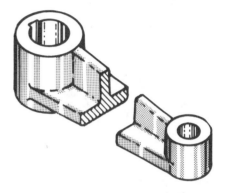

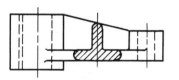

LINE SHOULD NOT GO THROUGH SECTION

AVOID

(B) REVOLVED SECTION

Revolved Sections

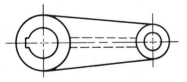

CROSSING LINES TEND TO CONFUSE

AVOID

(C) REVOLVED SECTION WITH VIEW BROKEN

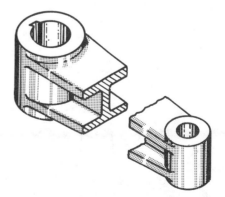

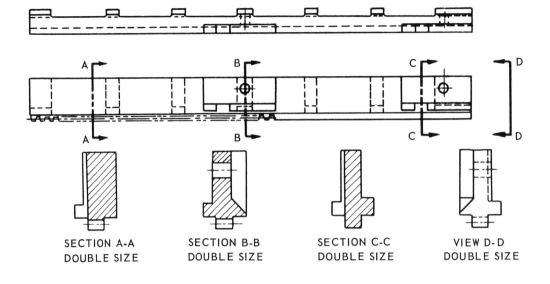

SECTION A-A
DOUBLE SIZE

SECTION B-B
DOUBLE SIZE

SECTION C-C
DOUBLE SIZE

VIEW D-D
DOUBLE SIZE

(A)   REMOVED SECTIONS AND REMOVED VIEW

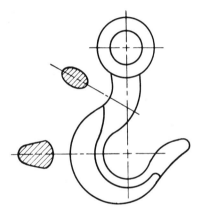

(B)   CRANE HOOK

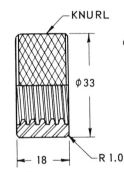

KNURL

⌀33

18

R 1.0

(C)   NUT

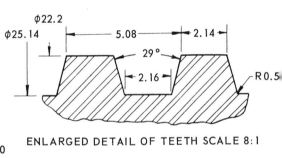

⌀22.2
⌀25.14
5.08
2.14
29°
2.16
R 0.5

ENLARGED DETAIL OF TEETH SCALE 8:1

Removed Sections

ANSI Y14.2 (SEE * P. 251)
CSA B78.1

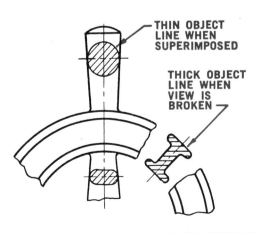

THIN OBJECT
LINE WHEN
SUPERIMPOSED

THICK OBJECT
LINE WHEN
VIEW IS
BROKEN

Revolved Sections

ANSI Y14.2 (SEE * P. 251)
CSA B78.1

PLACEMENT OF SECTION VIEWS

Whenever practical, except for revolved sections, section views should be projected perpendicularly to the cutting-plane, and be placed in the normal position for third angle projection.

When the preferred placement is not practical, the section view may be removed to some other convenient position on the drawing, but it must be clearly identified, usually by two capital letters, excluding I, O, Q, and Z, and be labelled.

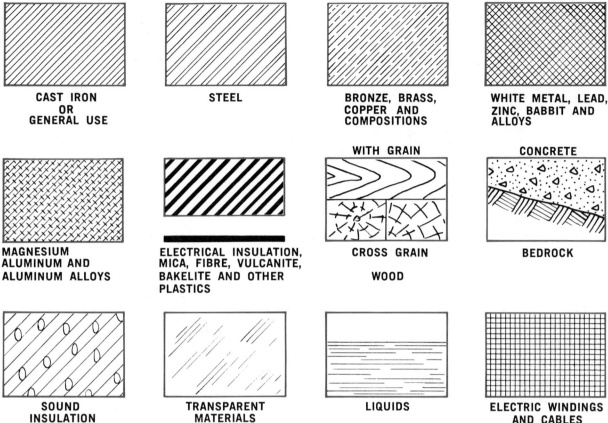

CAST IRON OR GENERAL USE	**STEEL**	**BRONZE, BRASS, COPPER AND COMPOSITIONS**	**WHITE METAL, LEAD, ZINC, BABBIT AND ALLOYS**
MAGNESIUM ALUMINUM AND ALUMINUM ALLOYS	**ELECTRICAL INSULATION, MICA, FIBRE, VULCANITE, BAKELITE AND OTHER PLASTICS**	**WITH GRAIN** / **CROSS GRAIN** / **WOOD**	**CONCRETE** / **BEDROCK**
SOUND INSULATION	**TRANSPARENT MATERIALS**	**LIQUIDS**	**ELECTRIC WINDINGS AND CABLES**

Symbolic Section Lining

ANSI Y14.2 (SEE * P. 251)
CSA B78.1

SECTION-LINING

Section-lining, sometimes referred to as cross-hatching, serves a double purpose. It indicates the surface that has been theoretically cut and makes it stand out clearly, thus helping the observer to understand the shape of the object. Section-lining also indicates the material from which the object is to be made. When it is not necessary to indicate the material of parts by a hatching symbol, all surfaces are hatched with single full lines like the symbol for cast iron. Hatching lines are thin and are usually drawn at an angle of 45° to the major outline of the object. The same angle is used for the whole "cut" surface of the object. If the part shape would cause section lines to be parallel, or nearly so, to one of the sides of the part, some angle other than 45° should be chosen. The spacing of the hatching lines should be reasonably uniform to give a good appearance to the drawing. The *pitch,* or distance between lines, varies between 1.0 and 2.5 mm depending on the size of the area to be sectioned.

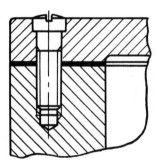

GASKETS   STEEL PLATE

Thin Sections

ANSI Y14.2 (SEE * P. 251)
CSA B78.1

THIN SECTIONS

When the part in section is very thin, no attempt is made to put on section-lining. A heavy solid line represents the thickness of the part, and a space is left between the thin part and adjacent parts that it would be touching.

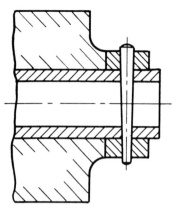

SPACING OF SECTION-LINES
ACCORDING TO THE SIZE OF
AREA TO BE SECTIONED

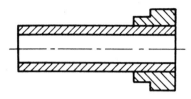

ADJACENT PARTS IN SECTION

Two adjacent parts are section-lined by lines at right angles to each other. A third part adjacent to both should be sectioned at 30° or 60° as shown.

LARGE AREAS

Large areas shown in section need not be entirely section-lined. Section-lining around the outline will usually be sufficient.

SECTIONS THROUGH SHAFTS, BOLTS, PINS, KEYS, ETC.

Shafts, bolts, nuts, rods, rivets, keys, pins and similar solid parts, the axes of which lie in the cutting plane, should not be sectioned except that a broken-out section of the shaft may be used to indicate clearly the key, keyseat or pin.

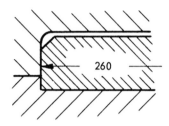

DIMENSIONS

Dimensions may be inserted in circular openings left in the section-lining.

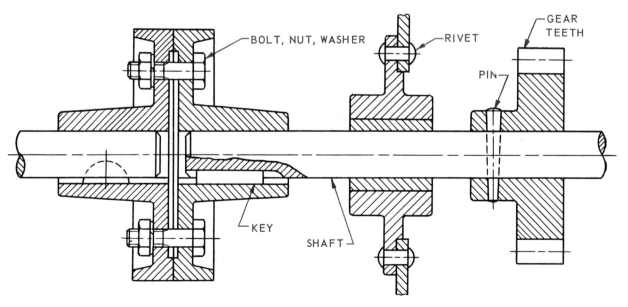

Parts That Are Not Section-Lined in Section Drawings Even Though the Cutting Plane Line Passes Through Them

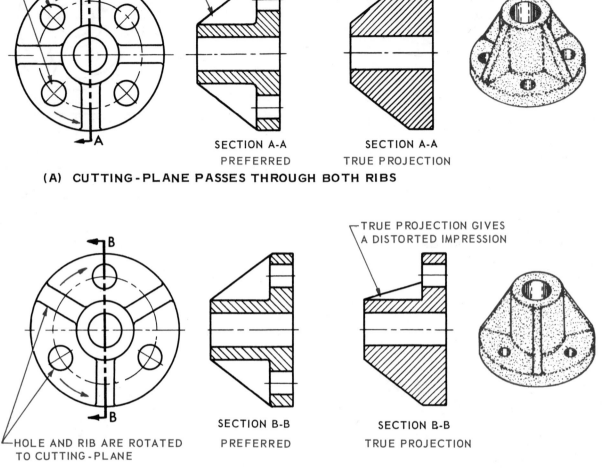

HOLES ARE ROTATED TO CUTTING-PLANE TO SHOW THEIR
TRUE RELATIONSHIP WITH THE REST OF THE ELEMENT

RIBS ARE NOT SECTIONED

SECTION A-A
PREFERRED

SECTION A-A
TRUE PROJECTION

(A) CUTTING-PLANE PASSES THROUGH BOTH RIBS

TRUE PROJECTION GIVES
A DISTORTED IMPRESSION

HOLE AND RIB ARE ROTATED
TO CUTTING-PLANE

SECTION B-B
PREFERRED

SECTION B-B
TRUE PROJECTION

(B) CUTTING-PLANE PASSING THROUGH ONE RIB AND ONE HOLE

Preferred and True Projection Through Ribs and Holes

HOLES IN SECTION

Holes, like ribs, are aligned in order to show their true relationship to the rest of the part.

RIBS IN SECTION

A true projection section view of a part will be misleading when the cutting-plane passes longitudinally through the center of the rib. To avoid this impression of solidity, a preferred section not showing the ribs section-lined or cross-hatched is used. When there is an odd number of ribs the top rib is aligned with the bottom rib to show its true relationship with the hub and flange. If the rib is not aligned or revolved it appears distorted on the section view and is misleading.

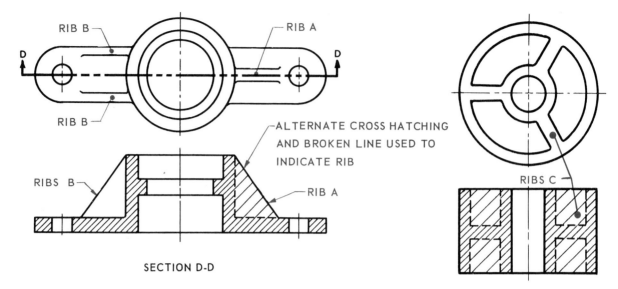

SECTION D-D

(A) BASE

(B) PULLEY

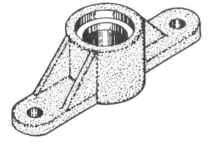

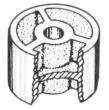

Alternate Method of Showing Ribs in Section

It may be necessary at times to use an alternative method of identifying ribs in a section view. If rib *A* of the base shown above is not sectioned as previously described, it appears exactly like rib *B* in the section view and is misleading. Similarly, the rib *C* shown on the pulley may be overlooked.

To distinguish between the ribs on the base and the ribs and spaces on the pulley, alternate section-lining on the ribs is used. The line between the rib and solid portions is shown as a broken line.

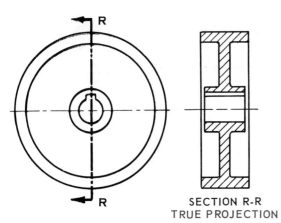

SECTION R-R
TRUE PROJECTION

WEB IS SECTIONED

(A) FLAT PULLEY WITH WEB

SECTION S-S
PREFERRED PROJECTION

SPOKES ARE NOT SECTIONED

(B) CROWNED PULLEY WITH EVEN

NUMBER OF SPOKES

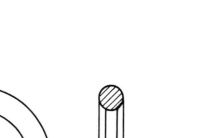

SECTION T-T
PREFERRED PROJECTION

SPOKE M IS ROTATED TO CUTTING-PLANE
LINE BUT NOT SECTIONED

(C) HANDWHEEL WITH ODD NUMBER

OF SPOKES

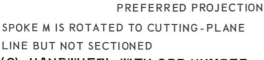

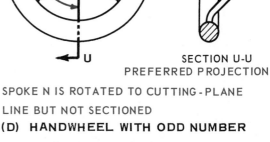

SECTION U-U
PREFERRED PROJECTION

SPOKE N IS ROTATED TO CUTTING-PLANE
LINE BUT NOT SECTIONED

(D) HANDWHEEL WITH ODD NUMBER

OF OFFSET SPOKES

Showing Webs and Spokes in Section Drawings

WEBS AND SPOKES IN SECTION

A comparison is shown between a wheel with spokes, and a pulley with a web. A preferred section for the wheel with spokes is desirable so that it will not appear to be a pulley with a solid web. In preferred sectioning, any part that is not solid or continuous around the hub is drawn without the section-lining, even though the cutting-plane passes through the spoke. When there is an odd number of spokes, such as shown, the bottom spoke is aligned with the top spoke to show its true relationship to the wheel and hub. If the spoke were not revolved or aligned it would appear distorted in the section view.

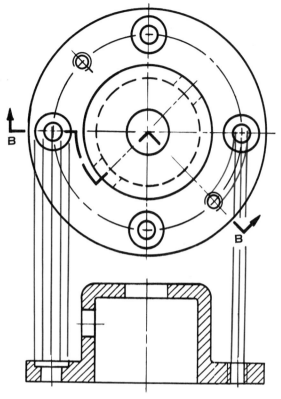

SECTION B-B

(1) HOLES ALIGNED

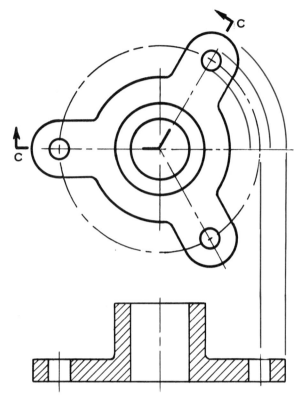

SECTION C-C

(2) LUGS ALIGNED AND SECTIONED

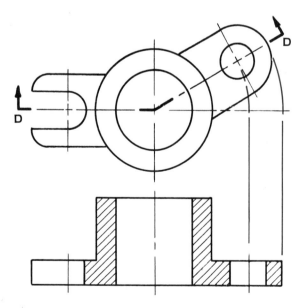

SECTION D-D

(3) LUGS ALIGNED AND SECTIONED

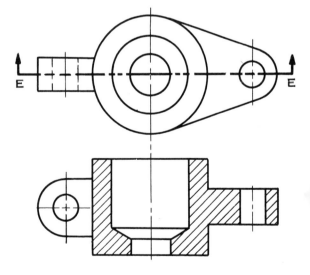

SECTION E-E

(4) LUGS NOT SECTIONED

Aligning Holes and Lugs in Section Drawings

LUGS IN SECTION

Like ribs and spokes, lugs are aligned to show their true relationship to the rest of the part because a true projection might be misleading. Shown above are several examples of lugs in section. Note how the cutting-plane line is bent or offset so that the features may be clearly understood in the section view.

Some lugs are shown in section and some not. When the cutting-plane passes through the lug crosswise the lug is sectioned; otherwise, the lugs are treated in the same manner as ribs.

References

CSA B78.1
ANSI Y14.2

Review Questions

1. What is a section view, and what is its main purpose?
2. What is the purpose of the cutting-plane line?
3. What is the difference between a full section and a half section?
4. How does an offset section differ from a full section?
5. What purposes are served by section-lining?
6. What is the rule concerning section-lining for adjacent parts in section?
7. What is the purpose served by revolved and removed sections?
8. What is the difference between a revolved and a removed section?
9. What technique is used for thin plates in sections?
10. Name four typical parts that would not be section-lined in a section view.

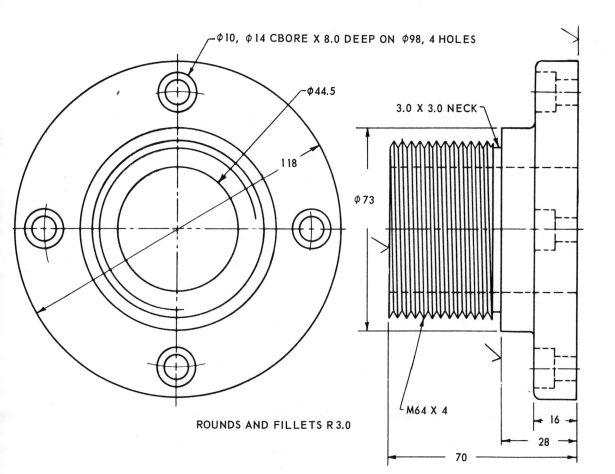

ø10, ø14 CBORE X 8.0 DEEP ON ø98, 4 HOLES

ø44.5

3.0 X 3.0 NECK

118

ø73

M64 X 4

ROUNDS AND FILLETS R 3.0

16

28

70

Figure 8.1   End Plate

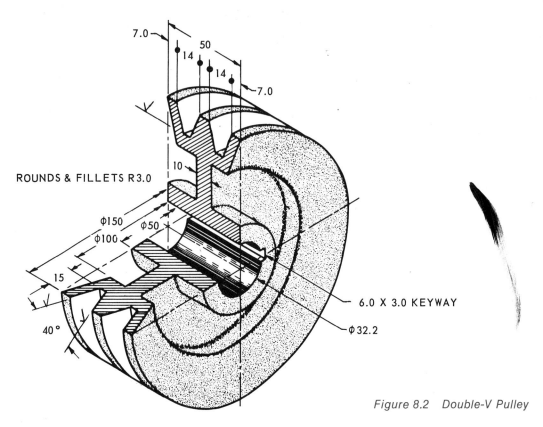

ROUNDS & FILLETS R3.0

φ150
φ100
φ50

15

40°

10

7.0
14
50
14
7.0

6.0 X 3.0 KEYWAY

φ32.2

Figure 8.2   Double-V Pulley

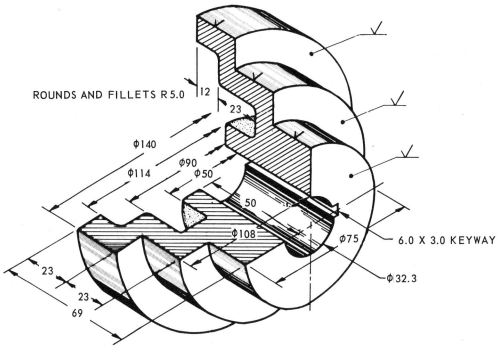

ROUNDS AND FILLETS R5.0

12
23

φ140
φ114
φ90
φ50

23
23
69

50

φ108
φ75

6.0 X 3.0 KEYWAY

φ32.3

Figure 8.3   Step Pulley

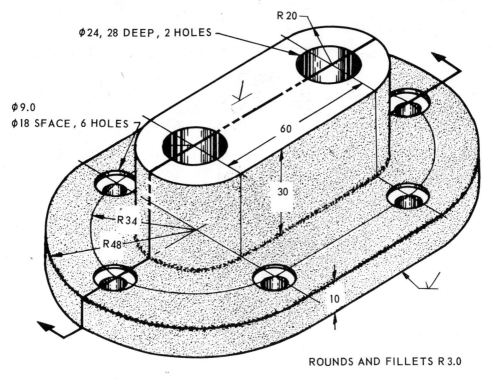

Ø24, 28 DEEP, 2 HOLES

R 20

Ø9.0
Ø18 SFACE, 6 HOLES

60

30

R34

R48

10

ROUNDS AND FILLETS R 3.0

Figure 8.4   Shaft Base

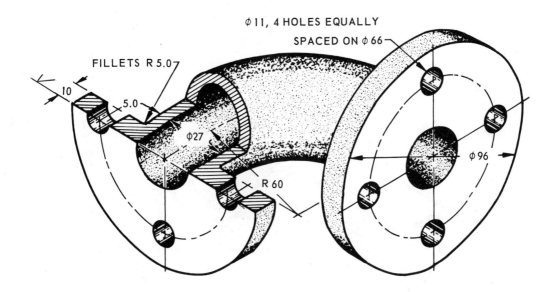

Ø11, 4 HOLES EQUALLY
SPACED ON Ø 66

FILLETS R 5.0

10

5.0

Ø27

R 60

Ø96

Figure 8.5   Flanged Elbow

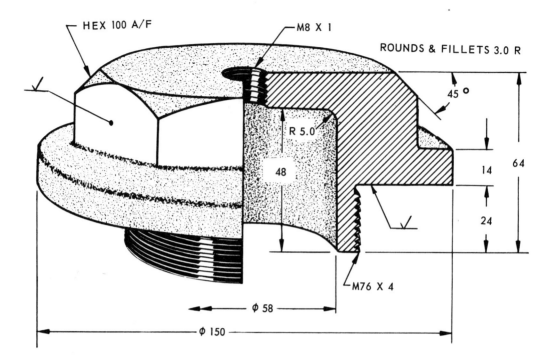

Figure 8.6   Pipe Plug

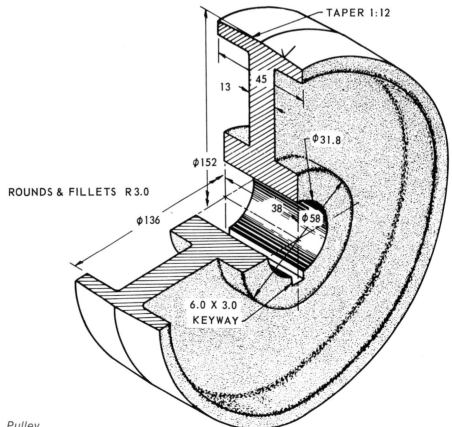

Figure 8.7   Pulley

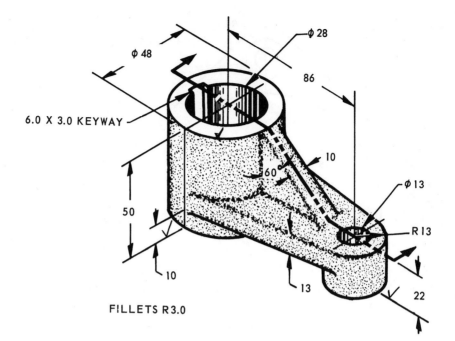

FILLETS R3.0

Figure 8.8   Bracket

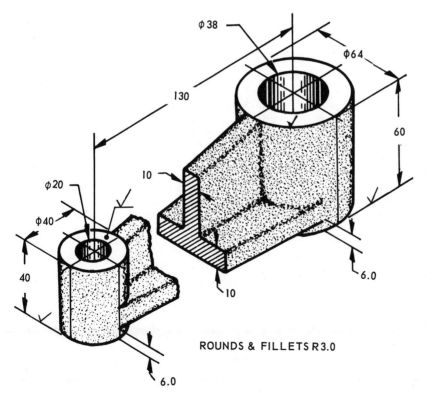

ROUNDS & FILLETS R3.0

Figure 8.9   Shaft Support

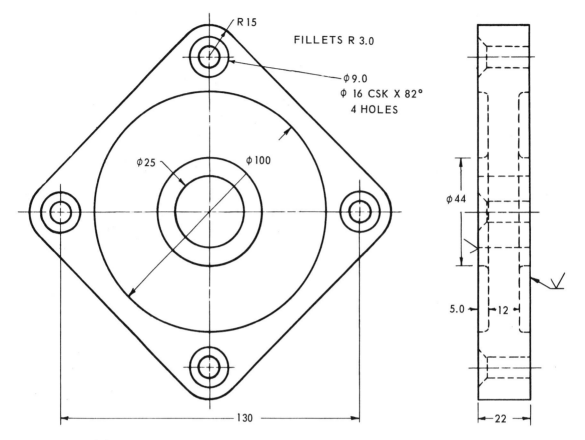

Figure 8.10   Adaptor

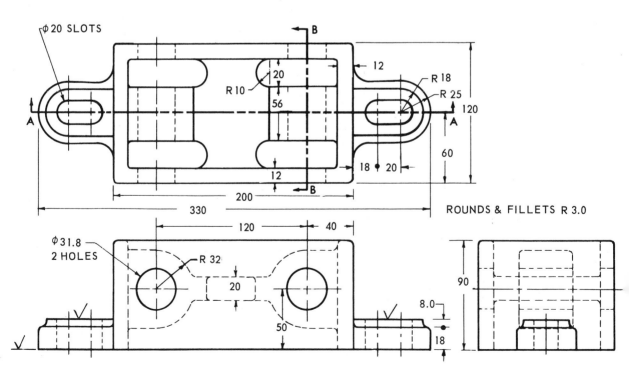

Figure 8.11   Adjustable Base

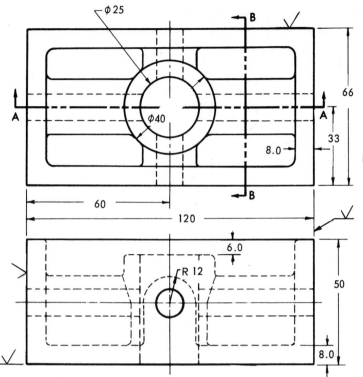

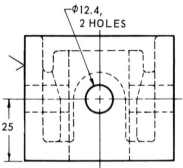

ROUNDS & FILLETS R 3.0

Figure 8.12   Cross Support

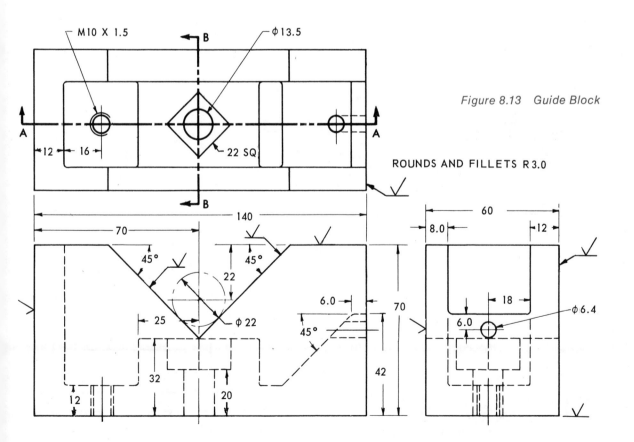

Figure 8.13   Guide Block

ROUNDS AND FILLETS R 3.0

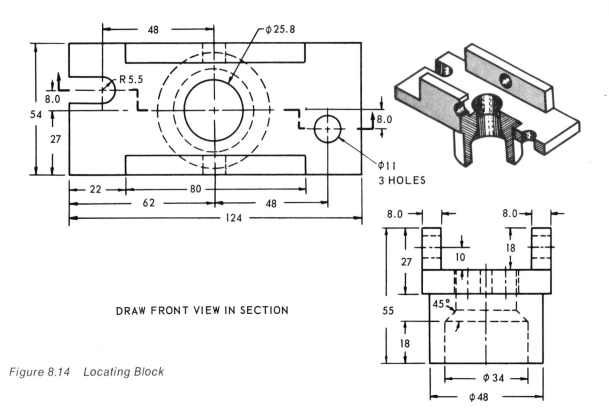

DRAW FRONT VIEW IN SECTION

Figure 8.14   Locating Block

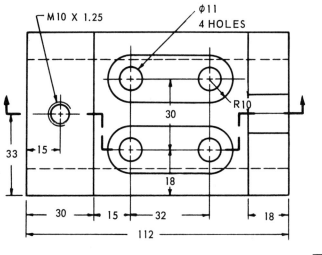

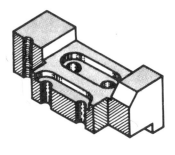

DRAW FRONT VIEW IN SECTION

Figure 8.15   Index Block

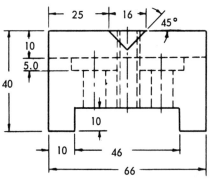

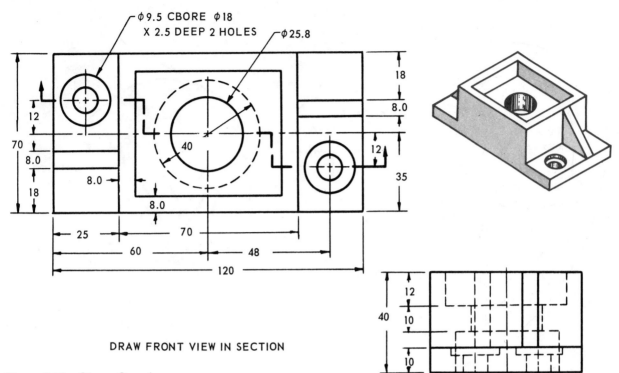

φ9.5 CBORE φ18
X 2.5 DEEP 2 HOLES   φ25.8

18
8.0
12
40
12
35
70
8.0
18
25
60
70
48
8.0
8.0
120

DRAW FRONT VIEW IN SECTION

Figure 8.16   Clamp Guard

12
40   10
10

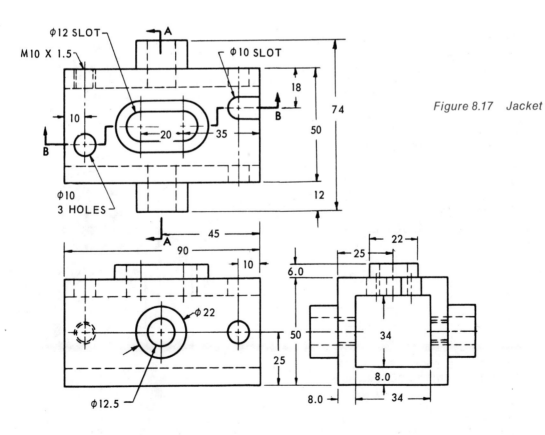

φ12 SLOT
M10 X 1.5
φ10 SLOT
A
18
B
74
10
50
20   35
B
12
φ10
3 HOLES

Figure 8.17   Jacket

A
45
90
10
φ22
50
25
φ12.5

22
25
6.0
50
34
8.0
8.0   34

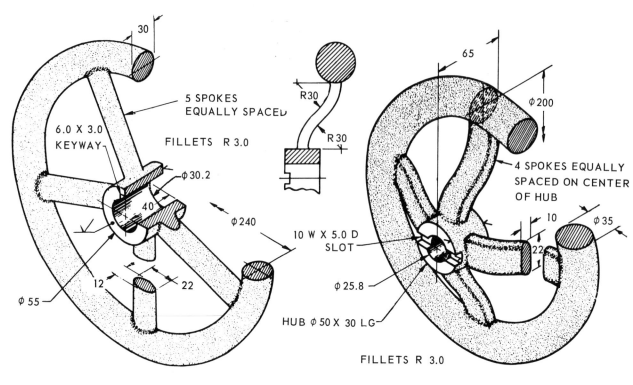

Figure 8.18   Handwheel

Figure 8.19   Offset Handwheel

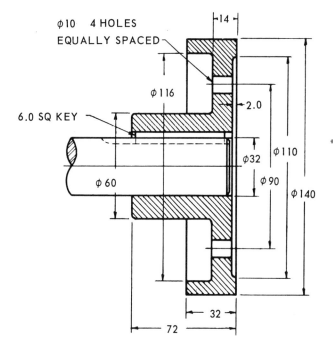

Figure 8.20   Flanged Coupling

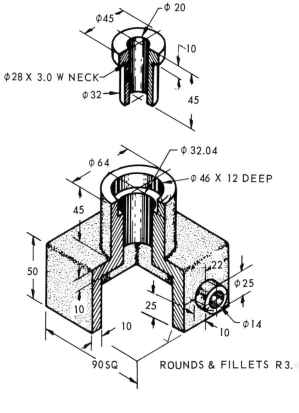

Figure 8.21   Drill Jig Stand

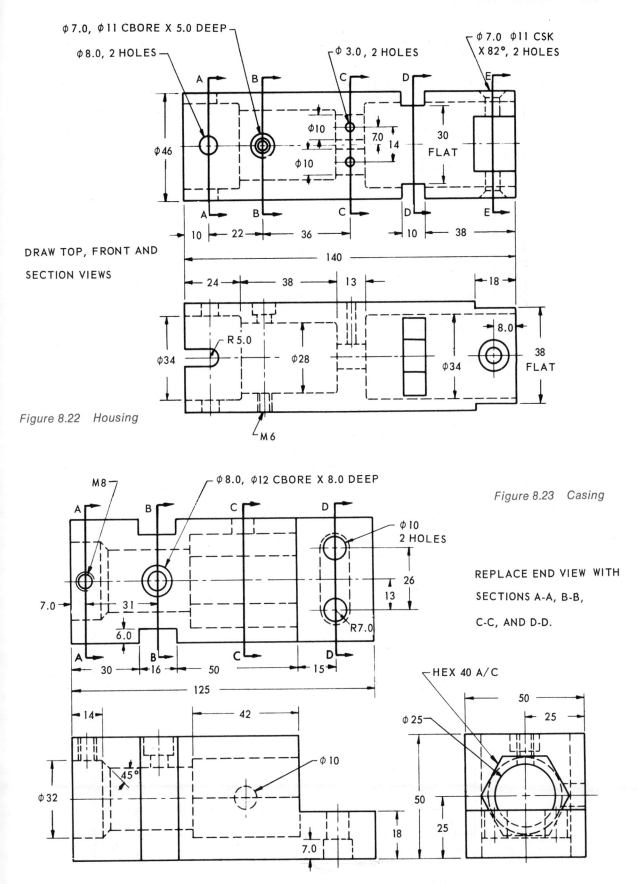

φ7.0, φ11 CBORE X 5.0 DEEP
φ8.0, 2 HOLES
φ3.0, 2 HOLES
φ7.0 φ11 CSK X 82°, 2 HOLES

φ46

φ10

φ10

7.0

14

30 FLAT

10 22 36 10 38

140

DRAW TOP, FRONT AND
SECTION VIEWS

24 38 13 18

R 5.0

φ34

φ28

8.0

φ34

38 FLAT

Figure 8.22   Housing

M 6

M8

φ8.0, φ12 CBORE X 8.0 DEEP

Figure 8.23   Casing

φ10
2 HOLES

26

13

7.0

31

6.0

R7.0

REPLACE END VIEW WITH
SECTIONS A-A, B-B,
C-C, AND D-D.

30 16 50 15

125

HEX 40 A/C

14 42

45°

φ32

φ10

18

7.0

φ25

50 25

50

25

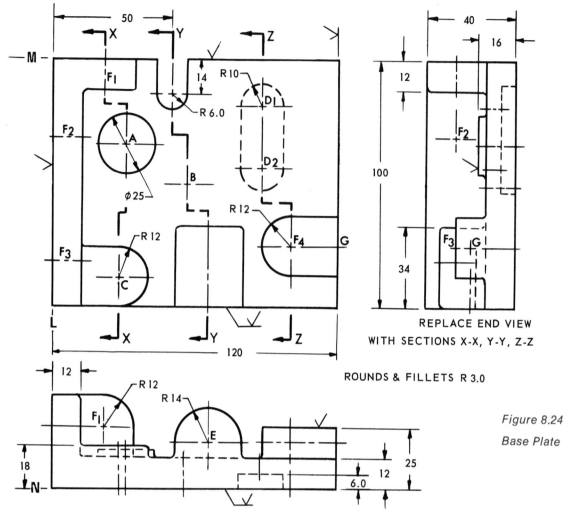

REPLACE END VIEW
WITH SECTIONS X-X, Y-Y, Z-Z

ROUNDS & FILLETS R 3.0

Figure 8.24

Base Plate

DRAW TOP, FRONT AND 3 SECTION VIEWS

HOLE	HOLE SIZE	LOCATION		
		L	M	N
A	M 12 X 1.75	32	35	
B	φ 7.0 φ12 CSK X 82°	58	50	
C	φ 8.0 φ12 CBORE X 6.0 DEEP	28	88	
D₁	φ 8.0	88	20	
D₂	φ 8.0	88	45	
E	M12 X 1.75 X 20 DEEP	66		20
F₁	φ12	22		25
F₂	φ12		32	25
F₃	φ12		82	25
F₄	φ12	100	75	
G	φ 3.0 THROUGH		75	20

CHAPTER NINE

AUXILIARY VIEWS

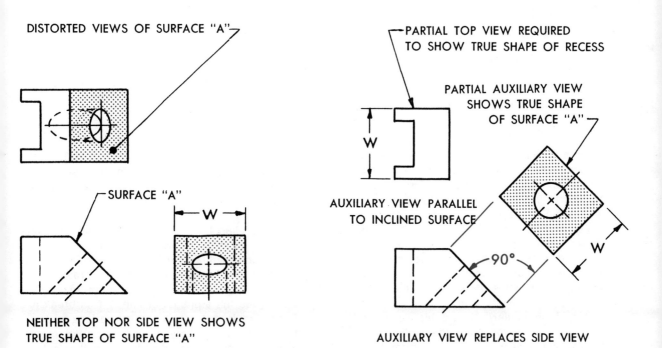

DISTORTED VIEWS OF SURFACE "A"

SURFACE "A"

NEITHER TOP NOR SIDE VIEW SHOWS TRUE SHAPE OF SURFACE "A"

PARTIAL TOP VIEW REQUIRED TO SHOW TRUE SHAPE OF RECESS

PARTIAL AUXILIARY VIEW SHOWS TRUE SHAPE OF SURFACE "A"

AUXILIARY VIEW PARALLEL TO INCLINED SURFACE

90°

AUXILIARY VIEW REPLACES SIDE VIEW

The Need for Auxiliary View Drawings

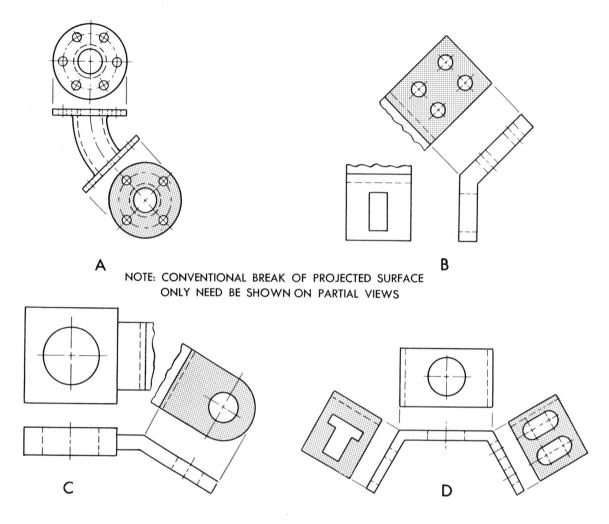

NOTE: CONVENTIONAL BREAK OF PROJECTED SURFACE
ONLY NEED BE SHOWN ON PARTIAL VIEWS

A

B

C

D

Examples of Auxiliary View Drawings

Many machine parts have surfaces that are not perpendicular or at right angles to the plane of projection. These surfaces are referred to as *sloping* or *inclined* surfaces. In the regular orthographic views such surfaces appear to be foreshortened, and their true shape is not shown. When an inclined surface has important characteristics that should be shown clearly and without distortion, so that the drawing completely and clearly explains the shape of the object, an *auxiliary view* is used.

One of the regular orthographic views will have an edge line representing the inclined surface. The auxiliary view is projected from this edge line, at right angles, and is drawn parallel to the edge line. Because the auxiliary view shows the

true shape and detail of the inclined surface, the other views, which show the inclined surface as being distorted, are usually altered. They then become partial views, showing the true shape portion only.

The broken lines that represent hidden background detail are often omitted on auxiliary views and regular partial views to simplify the drawing and to avoid confusion. A break line is used to signify the "break" in an incomplete view. (See the alphabet of lines.) This break line is not required if only the exact surface is drawn for either an auxiliary view or a partial regular view. Dimensions for the detail on the inclined face are placed on the auxiliary view, where such a detail is seen in its true shape.

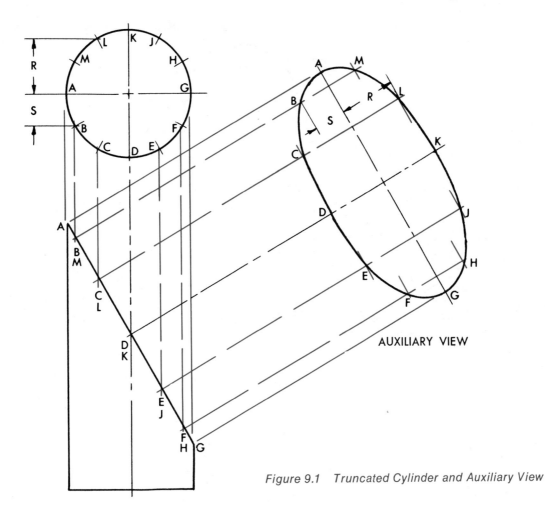

AUXILIARY VIEW

Figure 9.1   Truncated Cylinder and Auxiliary View

Figure 9.1 illustrates an auxiliary view of a truncated cylinder. The shape seen in the auxiliary view is an *ellipse.* This shape is drawn by plotting *lines of intersection.* The perimeter of the circle in the top view is divided to give a number of equally spaced points—in this case 12 points, A to M, spaced 30° apart ($\frac{360°}{12} = 30°$).

These points are projected down to the edge line on the front view, then at right angles to the edge line to the area where the auxiliary view will be drawn. A centerline for the auxiliary view is drawn parallel to the edge line, and width settings taken from the top view are transferred to the auxiliary view. Note width setting R for point L. Because the illustration shows a true cylinder and the point divisions in the top view are all equal, the width setting R taken at L is also the correct width setting for C, E, and J. Width setting S for B is also the correct width

setting for F, H, and M. When all the width settings have been transferred to the auxiliary view, the resulting points of intersection are connected with the use of a French curve to give the desired elliptical shape.

Review Questions

1. Why are auxiliary views used?

2. How are auxiliary views drawn?

3. What change may take place in the regular views when an auxiliary view is drawn?

4. Why is it desirable to place the dimensions for the detail on an inclined face on the auxiliary view?

5. What technique is used to draw the elliptical shape of a truncated cylinder?

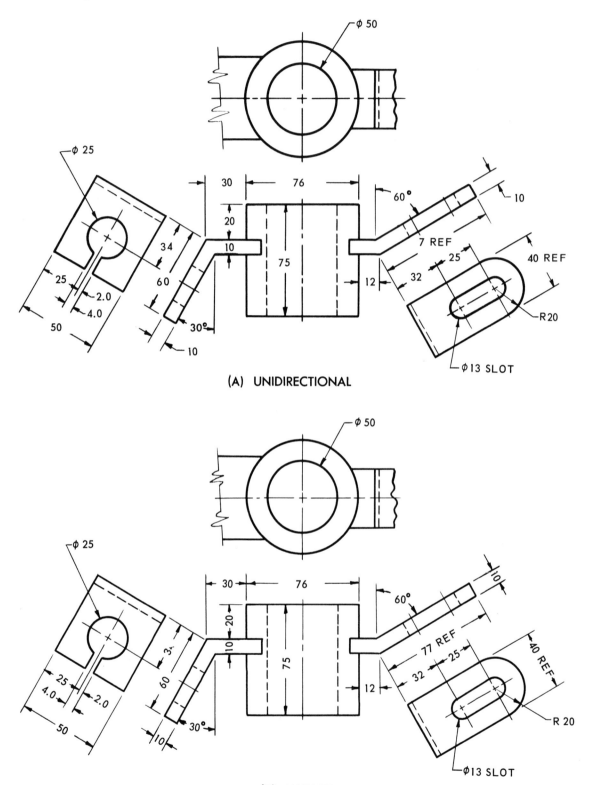

(A) UNIDIRECTIONAL

(B) ALIGNED

Dimensioning Auxiliary Drawings

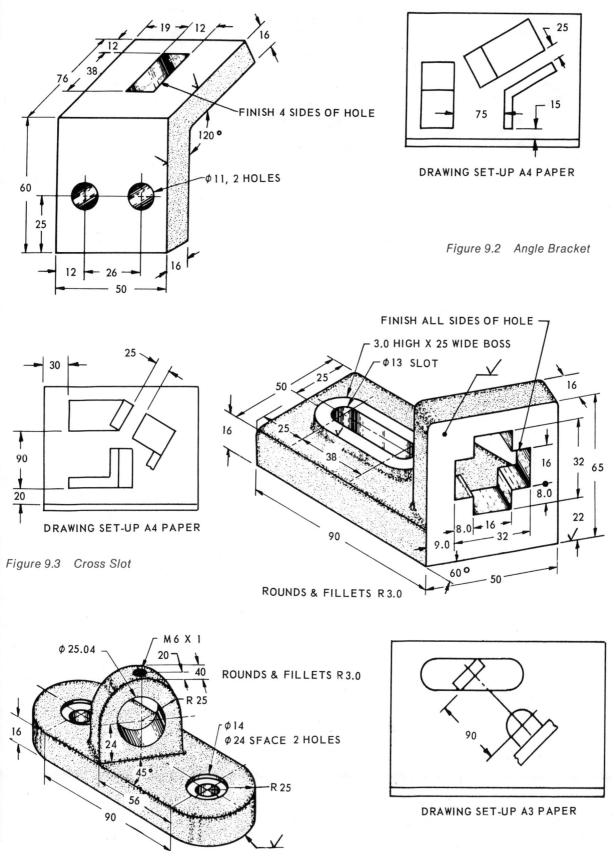

FINISH 4 SIDES OF HOLE

120°

⌀11, 2 HOLES

Figure 9.2   Angle Bracket

DRAWING SET-UP A4 PAPER

Figure 9.3   Cross Slot

DRAWING SET-UP A4 PAPER

FINISH ALL SIDES OF HOLE

3.0 HIGH X 25 WIDE BOSS

⌀13 SLOT

ROUNDS & FILLETS R3.0

M6 X 1

⌀ 25.04

R 25

ROUNDS & FILLETS R3.0

⌀14
⌀24 SFACE 2 HOLES

R 25

45°

DRAWING SET-UP A3 PAPER

Figure 9.4   Shaft Support

ROUNDS & FILLETS R 3.0

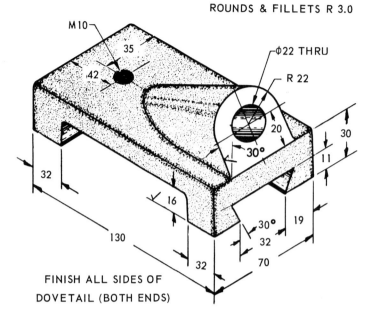

M10
35
42
Φ22 THRU
R 22
20
30°
30
11
32
16
130
30°
32
19
32
70

FINISH ALL SIDES OF
DOVETAIL (BOTH ENDS)

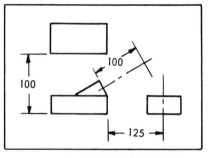

DRAWING SET-UP A3 PAPER
SCALE 1;1

100
100
125

Figure 9.5   Control Block

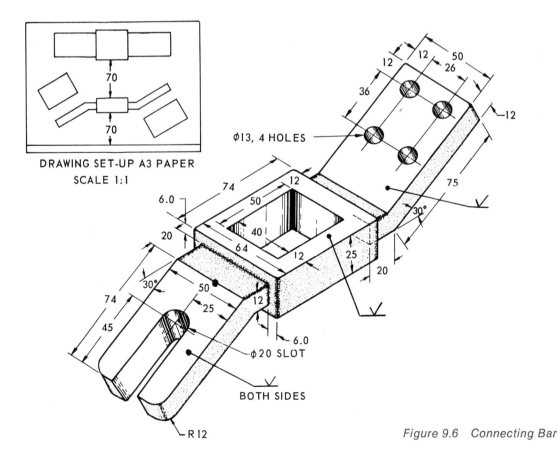

DRAWING SET-UP A3 PAPER
SCALE 1;1

70
70

Φ13, 4 HOLES

12   12   50
26
36
12

75
30°

74   12
6.0   50
20   40
64   12
25
50   20
30°
74   25
45   12
6.0
Φ20 SLOT
BOTH SIDES
R12

Figure 9.6   Connecting Bar

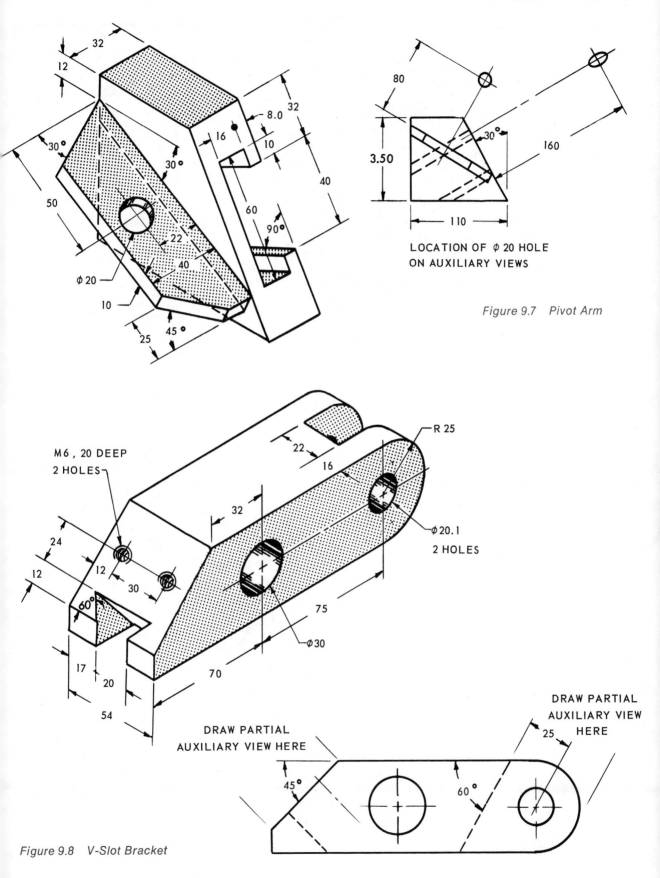

Figure 9.7   Pivot Arm

LOCATION OF φ 20 HOLE
ON AUXILIARY VIEWS

Figure 9.8   V-Slot Bracket

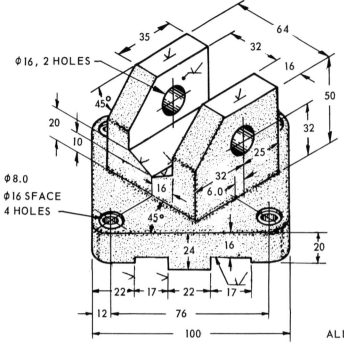

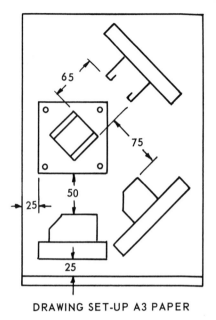

DRAWING SET-UP A3 PAPER

ALL ROUNDS & FILLETS 3.0

Figure 9.9   Angle Slide

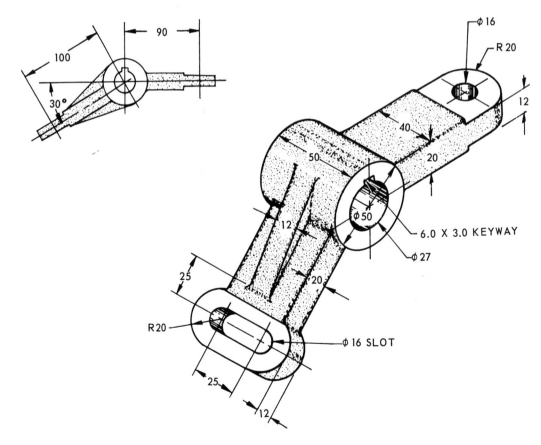

Figure 9.10   Link

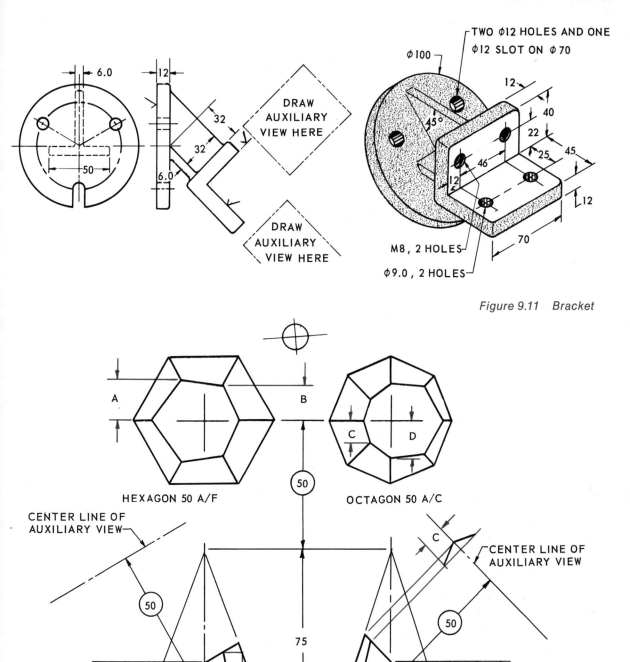

Figure 9.11   Bracket

NOTE: METHOD USED TO OBTAIN DISTANCES "A" AND "B" ON TOP VIEW
MAY BE USED TO OBTAIN DISTANCE "D" ON OCTAGON

Figure 9.12   Statue Bases

CHAPTER TEN

PICTORIAL DRAWING

As the name indicates, pictorial drawings are single-view "picture" drawings. Numerous pictorial drawings were used as illustrations in the previous chapters and in the selections of drafting projects. Although separate views and orthographic projections provide a more precise method of shape description in a working drawing, pictorial drawings are used extensively in preliminary design sketching. They assist others to visualize the shape of an object and are helpful in explaining design ideas. Pictorial drawings are also valuable in illustrating written articles and reports. A basic part of a draftsman's training is pictorial drawing, both by freehand sketching and with the use of instruments. Shown is a comparison between orthographic projection and the various pictorial methods of projection (isometric, oblique and perspective). Perspective drawings are quite accurate representations of what the human eye sees; isometric and oblique drawings are close approximations of what is seen. Isometric and oblique drawings can be made quickly and accurately because the principal lines can be measured directly.

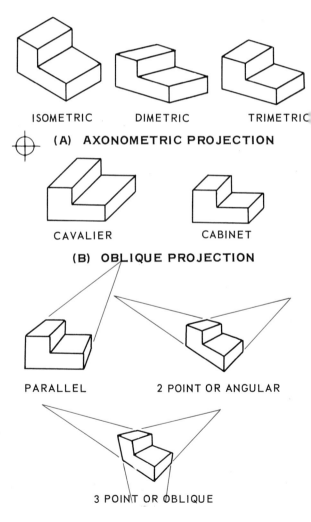

ISOMETRIC   DIMETRIC   TRIMETRIC

(A) AXONOMETRIC PROJECTION

CAVALIER   CABINET

(B) OBLIQUE PROJECTION

PARALLEL   2 POINT OR ANGULAR

3 POINT OR OBLIQUE

Types of Pictorial Drawing   **(C) PERSPECTIVE PROJECTION**

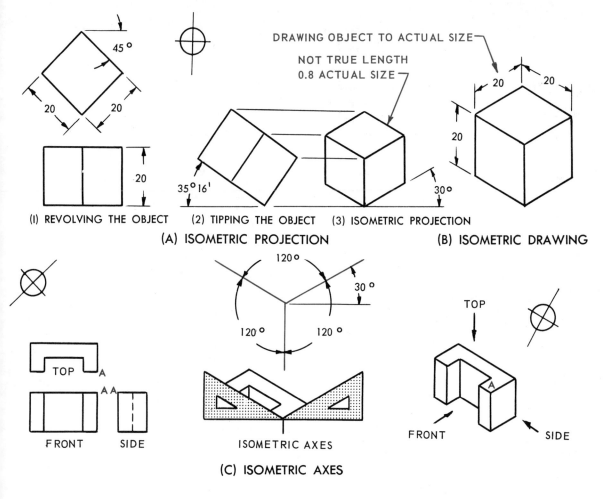

(I) REVOLVING THE OBJECT   (2) TIPPING THE OBJECT   (3) ISOMETRIC PROJECTION

(A) ISOMETRIC PROJECTION

(B) ISOMETRIC DRAWING

(C) ISOMETRIC AXES

Isometric Axes and Projection

ISOMETRIC PROJECTION

This method is based on a procedure of revolving the object at an angle of 45° to the horizontal, so that the front corner is toward the viewer, then tipping the object up or down at an angle of 35° —16'. When this is done to a cube, the three faces visible to the viewer appear equal in shape and size, and the side faces are at angle of 30° to the horizontal. If the isometric view were actually projected from a view of the object in the tipped position, the lines in the isometric view would be foreshortened and would therefore not be seen in their true length. To simplify the drawing of an isometric view, the actual measurements of the object are used. Although the object appears slightly larger without the allowance for

foreshortening, the proportions are not affected. All isometric drawings are started by constructing the isometric axes—a vertical line for heights, and isometric lines to left and right, at an angle of 30° from the horizontal, for lengths and widths. The three faces seen in the isometric view are the same faces that would be seen in the normal orthographic views—top, front, and side. Figure (B) above illustrates the selection of the front corner (A), the construction of the isometric axes, and the completed isometric view. Note that all lines are drawn to their true length, measured along the isometric axes, and that hidden lines are usually omitted. Vertical edges are represented by vertical lines, and horizontal edges by lines at 30° to the horizontal.

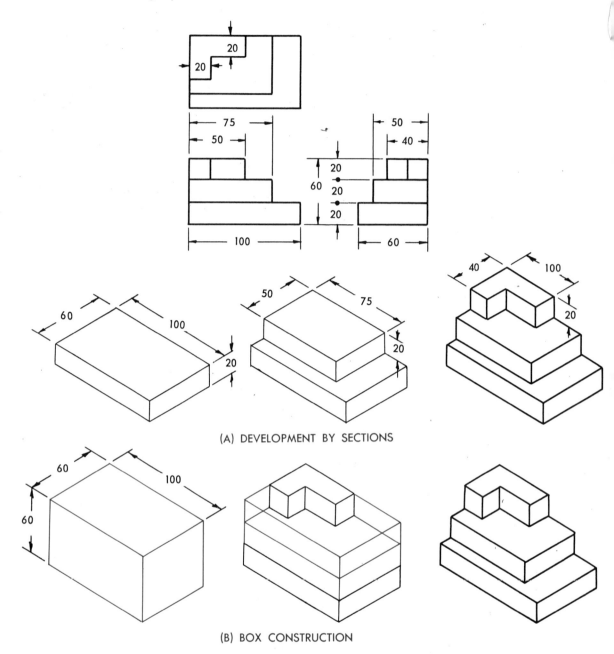

(A) DEVELOPMENT BY SECTIONS

(B) BOX CONSTRUCTION

Developing an Isometric Drawing

Shown above are two techniques for making an isometric drawing of an irregularly shaped object. By one method the object is divided mentally into a number of sections, and the sections are drawn one at a time in their proper relationship to each other. By the second method a box is drawn with the maximum height, width, and depth of the object; then the parts of the box that are not part of the object are removed, leaving the pieces that form the total object.

DRAWING NON-ISOMETRIC LINES

Many objects have sloping surfaces that are represented by sloping lines in the orthographic views. In isometric drawing, sloping surfaces ap-

pear as non-isometric lines; to draw them, locate their end points and join them with a straight line. Figures 10.1 and 10.2 illustrate the construction of non-isometric lines.

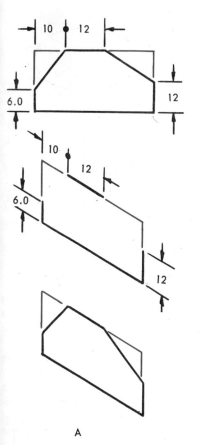

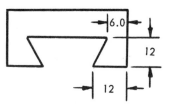

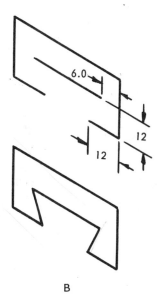

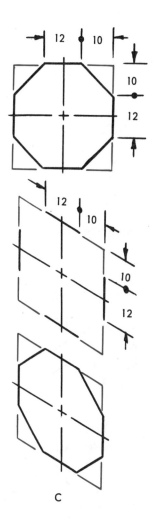

A   B   C

Figure 10.1   Examples in the Construction of Non-Isometric Lines

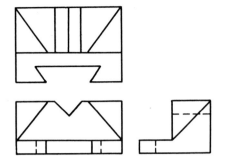

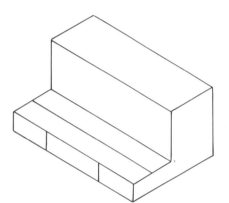

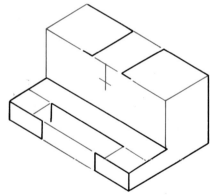

(A) BLOCK IN FEATURES

(B) DARKEN IN ISOMETRIC LINES

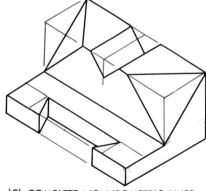

(C) COMPLETE NON-ISOMETRIC LINES

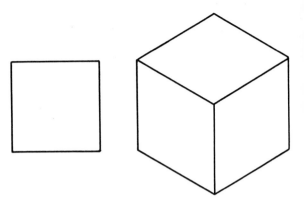

(A) A SQUARE DRAWN IN THE THREE ISOMETRIC POSITION

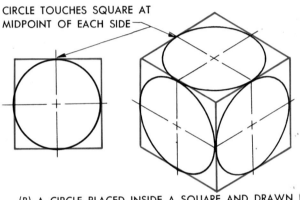

CIRCLE TOUCHES SQUARE AT MIDPOINT OF EACH SIDE

(B) A CIRCLE PLACED INSIDE A SQUARE AND DRAWN THREE ISOMETRIC POSITIONS

Circles in Isometric

DRAWING CIRCLES IN ISOMETRIC

A circle on any of the three regular faces of an object drawn in isometric has the shape of an ellipse. The steps in drawing isometric circles are shown above and overleaf.

1. Draw the centerlines and a square, with sides equal to the circle diameter, in isometric.
2. Using the obtuse-angled (120°) corners as centers, draw arcs tangent to the sides forming the obtuse-angled corners, stopping at the points where the centerlines cross the sides of the square.
3. Draw construction lines from those same points to the opposite obtuse-angled corners. The points at which these construction lines intersect are the centers for arcs drawn tangent to the sides forming the acute-angled corners, meeting the first arcs.

Figure 10.2   Sequence in Drawing an Object Having Non-Isometric Lines

DRAWING ARCS IN ISOMETRIC

The same technique is used for drawing part-circles (arcs). Construct an isometric square with sides equal to twice the radius, and draw that portion of the ellipse necessary to join the two faces. When these faces are parallel, draw one-half of an ellipse (one long radius and one short radius); when they are at an obtuse angle (120°), draw one long radius; and when they are at an acute angle (60°), draw one short radius.

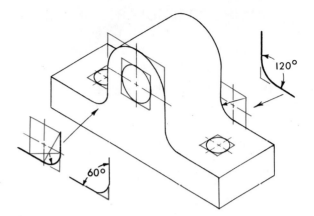

Drawing Isometric Arcs

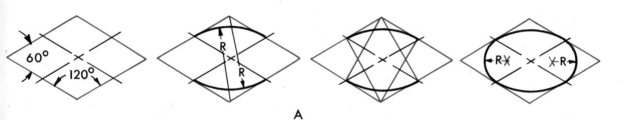

A

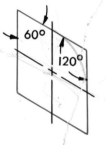
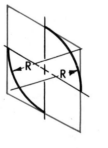

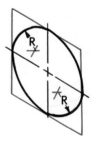

B

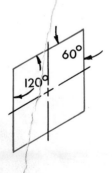
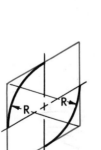
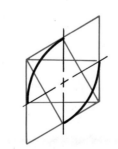
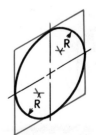

C

Sequence in Drawing Isometric Circles

DRAWING IRREGULAR CURVES IN ISOMETRIC

To draw curves other than circles or arcs, the following plotting method is used.

1. Draw an orthographic view, and divide the area enclosing the curved line into equal squares.
2. Produce an equivalent area on the isometric drawing, showing the offset squares.
3. Take positions relative to the squares from the orthographic view, and plot them on the corresponding squares on the isometric view.
4. Draw a smooth curve through the established points with the aid of an irregular curve.

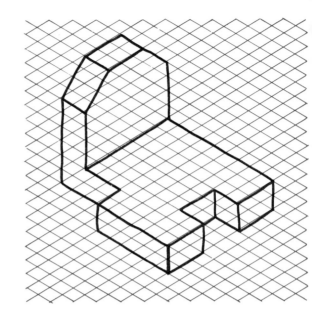

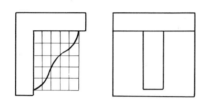

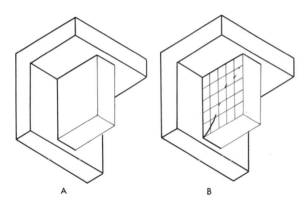

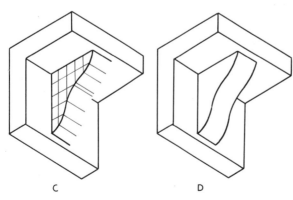

Curves Drawn in Isometric by Means of Offset Measurements

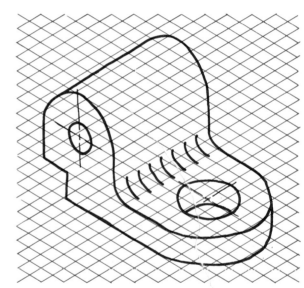

Isometric Sketching Paper

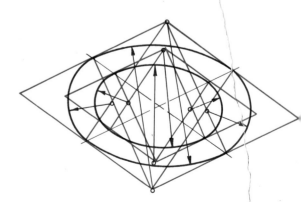

Drawing Concentric Isometric Circles

DIMENSIONING ISOMETRIC DRAWINGS

Sometimes an isometric drawing of a simple object may serve as a working drawing. In such cases the necessary dimensions and specifications are placed on the drawing.

Dimension lines, extension lines, and the line being dimensioned should be in the same plane. Arrow heads, which should be long and narrow, should be in the plane of the dimension and extension lines.

There are two acceptable methods of dimensioning an isometric drawing, pictorial plane dimensioning and unidirectional dimensioning. In pictorial plane dimensioning, the lettering should lie in one of the pictorial planes.

In unidirectional dimensioning, which is most commnoly used, the letters and numbers are vertical and read from the bottom of the sheet. An example of this type of dimensioning is shown.

Since the isometric is a one-view drawing, it is not usually possible to avoid placing dimensions on the view or across dimension lines but doing so should be avoided whenever possible.

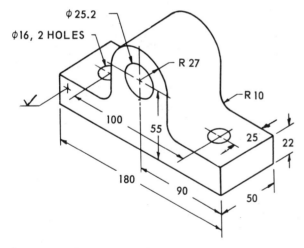

Isometric Dimensioning

CONVENTIONAL TREATMENT OF COMMON FEATURES

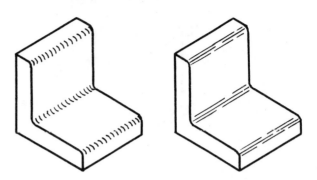

Representation of Fillets and Rounds

ANSI Y14.4-1957 (SEE * P. 251)

Fillets and Rounds

For most isometric drawings of parts having small fillets and rounds, the adopted practice is to draw the corners as sharp features. However, when it is desirable to represent the part—normally a casting—more realistically, either of the methods shown may be used. The isometric illustrations used throughout this text are common forms of technical illustration used in publications. They should not be confused with production drawings.

Representation of Threads in Isometric

ANSI Y14.4-1957 (SEE * P. 251)

Threads

The conventional method of showing threads in pictorial form is shown. The threads are represented by a series of ellipses (isometric) or circles (oblique) which are uniformly spaced along the center of the thread. The spacing of the circles need not be the spacing of the pitch. Shading may be used if desired.

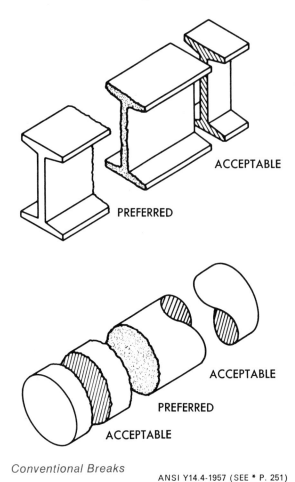

ACCEPTABLE

PREFERRED

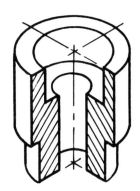

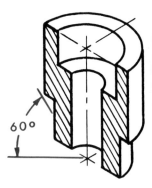

(A) HALF SECTION   **(B) FULL SECTION**

Section Views and Section Lining

ISOMETRIC SECTIONING

When a section drawing is drawn in isometric, the section lines are drawn at an angle of 60° to the horizontal. In half sections, the section lines are sloped in the opposite direction.

ACCEPTABLE

PREFERRED

ACCEPTABLE

Conventional Breaks

ANSI Y14.4-1957 (SEE * P. 251)

Break Lines

For long parts, break lines should be used to shorten the length of the drawing. Freehand breaks are preferred.

OBLIQUE PROJECTION

This method of pictorial drawing is based on a procedure of placing the object with one face parallel to the frontal plane and considering the other two faces on oblique (or receding) planes, to left or right, top or bottom, at a convenient angle. The three axes of projection are vertical, horizontal, and receding. Shown below is a cube drawn in typical positions with the receding axis at 60°, 45°, and 30°. This form of projection has the advantage of showing one face of the object without distortion. The face with the greatest irregularity of outline or contour, or the face with the longest dimension, faces the front.

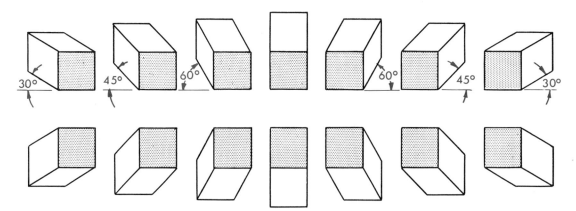

Typical Positions of the Receding Axes for Oblique Projection

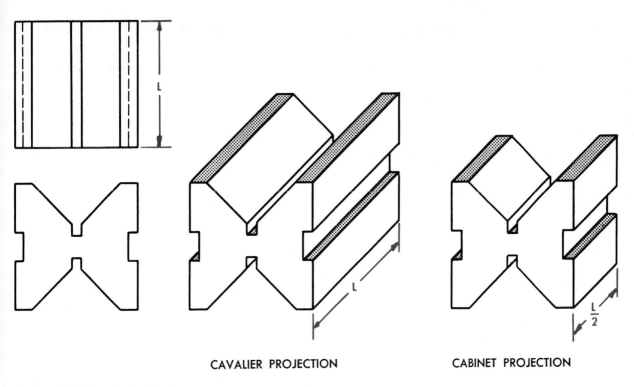

CAVALIER PROJECTION   **CABINET PROJECTION**

Types of Oblique Projection

Two types of oblique projection are used. In *cavalier oblique,* all lines are drawn to their true length, measured on the axes of the projection. In *cabinet oblique,* the lines on the receding axis are shortened to two-thirds or one-half their true length to compensate for distortion and to approximate more closely what the human eye would see. For this reason, and because of the simplicity of projection, cabinet oblique is a commonly used form of pictorial representation, especially where circles and arcs are to be drawn.

Many of the drawing techniques for isometric projection apply to oblique projection.

In the *box method* the lines for sloping surfaces are drawn by establishing the end points and joining them. Start the drawing by establishing the three axes at the front corner position. Then "box" in the overall length, height, and depth, and proceed to construct the shape, working from the front face towards the back. The construction of an irregularly shaped object by the box method is shown below.

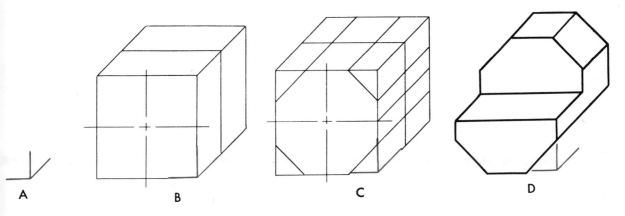

Oblique Construction by the Box Method

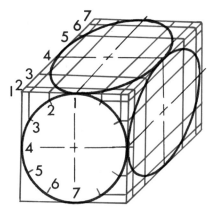

Drawing Oblique Circles by Means of Offset Measurements

DRAWING CIRCLES AND ARCS IN OBLIQUE

Whenever possible, the face of the object having circles or arcs should be selected as the "front" face, so that such circles or arcs can be easily drawn in their true shape. When circles or arcs must be drawn on one of the oblique faces, the offset measurement method illustrated may be used.

1. Draw an oblique square about the center lines, with sides equal to the diameter.

2. Draw a true circle adjacent to the oblique square, and establish equally spaced points about its circumference.

3. Project these point positions to the edge of the oblique square, and draw lines on the oblique axis from these positions. Similarly spaced lines are drawn on the other axis, forming offset squares and giving intersection points for the oval shape.

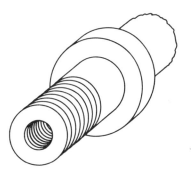

Representation of Threads in Oblique
ANSI Y14.4 (SEE * P. 251)

DIMENSIONING AN OBLIQUE DRAWING

Dimension lines are drawn parallel to the axes of projection. Extension lines are projected from the horizontal and vertical object lines whenever possible.

The dimensioning of an oblique drawing is similar to the dimensioning of an isometric drawing. The two acceptable methods of dimensioning are: pictorial plane dimensioning and unidirectional dimensioning, the latter being preferred.

As in isometric dimensioning, it is usually necessary to place some dimensions directly on the view.

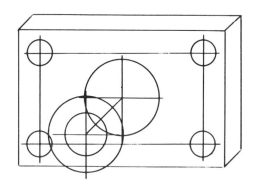

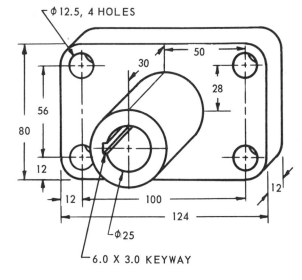

Construction and Dimensioning of an Oblique Object

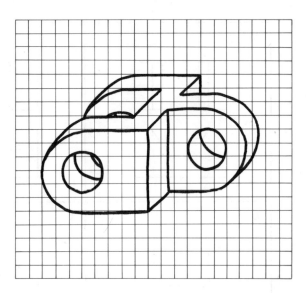

Oblique Sketching Paper

CONVENTIONAL TREATMENT OF COMMON FEATURES

Fillets and Rounds

Small fillets and rounds are normally drawn as sharp corners. When it is desirable to show the corners rounded, then either of the methods shown for isometric drafting is recommended.

Breaks

The conventional method for representing breaks is the same as that shown for isometric drawing.

References

ANSI Y14.4

Review Questions

1. What two methods of pictorial drawing are commonly used?

2. What are the angles for the isometric axes?

3. Formulate four rules that apply to isometric drawing.

4. How are non-isometric lines drawn?

5. What shape do circles have in an isometric view?

6. What technique is used for drawing irregular curves in isometric?

7. Formulate two basic rules for oblique projection.

8. What are the three axes for oblique projection?

9. What is the difference between cavalier oblique and cabinet oblique?

10. What technique is used for constructing the shape of circles on an oblique face?

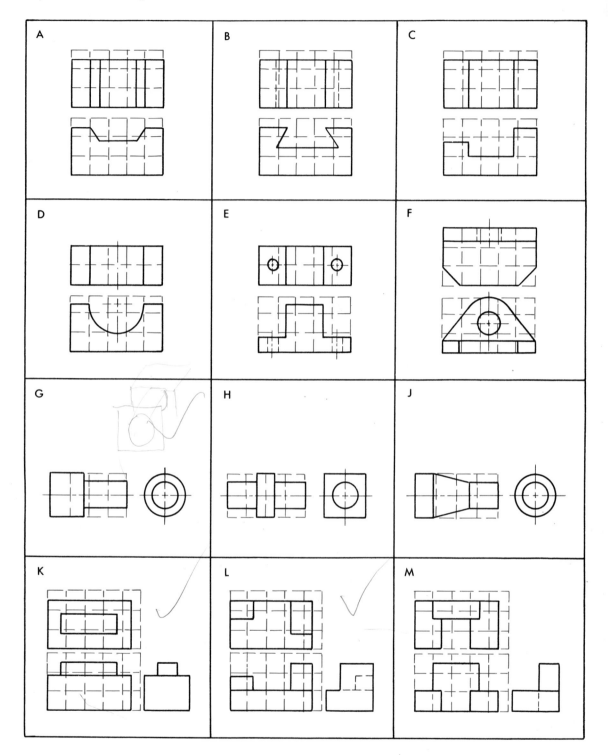

Figure 10.3   Sketching Problems

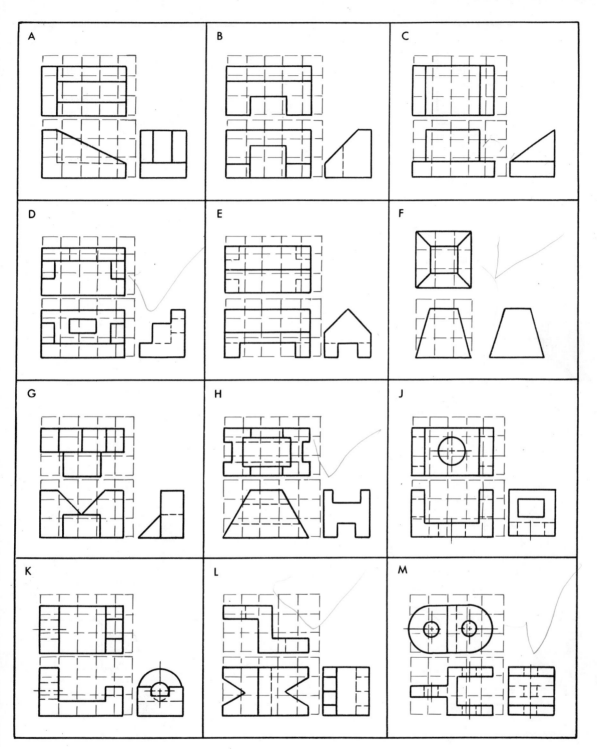

Figure 10.4   Sketching Problems

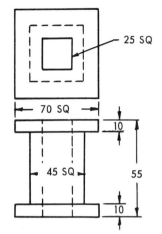

25 SQ

70 SQ

45 SQ

10

55

10

10

Figure 10.5   Guide Block

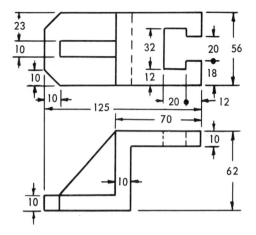

Figure 10.8   T-Slot Bracket

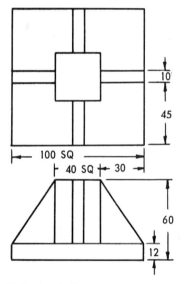

100 SQ

40 SQ   30

10

45

60

12

Figure 10.6   Lock Base

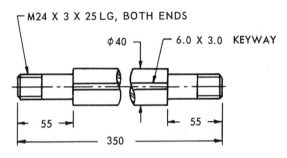

M24 X 3 X 25 LG, BOTH ENDS

φ40   6.0 X 3.0   KEYWAY

55   55

350

Figure 10.9   Roller Shaft

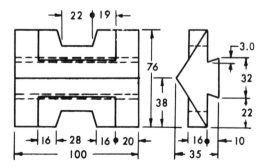

22 19

76

38

3.0

32

22

16   28   16 20

100

16 10

35

NOTE: ALL DIMENSIONS SHOWN ARE IN MILLIMETERS

Figure 10.7   Dovetail Guide

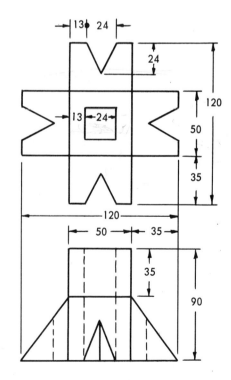

13 24

24

13 24

120

50

35

120

50   35

35

90

Figure 10.10   V-Stop

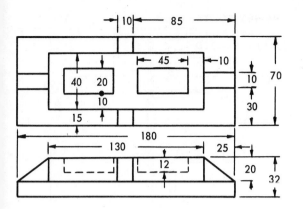

Figure 10.11 Base Plate

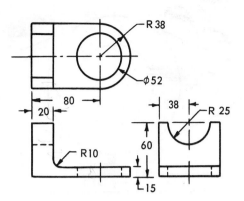

Figure 10.14 Cradle Bracket

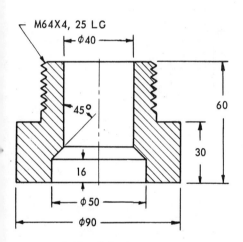

Figure 10.12 Adapter

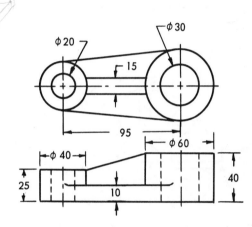

Figure 10.15 Link

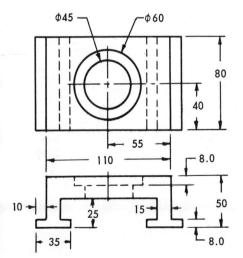

Figure 10.13 T-Guide

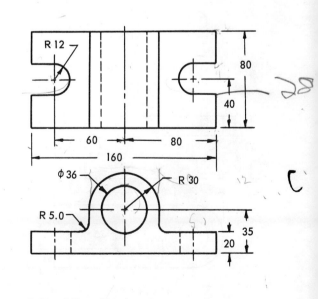

Figure 10.16 Pillow Block

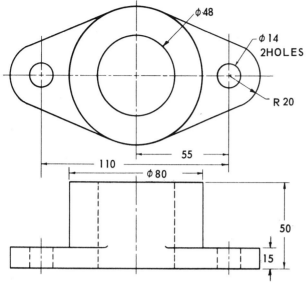

φ48

φ14
2HOLES

R20

55

110

φ80

50

15

Figure 10.17   *Bearing Support*

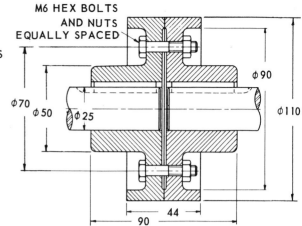

M6 HEX BOLTS
AND NUTS
EQUALLY SPACED

φ90

φ70

φ50

φ25

φ110

44

90

Figure 10.20   *Flanged Coupling*

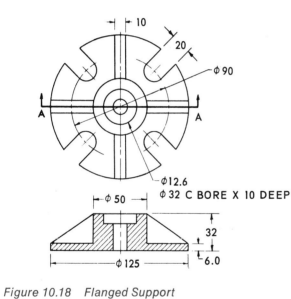

10

20

φ90

A   A

φ12.6
φ32 C BORE X 10 DEEP

φ50

32

6.0

φ125

Figure 10.18   *Flanged Support*

φ36 X 15 DEEP

100

50

150

75

50   50

125

32

32

25   50

50   32

φ28

35   35   12   35   35

75   40

Figure 20.21   *Sliding Block*

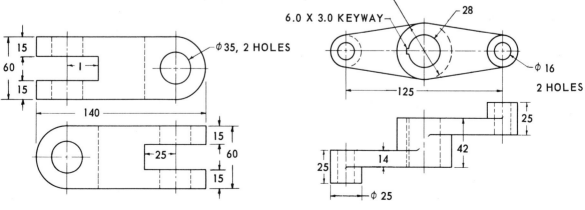

15

60

15

1

φ35, 2 HOLES

140

15

60

15

25

Figure 10.19   *Coupling*

φ46

6.0 X 3.0 KEYWAY

28

φ16

2 HOLES

125

25

42

25

14

φ25

Figure 10.22   *Rocker Arm*

CHAPTER ELEVEN

DEVELOPMENT DRAWINGS AND INTERSECTIONS

Many objects, such as cardboard and metal boxes, "tin" cans, funnels, cake pans, furnace pipes, elbows, ducts, and eavestroughing, are made from flat sheet material that is cut so that, when folded, formed, or rolled, it will take the shape of the object. Since a definite shape and size is desired, a regular orthographic drawing of the object is made first; then a development drawing is made to show the complete surface or surfaces laid out in a flat plane.

Surface development drawing is sometimes referred to as *pattern* drawing, because the layout, when made on heavy cardboard, thin metal, or wood, is used as a pattern for tracing out the developed shape on flat material. Such patterns are used extensively in sheet metal shops.

When he is making a development drawing, the draftsman must be concerned not only with the developed surfaces, but also with the joining of the edges of these surfaces and with exposed edges. An allowance must be made for the additional material necessary for seams and edges. Figure 11.5 shows a number of common methods that are used for seaming and edging. Seams are used to join edges together. Exposed edges are folded or wired to give the edge added strength and to eliminate the sharp edge.

A surface is said to be developable if a thin sheet of flexible material, such as paper, can be wrapped smoothly about it. Objects that have plane or flat surfaces and single-curved surfaces are developable; but if a surface is double-curved or warped, approximate methods must be used to develop the surface. The development of a spherical shape would thus be approximate, and the material would have to be stretched to com-

pensate for small inaccuracies. The covering for a football or a basketball is made in segments, each segment being cut to an approximate developed shape; the segments are then stretched and sewn together to give the desired shape.

GAUGE NO.	U.S. STANDARD STEEL	GALVANIZED STEEL	ALUMINUM	COPPER BWG
32	0.25	0.33		
31	0.27	0.36		
30	0.31	0.41		
29	0.34	0.44		
28	0.38	0.48		
27	0.42	0.51		
26	0.46	0.56	0.41	0.46
25	0.53	0.64		
24	0.61	0.71	0.51	0.53
23	0.68	0.79		
22	0.76	0.86	0.64	
21	0.84	0.94		0.81
20	0.91	1.02	0.81	
19	1.06	1.17		
18	1.21	1.32	1.02	0.94
17	1.37	1.47		
16	1.52	1.63	1.30	1.63
15	1.71	1.80		
14	1.90	2.01	1.63	
13	2.28	2.36		
12	2.66	2.74	2.06	
11	3.04	3.12		
10	3.42	3.50	2.59	

Figure 11.1 *Sheet Metal Thicknesses in Millimetres.*

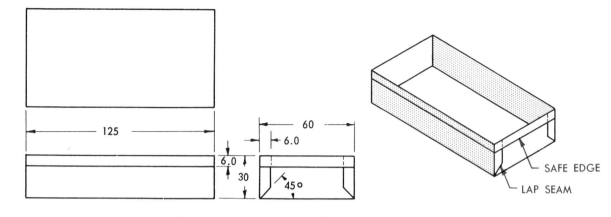

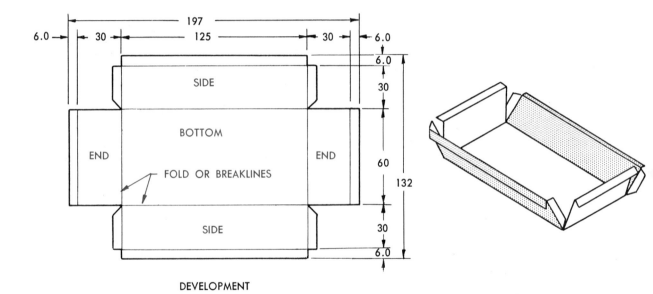

Figure 11.2   Development of a Rectangular Box

STRAIGHT LINE DEVELOPMENT

This is the term given to the development of an object that has surfaces on a flat plane of projection. The true size of each side of the object is known, and these sides can be laid out in successive order. Figure 11.2 shows the development of a simple rectangular box having a bottom and four sides. Note that in the development of the box an allowance is made for lap seams at the corners and for a folded edge. Note also that all lines for each surface are straight.

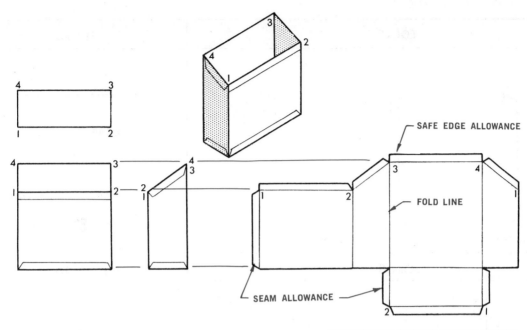

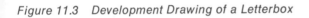

SAFE EDGE ALLOWANCE

FOLD LINE

SEAM ALLOWANCE

DEVELOPMENT (OUTSIDE SURFACE SHOWN)

Figure 11.3 Development Drawing of a Letterbox

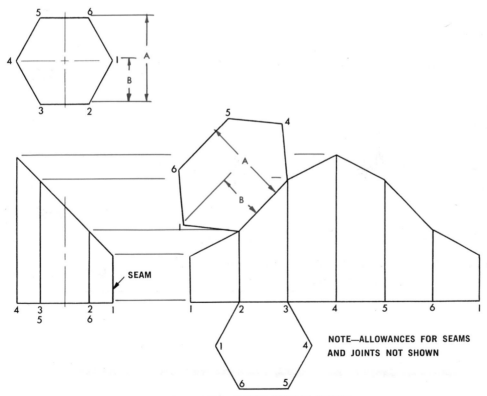

SEAM

NOTE—ALLOWANCES FOR SEAMS AND JOINTS NOT SHOWN

DEVELOPMENT (INSIDE SURFACE SHOWN)

Figure 11.4 Development of a Truncated Hexagon

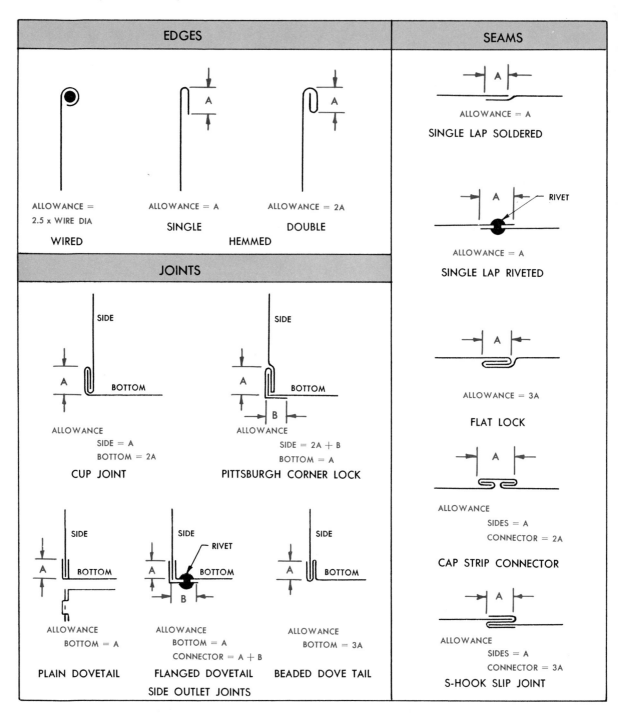

Figure 11.5   *Allowances for Joints, Seams and Edges*

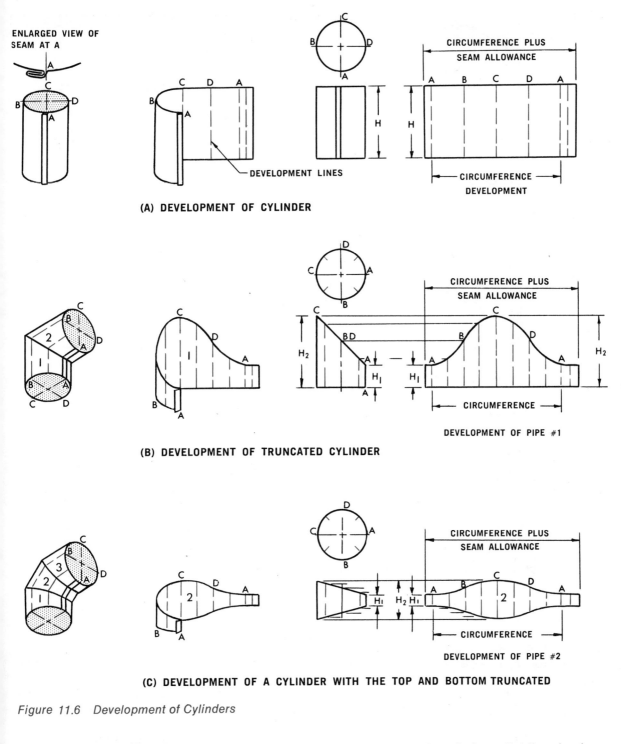

ENLARGED VIEW OF SEAM AT A

DEVELOPMENT LINES

(A) DEVELOPMENT OF CYLINDER

CIRCUMFERENCE PLUS SEAM ALLOWANCE

CIRCUMFERENCE DEVELOPMENT

DEVELOPMENT OF PIPE #1

(B) DEVELOPMENT OF TRUNCATED CYLINDER

DEVELOPMENT OF PIPE #2

(C) DEVELOPMENT OF A CYLINDER WITH THE TOP AND BOTTOM TRUNCATED

Figure 11.6   Development of Cylinders

PARALLEL LINE DEVELOPMENT

The lateral, or curved surface of a cylindrically shaped object, such as a "tin" can, is developable since it has a single-curved surface of one constant radius. The development technique used for such objects is called parallel line development. Figure 11.6 (A) shows the development of the lateral surface of a simple hollow cylinder. The width of the development is equal to the height of the cylinder, and the length of the development is equal to the circumference of the cylinder (πD) plus the seam allowance. Figure

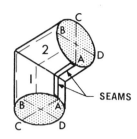
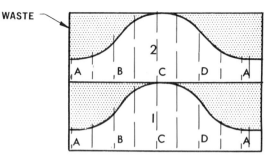

SEAMS

WASTE

(A) DEVELOPMENT OF A 2-PIECE ELBOW. BOTH SEAMS ON LINE A

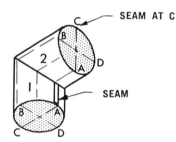
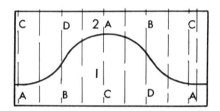

SEAM AT C

SEAM

(B) DEVELOPMENT OF A 2-PIECE ELBOW. SEAMS ON LINES A AND C

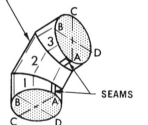

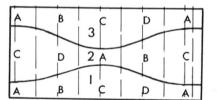

SEAM ON LINE C FOR PIPE #2

SEAMS

(C) DEVELOPMENT OF A 3-PIECE ELBOW. SEAMS ALTERNATED ON LINES A AND C

Figure 11.7   *Location of Seams and Elbows*

11.6 (B) shows the development of a cylinder with the top truncated at a 45° angle (one-half of a two-piece 90° elbow). Points of intersection are established to give the curved shape on the development. These points are derived from the intersection of a *length* location, representing a certain distance around the circumference from a starting point, and the *height* location at the same point on the circumference. The closer the points of intersection are to each other, the greater the accuracy of the development. An irregular curve is used to connect the points of intersection.

Figure 11.6 (C) shows the development of the surface of a cylinder with both the top and the bottom truncated at an angle of 22½° (the center part of a three-piece elbow). It is normal practice in sheet metal work to place the seam on the shortest side. In the development of elbows, however, this practice would result in considerable waste of material, as illustrated by figure 11.7 (A). To avoid this wastage and to simplify cutting the pieces, the seams are alternately placed 180° apart, as illustrated by figure 11.7 (B) for a two-piece elbow, and by figure 11.7 (C) for a three-piece elbow. Refer to figures 11.8 and 11.9 for complete developments of two- and four-piece elbows.

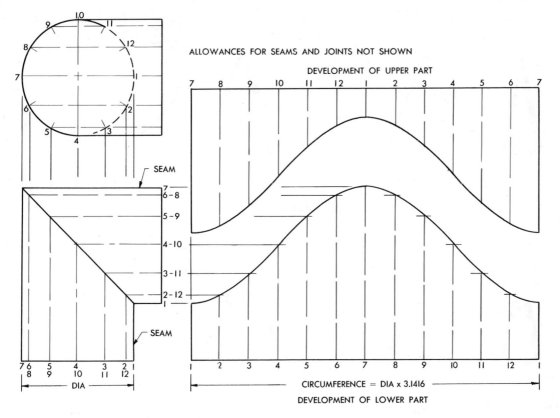

ALLOWANCES FOR SEAMS AND JOINTS NOT SHOWN

DEVELOPMENT OF UPPER PART

CIRCUMFERENCE = DIA x 3.1416

DEVELOPMENT OF LOWER PART

Figure 11.8   Development of a Two-Piece Elbow

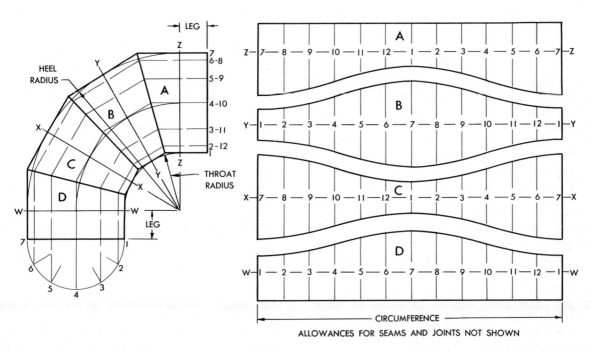

CIRCUMFERENCE

ALLOWANCES FOR SEAMS AND JOINTS NOT SHOWN

Figure 11.9   Development of a Four-Piece Elbow

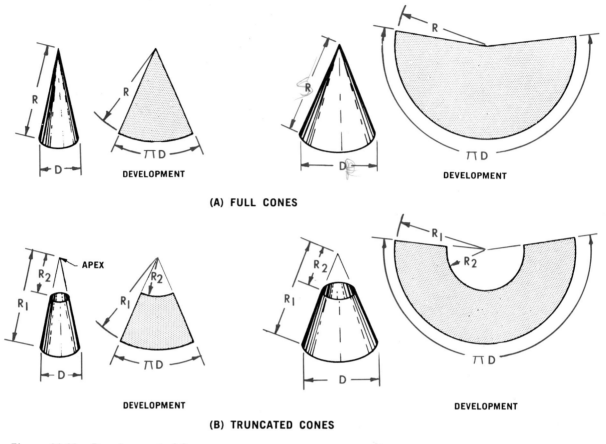

(A) FULL CONES

(B) TRUNCATED CONES

Figure 11.10   Development of Cones

RADIAL LINE DEVELOPMENT

The surface of a cone is developable, because a thin sheet of flexible material can be wrapped smoothly about it. The two dimensions necessary to make the development of the surface are the *slant height* of the cone and the *circumference* of its base. For a right-circular cone (symmetrical about the vertical axis), the developed shape is a sector of a circle. The radius for this sector is the slant height of the cone, and the length around the perimeter of the sector is equal to the circumference of the base. The proportion of height to base diameter determines the size of the sector, as illustrated by figure 11.10 (A). The development of a frustrum of a cone is the development of a full cone less the development of the upper part removed, as shown in figure 11.10 (B). Note that, at all times, the radius setting, either R^1 or R^2, is a *slant height*, a distance taken on the surface of the cone.

Figure 11.11 (A) shows the steps in the development of a cone. The top view is divided into a convenient number of equal divisions, in this

instance, 12. The chordal distance between these points is used to step off the length of arc on the development. The radius R for the development is seen as the slant height in the front view. If a cone is truncated at an angle to the base, the inside shape on the development no longer has a constant radius; that is, it is an ellipse, which must be plotted by establishing points of intersection. The divisions made on the top view are projected down to the base of the cone in the front view. Element lines are drawn from these points to the apex of the cone. These element lines are seen in their true length only when the viewer is looking in at right angles to them. Thus the points at which they cross the truncation line must be carried across, parallel to the base, to the outside element line, which is seen in its true length. The development is first made to represent the complete surface of the cone. Element lines are drawn from the step-off points about the circumference to the center point. True length settings for each element line are taken from the front view and marked off on the corresponding element line in the development.

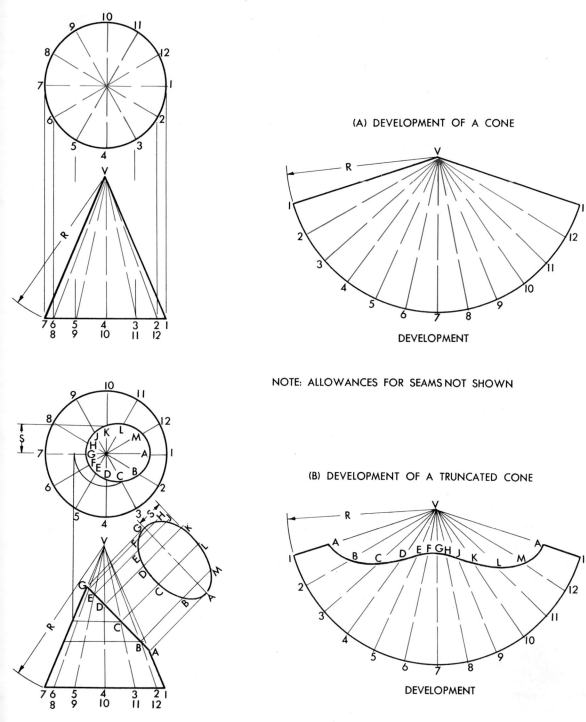

(A) DEVELOPMENT OF A CONE

DEVELOPMENT

NOTE: ALLOWANCES FOR SEAMS NOT SHOWN

(B) DEVELOPMENT OF A TRUNCATED CONE

DEVELOPMENT

Figure 11.11   Cone Development

An irregular curve is used to connect these points of intersection, giving the proper inside shape.

When the top of a cone is truncated at an angle to the base, the top surface will not be seen as a true circle. This shape must also be plotted by establishing points of intersection. True radius settings for each element line are taken from the front view and marked off on the corresponding element line in the top view. These points are connected with an irregular curve to give the correct oval shape for the top surface. If a development of the sloping top surface is required, an auxiliary view of this surface will show its true shape.

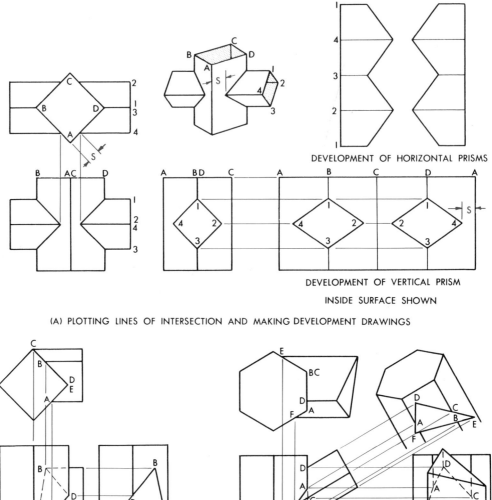

(A) PLOTTING LINES OF INTERSECTION AND MAKING DEVELOPMENT DRAWINGS

DEVELOPMENT OF HORIZONTAL PRISMS

DEVELOPMENT OF VERTICAL PRISM

INSIDE SURFACE SHOWN

(B) INTERSECTING PRISMS AT RIGHT ANGLES

(C) INTERSECTING PRISMS NOT AT RIGHT ANGLES

Figure 11.12   Developing Lines of Intersection for Flat Surfaces

INTERSECTIONS

When two surfaces at different angles meet, there is a line common to both called the *line of intersection.* When making the orthographic drawing of objects that comprise two or more intersecting parts, the lines of intersection of these parts must be plotted on the orthographic views. Figure 11.12 illustrates this plotting technique for the *intersection of flat-sided prisms* and shows the development of the parts. A numbering technique is very valuable in plotting lines of intersection. In the illustration shown, the lines of intersection appear in the front view. The

end points for these lines are established by projecting the height position from the right-side view to intersect the corresponding length position projected from the top view. When the prisms are flat-sided, the lines of intersection are straight, and the lines in the development will be straight.

Figure 11.13 (A) illustrates the plotting technique for the intersection of cylinders. Because there are no edges on the cylinders, element lines of reference are established about the cylinders in their orthographic views. In the top view the element lines for the small cylinder are drawn to

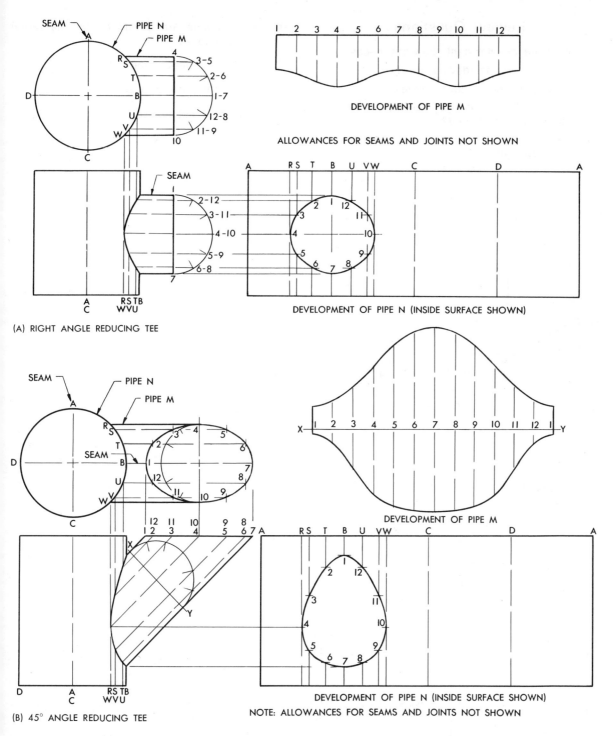

DEVELOPMENT OF PIPE M

ALLOWANCES FOR SEAMS AND JOINTS NOT SHOWN

DEVELOPMENT OF PIPE N (INSIDE SURFACE SHOWN)

(A) RIGHT ANGLE REDUCING TEE

DEVELOPMENT OF PIPE M

DEVELOPMENT OF PIPE N (INSIDE SURFACE SHOWN)

NOTE: ALLOWANCES FOR SEAMS AND JOINTS NOT SHOWN

(B) 45° ANGLE REDUCING TEE

Figure 11.13 Plotting Lines of Intersection and Making Development Drawing for Intersecting Cylinders

touch the surface of the large cylinder; for example, line 12 touches at U. This point location is then projected down to the front view to intersect the corresponding element line, establishing the height at that point. The points of intersection thus established are connected by an irregular curve to produce the line of intersection. The same points of reference used to establish the line of intersection are used to draw the development.

The same techniques of plotting reference points are used for figure 11.13 (B).

Review Questions

1. Why are development drawings necessary?
2. When is a surface developable?
3. What surfaces are developable?
4. What shapes can be developed by the straight line technique?
5. What shapes are developed by the parallel line technique?
6. What shapes are developed by the radial line technique?
7. What is a "right-circular" cone?
8. What is the purpose of seams?
9. Why are exposed edges folded or wired?
10. What is meant by "establishing points of intersection"?

PROBLEMS

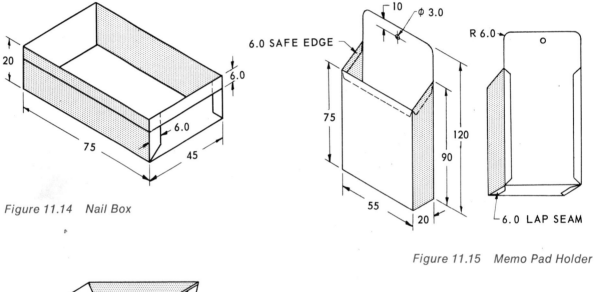

Figure 11.14   Nail Box

Figure 11.15   Memo Pad Holder

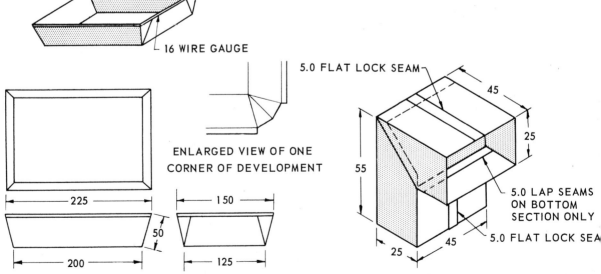

Figure 11.16   Cake Tin

Figure 11.17   Rectangular Two-Piece Elbow

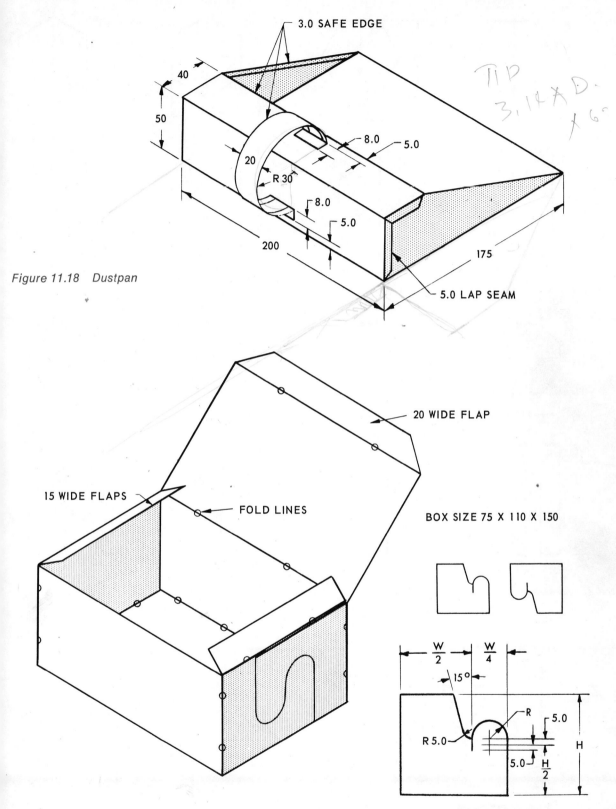

3.0 SAFE EDGE

40

50

20

R 30

8.0

5.0

8.0

5.0

200

175

5.0 LAP SEAM

Figure 11.18   Dustpan

20 WIDE FLAP

15 WIDE FLAPS

FOLD LINES

BOX SIZE 75 X 110 X 150

$\frac{W}{2}$ $\frac{W}{4}$

15°

R 5.0   R   5.0

5.0

H

$\frac{H}{2}$

LOCK FLAP DETAILS

Figure 11.19   Candy Carton

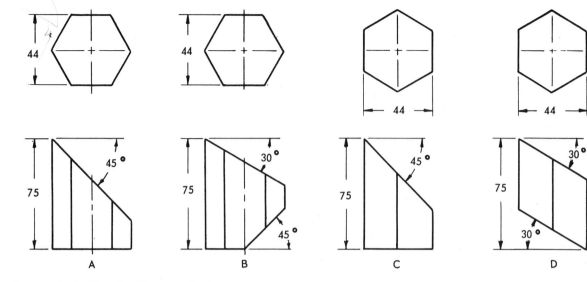

Figure 11.20   Regular Hexagon Problems

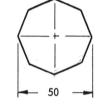
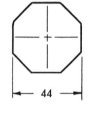
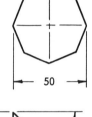
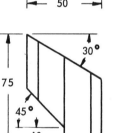
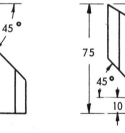
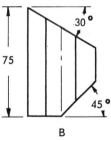
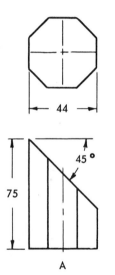

Figure 11.21   Regular Octagon Problems

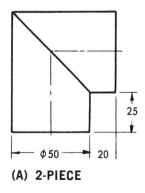
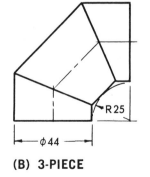
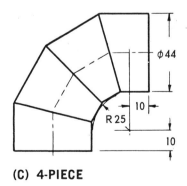

(A) 2-PIECE   **(B) 3-PIECE**   **(C) 4-PIECE**

Figure 11.22   Elbow Problems

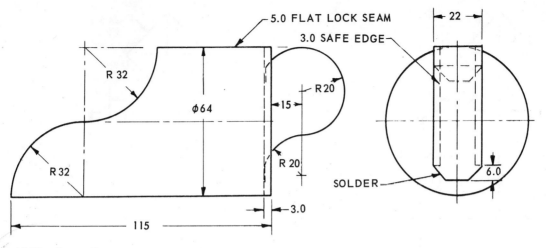

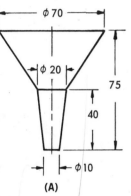

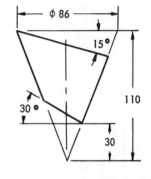

Figure 11.23   Sugar Scoop

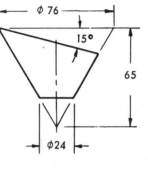

(A)   (B)   (C)

Figure 11:24   Cone Development Problems

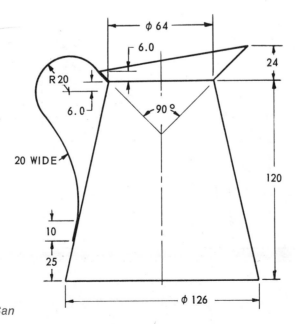

Figure 11.25   Measuring Can

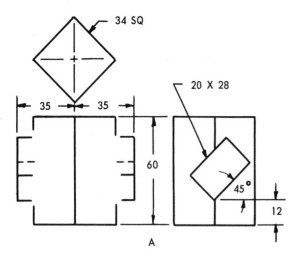

A

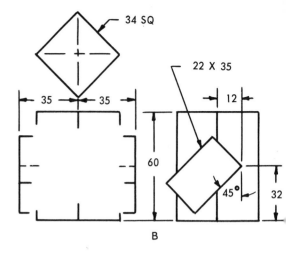

B

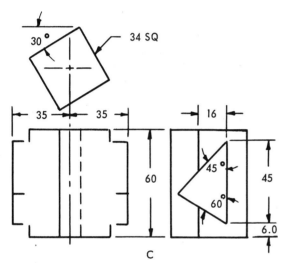

C

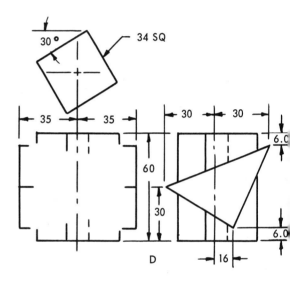

D

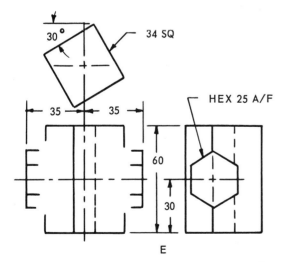

E

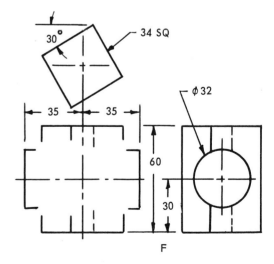

F

Figure 11.26   *Problems in Finding the Lines of Intersection. Intersecting Prisms Open Into Each Other*

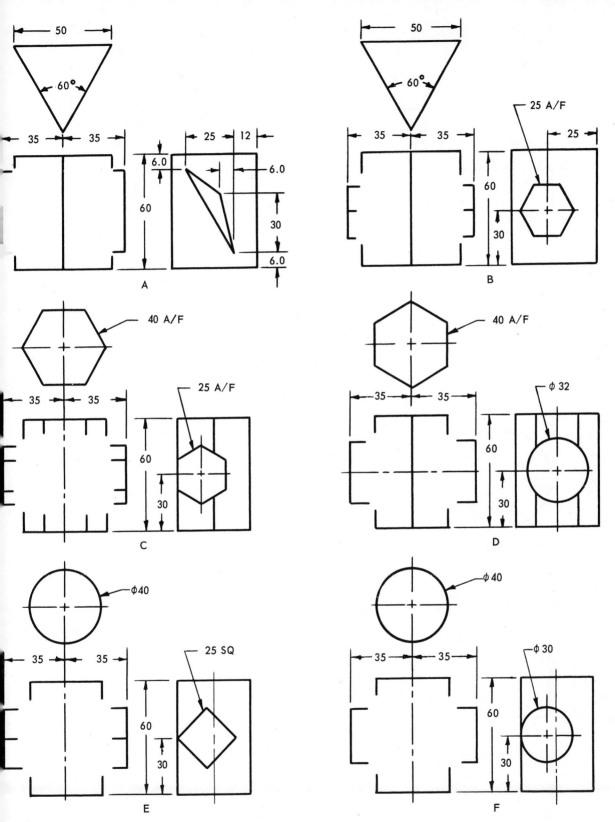

Figure 11.27 Problems in Finding the Lines of Intersection. Intersecting Prisms Open Into Each Other

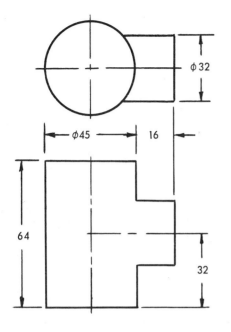

$\phi 32$

$\phi 45$ 16

64

32

(A) 90° REDUCING TEE

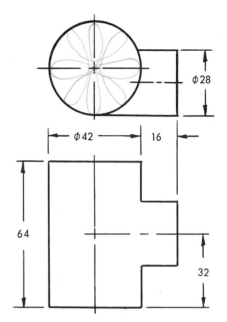

$\phi 28$

$\phi 42$ 16

64

32

(B) 90° OFFSET REDUCING TEE

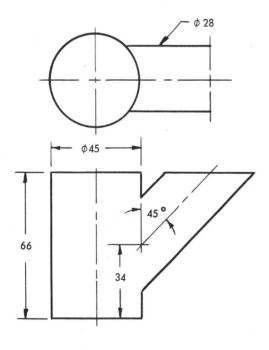

$\phi 28$

$\phi 45$

66

45°

34

(C) 45° REDUCING TEE

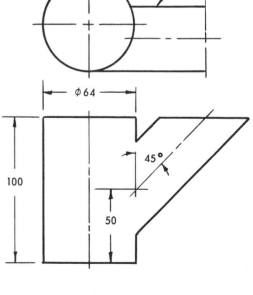

$\phi 44$

$\phi 64$

100

45°

50

(D) 45° OFFSET REDUCING TEE

Figure 11.28   Problems in Parallel Line Development and Completing Lines of Intersection

CHAPTER TWELVE

ARCHITECTURAL DRAFTING

Architectural drafting is concerned with the design, representation, and specifications for a variety of buildings and structures. The principles of architectural drawing are basically those used in other technical drawings. There are, however, many conventional symbols and practices peculiar to architectural drawing because of the nature of the work and the smaller scale used. This chapter will deal with the basic principles of architectural drawing as related to home design.

There are five basic house types:

1. The one-story or bungalow

2. The 1½-story

3. The two-story

4. The split-level

5. The bi-level

Information on these house types is found in figures 12.1 and 12.2.

Architectural drawings are of two types: presentation drawings and working drawings.

PRESENTATION DRAWINGS

The architectural draftsman is concerned with presentation drawings, which are used in mag- azines and other publications read by the general public. These drawings are pictorial in form, showing only the basic room arrangements and exterior features. They are drawn omitting the complicated building detail so that the general public may readily understand them. A floor plan is the central feature of such drawings, and a pictorial view and elevations (views) are usually shown also.

Landscaping and rendering is used on presentation drawings to make the house more attractive.

Only the overall house size is shown by the means of dimension and extension lines. Finished room sizes are given along with the room names, and the overall floor area in square feet is shown beside the floor plan.

The floor plan represents a horizontal slice through the house. Figure 12.3 shows the slice and the resulting floor-plan drawing. The floor plan gives the information that a person would need to know when selecting a house design. It gives the location of doors, windows, fireplaces, closets, and other features of the building. Also the floor plan shows the relationships of the rooms to one another. Figure 12.5 illustrates the symbols used for presentation floor-plan drawings. A knowledge of these symbols is necessary for a full understanding of the architect's design.

ONE-STORY Pitched Roof and Flat Ceiling	ONE-STORY Pitched Roof and Sloping Ceiling—Flat Roof	1½-STORY Two Living Levels—Varying Second Floor Area and Ceiling	TWO-STORY Two Living Levels—Varying Roof and Ceiling Types

Home building statistics reveal that one-story houses, with and without basements, are built in larger numbers each year than any other basic house type. There are more size, shape, and design variations in one-story houses than in any other type. Despite these variables, the construction simplicity of most one-story designs provides an excellent basis for studies of construction methods which may result in important cost savings.

From a livability standpoint, one-level houses are advantageous. Families of all ages, including the elder retirement group, favor the convenience of one-story houses. Many multilevel houses are designed with a variety of one-story additions as a basic feature of the composite architectural design.

The roof design and load-bearing elements of houses with flat roofs and those with continuous sloping roofs and ceilings are similar. Both types are significantly different, in structural design, from houses with trusses or with rafters and ceiling joists. Good architectural detail, in the functional design of these basic house types, will result in exciting examples of contemporary living. These same roof construction details are often used in multi-level houses.

The traditional homes of New England have been popular for two centuries. Probably the most familiar of these is the 1½-story "Cape Cod." The basic simplicity of the Cape Cod design should be retained, in proportion and detail, if an approach to historical authenticity is desired. The 1½-story basic shape permits a wide design variety other than traditional. The steep, sloping roof can be the basis for many outstanding contemporary designs. The second-floor living area, which varies in size with the house dimensions and use of dormers, provides for flexible planning.

Like 1½-story houses, two-story house types are rich in traditional heritage. They, too, should be designed with great respect for proportion and detail, regardless of their architectural style. The box-like, two-story form provides maximum living area at the least cost. A wide range of roof types can be used to vary the design characteristics of the two-story house. Lower- and upper-level walls can be in the same plane or, in some cases, the upper-level walls may be projected to gain more floor area and break the high wall appearance. Various types of additions, to the two-story box, often enhance overall design composition.

Canadian Wood Council

Figure 12.1   House Designs for Level Lots

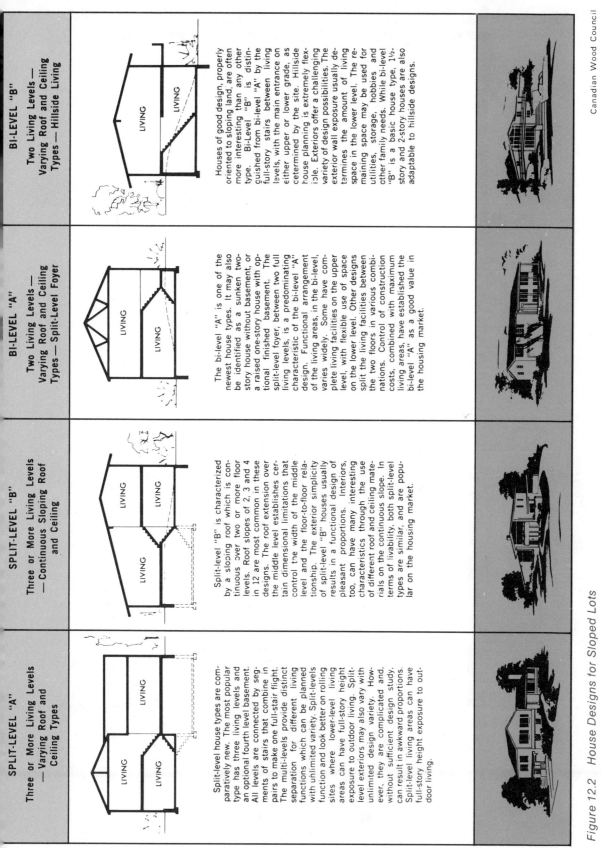

SPLIT-LEVEL "A" Three or More Living Levels — Varying Roof and Ceiling Types	SPLIT-LEVEL "B" Three or More Living Levels — Continuous Sloping Roof and Ceiling	BI-LEVEL "A" Two Living Levels — Varying Roof and Ceiling Types — Split-Level Foyer	BI-LEVEL "B" Two Living Levels — Varying Roof and Ceiling Types — Hillside Living

Split-level house types are comparatively new. The most popular type has three living levels and an optional fourth level basement. All levels are connected by segments of stairs that combine in pairs to make one full-stair flight. The multi-levels provide distinct separation for different living functions which can be planned with unlimited variety. Split-levels function and look better on rolling sites where lower-level living areas can have full-story height exposure to outdoor living. Split-level exteriors may also vary with unlimited design variety. However, they are complicated and, without sufficient design study, can result in awkward proportions. Split-level living areas can have full-story height exposure to outdoor living.

Split-level "B" is characterized by a sloping roof which is continuous over two or more floor levels. Roof slopes of 2, 3 and 4 in 12 are most common in these designs. The roof extension over the middle level establishes certain dimensional limitations that control the width of the middle level and the floor-to-floor relationship. The exterior simplicity of split-level "B" houses usually results in a functional design of pleasant proportions. Interiors, too, can have many interesting characteristics through the use of different roof and ceiling materials on the continuous slope. In terms of livability, both split-level types are similar, and are popular on the housing market.

The bi-level "A" is one of the newest house types. It may also be identified as a sunken two-story house without basement, or a raised one-story house with optional finished basement. The split-level foyer, between two full living levels, is a predominating characteristic of the bi-level "A" design. Functional arrangement of the living areas, in the bi-level, varies widely. Some have complete living facilities on the upper level, with flexible use of space on the lower level. Other designs split the living facilities between the two floors in various combinations. Control of construction costs, combined with maximum living areas, have established the bi-level "A" as a good value in the housing market.

Houses of good design, properly oriented to sloping land, are often more interesting than any other type. Bi-Level "B" is distinguished from bi-level "A" by the full-story stairs between living levels, with the main entrance on either upper or lower grade, as determined by the site. Hillside house planning is extremely flexible. Exteriors offer a challenging variety of design possibilities. The exterior wall exposure usually determines the amount of living space in the lower level. The remaining space may be used for utilities, storage, hobbies and other family needs. While bi-level "B" is a basic house type, 1½-story and 2-story houses are also adaptable to hillside designs.

Canadian Wood Council

Figure 12.2   House Designs for Sloped Lots

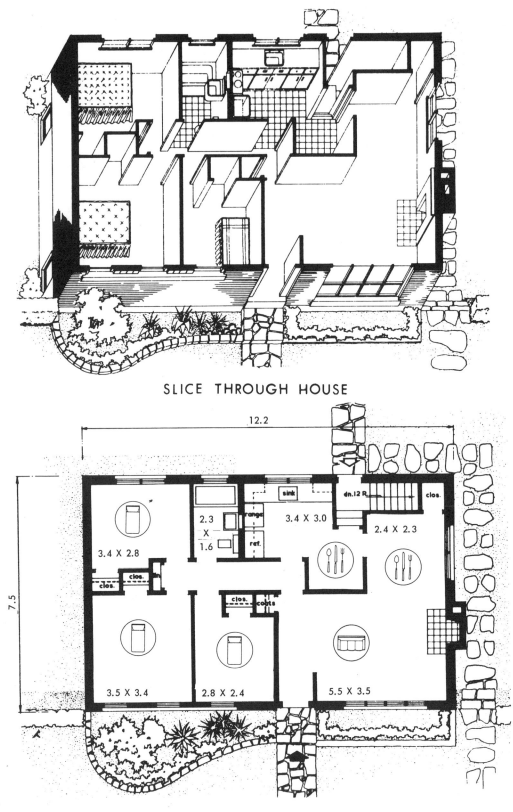

SLICE THROUGH HOUSE

RESULTING FLOOR PLAN

Figure 12.3   How to Read Presentation Floor Plan Drawings   Courtesy Central Mortgage and Housing Corporation

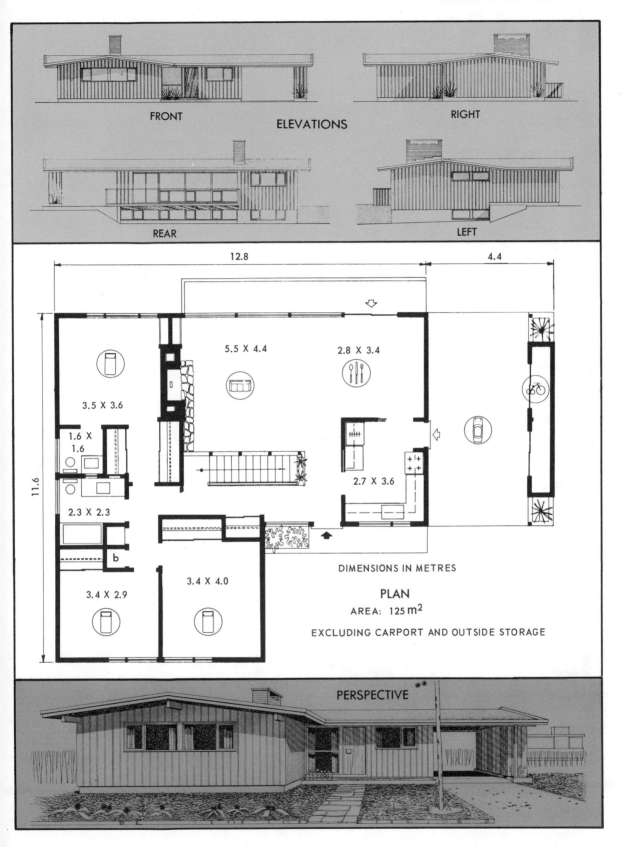

Figure 12.4   Presentation Drawing of a Home

Central Mortgage and Housing Corporation

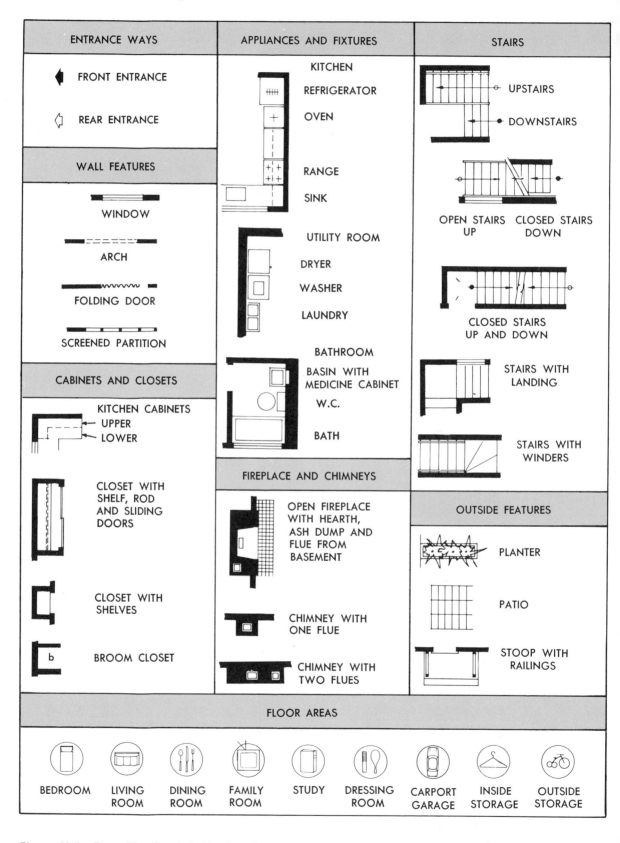

Figure 12.5   Floor Plan Symbols Used on Presentation Drawings

Central Mortgage and Housing Corporation

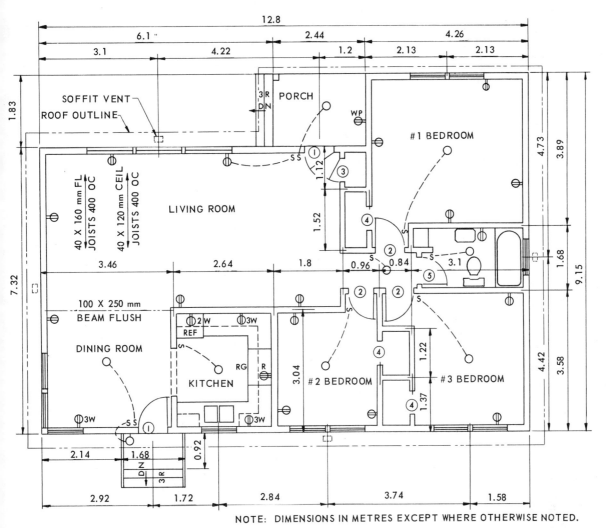

NOTE: DIMENSIONS IN METRES EXCEPT WHERE OTHERWISE NOTED.

Figure 12.6   Floor Plan of a Summer Cottage

WORKING DRAWINGS

Architectural working drawings contain the information required by the builder to erect the building. In order to understand and read working drawings, it is necessary to become familiar with architectural symbols and terms. Figures 12.7 and 12.8 illustrate the framing for a bungalow and give the architectural terms for the principal parts of the house. A typical set of working drawings for a house includes: floor plans for each level, a basement plan, a typical section through a wall, and elevations of the front, the back, and the two sides of the house. The floor plan and typical section view for a summer cottage are shown in figures 12.6 and 12.9.

LETTERING [2]

It is not considered practical or desirable to suggest a specific standard form of lettering for architectural drawings. The logical goal is to provide distinct, uniform letters and figures that will ensure the production of clear, legible prints.

It is recommended, however, that vertical upper case lettering and a minimum number of basic letter sizes be used. Three basic sizes are sufficient for most architectural drawing applications. The largest size is reserved for major headings. An intermediate size is used for sub-headings. The smallest size is used for notes. The letter size for notes and for dimensions should be not less than 3 mm.

DRAWING SCALES

Floor plans and elevations for houses are usually drawn to the scale 1:50. Section views which show close detail are drawn to a larger scale such as 1:10.

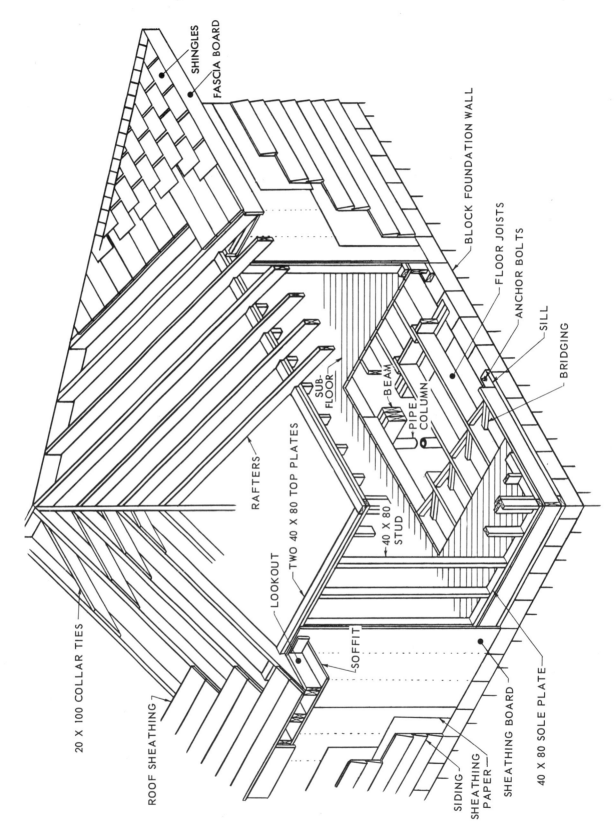

Figure 12.7   House Framing

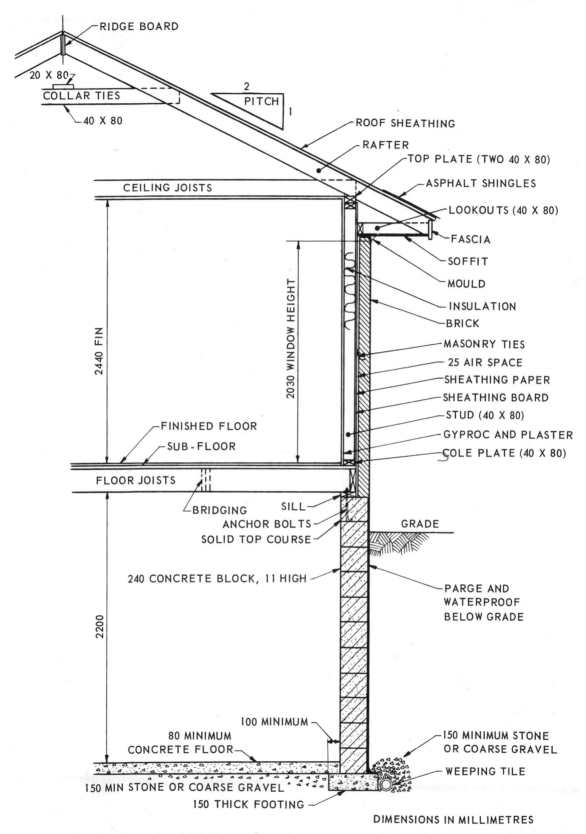

Figure 12.8 Section Through a Brick Veneer Bungalow

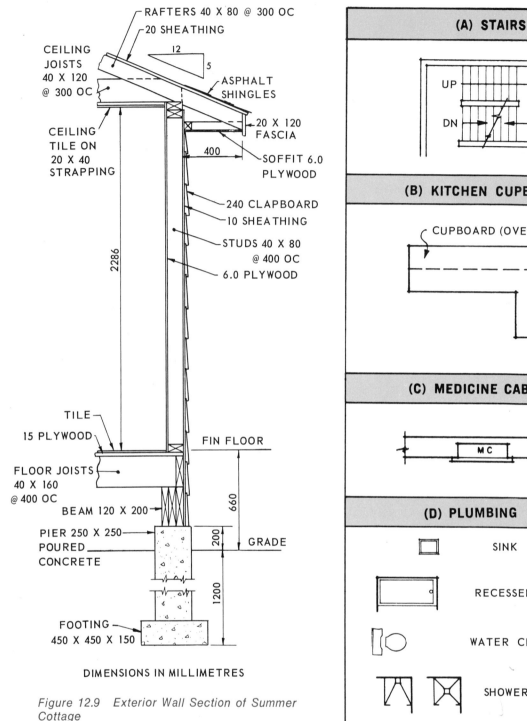

Figure 12.9 *Exterior Wall Section of Summer Cottage*

DRAWING SYMBOLS[2]

Figure 12.11 shows the symbols used to indicate the four basic types of wall construction used in the design of homes. Drawing symbols for common house features are shown in figures 12.10, 12.12 and 12.13.

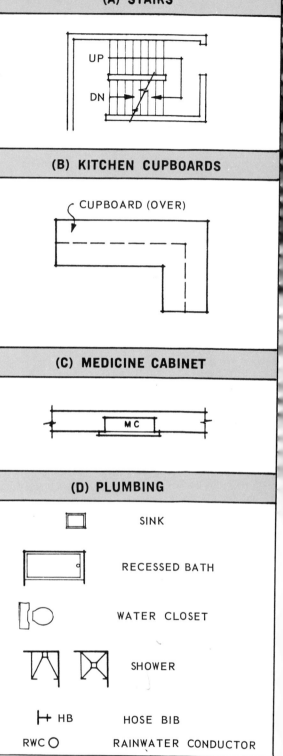

Figure 12.10 *Miscellaneous Working Drawing Symbols*

Canadian Government Specifications Board

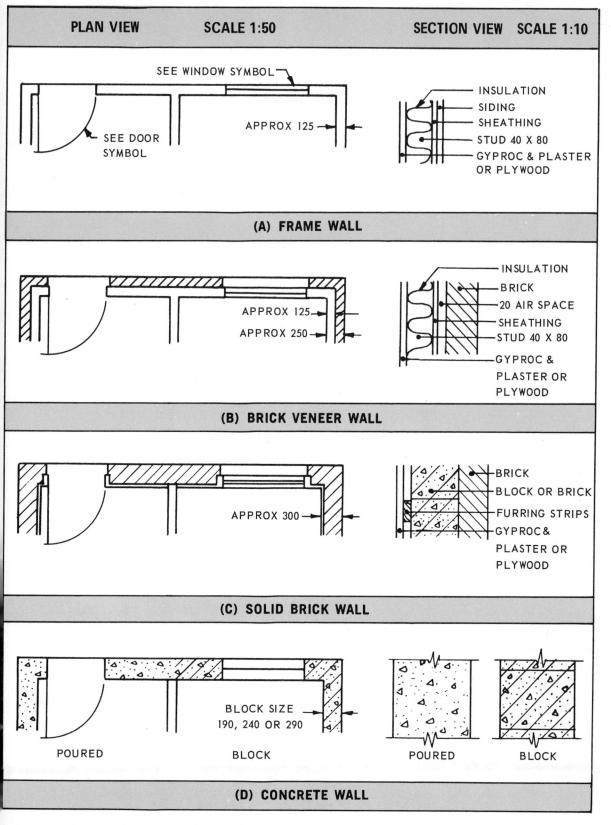

Figure 12.11 *Wall Symbols for Working Drawings*

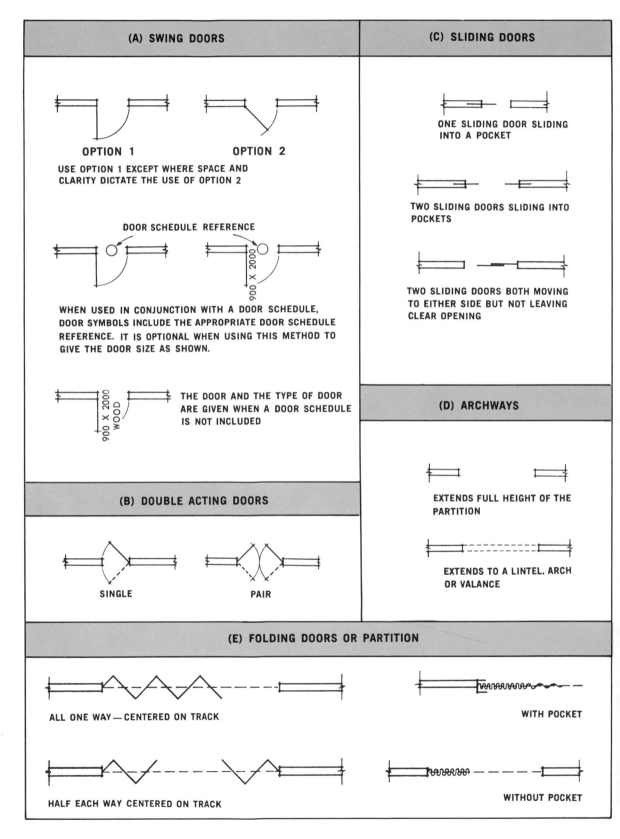

Figure 12.12   Door Symbols for Working Drawings

Canadian Government Specifications Board

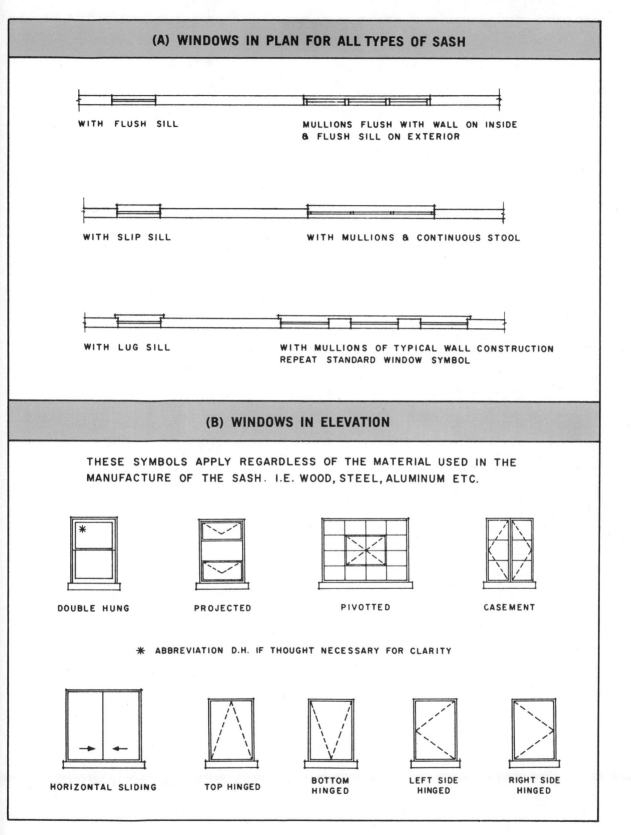

Figure 12.13 Window Symbols for Working Drawings

Canadian Government Specifications Board

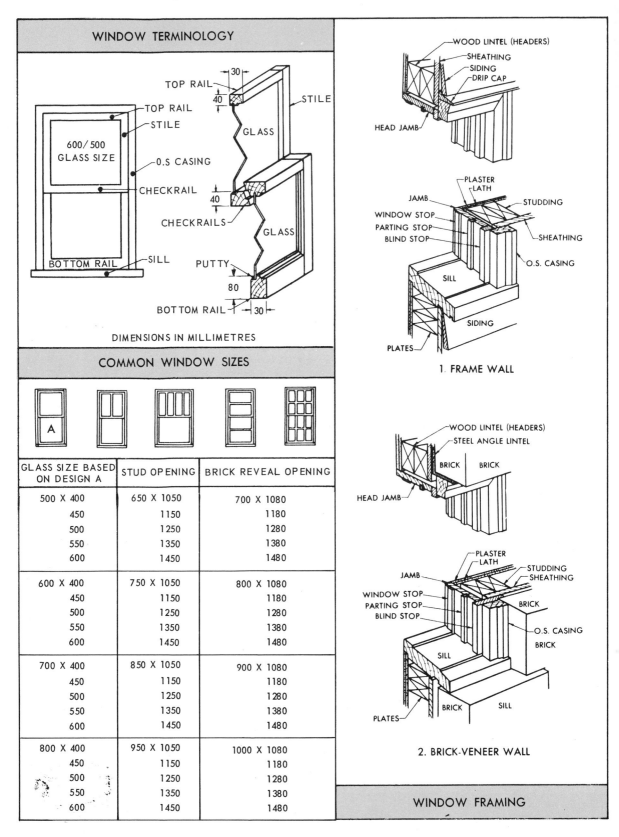

WINDOW TERMINOLOGY

600/500 GLASS SIZE

TOP RAIL
TOP RAIL
STILE
O.S CASING
CHECKRAIL
CHECKRAILS
BOTTOM RAIL — SILL
STILE
GLASS
GLASS
PUTTY
BOTTOM RAIL
30
40
40
80
30

DIMENSIONS IN MILLIMETRES

COMMON WINDOW SIZES

A

GLASS SIZE BASED ON DESIGN A	STUD OPENING	BRICK REVEAL OPENING
500 X 400	650 X 1050	700 X 1080
450	1150	1180
500	1250	1280
550	1350	1380
600	1450	1480
600 X 400	750 X 1050	800 X 1080
450	1150	1180
500	1250	1280
550	1350	1380
600	1450	1480
700 X 400	850 X 1050	900 X 1080
450	1150	1180
500	1250	1280
550	1350	1380
600	1450	1480
800 X 400	950 X 1050	1000 X 1080
450	1150	1180
500	1250	1280
550	1350	1380
600	1450	1480

WOOD LINTEL (HEADERS)
SHEATHING
SIDING
DRIP CAP
HEAD JAMB

PLASTER
LATH
JAMB
STUDDING
WINDOW STOP
PARTING STOP
BLIND STOP
SHEATHING
O.S. CASING
SILL
SIDING
PLATES

1. FRAME WALL

WOOD LINTEL (HEADERS)
STEEL ANGLE LINTEL
BRICK   BRICK
HEAD JAMB

PLASTER
LATH
JAMB
STUDDING
SHEATHING
WINDOW STOP
PARTING STOP
BLIND STOP
BRICK
O.S. CASING
BRICK
SILL
PLATES
BRICK   SILL

2. BRICK-VENEER WALL

WINDOW FRAMING

Figure 12.14   Window Details

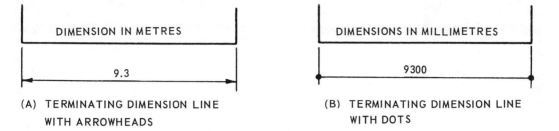

(A) TERMINATING DIMENSION LINE
   WITH ARROWHEADS

(B) TERMINATING DIMENSION LINE
   WITH DOTS

Figure 12.15   Alternate Methods of Dimensioning Working Drawings

DIMENSIONING [2]

The two approved methods for dimensioning architectural drawings are shown in figure 12.15. Note that the dimension line is not broken and that the dimension appears above the dimension line. Dimensions are given in metres (a minimum of two digits for each dimension) for floor plans and elevation drawings. When showing dimensions less than one metre in size, a zero must

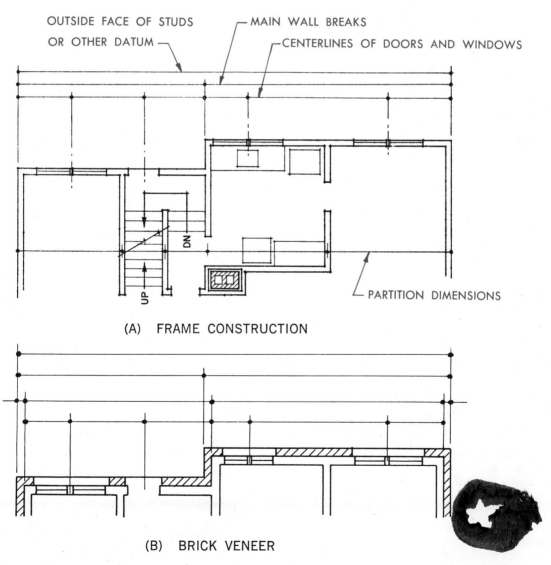

OUTSIDE FACE OF STUDS
OR OTHER DATUM

MAIN WALL BREAKS

CENTERLINES OF DOORS AND WINDOWS

PARTITION DIMENSIONS

DN

UP

(A)   FRAME CONSTRUCTION

(B)   BRICK VENEER

Figure 12.16   Dimensioning a Floor Plan

Canadian Government Specifications Board

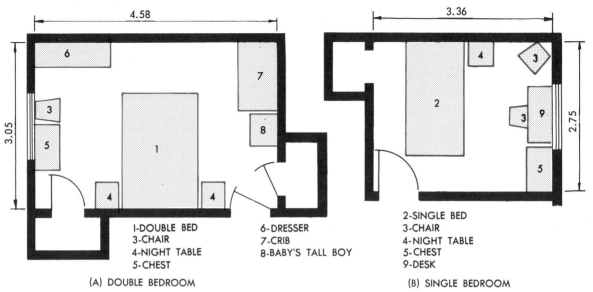

I-DOUBLE BED
3-CHAIR
4-NIGHT TABLE
5-CHEST

6-DRESSER
7-CRIB
8-BABY'S TALL BOY

2-SINGLE BED
3-CHAIR
4-NIGHT TABLE
5-CHEST
9-DESK

(A) DOUBLE BEDROOM

(B) SINGLE BEDROOM

Figure 12.17   Bedroom Layouts

DIMENSIONS IN METRES

be placed in front of the decimal point. For detail drawings of smaller features such as joist sizes, wall sections, and window details, the dimensions are in millimetres. However, the unit of measurement should be clearly indicated so the dimensions will not be interpreted as metre sizes. Figure 12.16 shows how to dimension walls, doors and windows.

DEVELOPING A HOUSE PLAN [1]

ROOM SIZES

How much space is required for the furniture in a small house? This is an important consideration in trying to devise an economical house plan with reasonable minimum dimensions. In buying furniture, it is important to select pieces that do not occupy too much floor space. Bulky old-fashioned furniture wastes space. Furniture is well designed if it is comfortable, convenient, compact, light, easily cleaned, and assists in giving the effect of free floor space.

BEDROOMS

The three-bedroom house is most popular because it provides for a typical family of parents with children of both sexes. Each individual in a family spends more time in the bedroom than in any other room in the house. The bedroom should be tailored to suit the individual, to offer opportunity for reasonable self-expression and provide a haven from the rest of the family. A well designed bedroom gives the maximum in pleasure, comfort, leisure, and quiet.

Youngsters are generally active and noisy, so that, while their rooms should be close by those of the parents, there should be some form of sound barrier, possibly a bank of closets, separating them. Children's bedrooms should also be near the bathroom. Bedrooms vary in size, usually between 7.5 and 14 m^2. Furniture is likely to occupy almost half of the floor area. The remaining space is necessary for dressing, to give access to drawers and cupboards, and to make beds and clean with mop and vacuum cleaner.

Minimum Furniture for a Single Bedroom

Bed	1.1 x 2.1	2.3	m^2
Chest of Drawers	0.5 x 0.8	0.4	"
Chair	0.5 x 0.5	0.25	"
Night Table	0.5 x 0.5	0.25	"
		Total 3.2	m^2

Minimum Furniture for a Double Bedroom

Bed	1.5 x 2.1	3.15	m^2
Night Tables (2)	0.5 x 0.5	0.25	"
	0.5 x 0.5	0.25	"
Dressing Table	0.5 x 1.5	0.75	"
Chest	0.5 x 0.8	0.4	"
Chair	0.5 x 0.5	0.25	"
		Total 5.05	m^2
Optional Furniture			
Baby Crib	0.6 x 0.9	0.55	m^2
Baby's Chest of Drawers	0.5 x 0.6	0.3	"
		Total 5.9	m^2

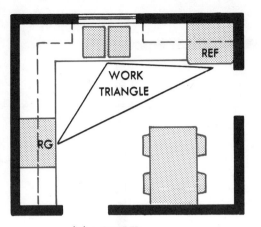

(A) L-SHAPED

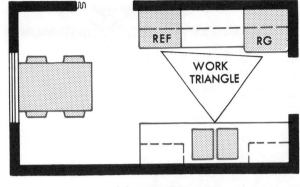

(B) CORRIDOR-TYPE

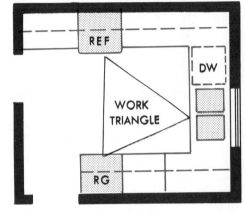

(C) U-SHAPED

Figure 12.18   Basic Kitchen Layouts

KITCHENS

The kitchen serves both as a food preparation center and as a food store. Often, food is eaten in the kitchen. Apart from regular meal preparation, other activities such as canning, baking, and pickle-making are done here. The kitchen is also used as a "home base" for cleaning the house, for doing laundry work, and for ironing. Children's home-work and hobbies are sometimes done in the kitchen. The cleaning of items such as shoes and silver and even minor repair jobs also take place in the kitchen. In fact, the kitchen is the hardest used and most useful room in the house.

A regular sequence of actions takes place in preparing a meal. This sequence is:

1. The assembling of the foods,
2. Preparation of food,
3. Cooking,
4. Serving up, and
5. Washing up and storage.

To make the handling of meals easy this sequence of food preparation should be provided for in the layout of the kitchen and its equipment. Three work centers are necessary. They are:

1. Mix Center
2. Sink Center
3. Cook Center

Supplies and equipment for use at each center should be stored there, close at hand.

There is a direct path between these centers forming a work triangle by which the efficiency of the kitchen may be gauged. The sum of the distances between these centers should not be less than 3.6 m and not more than 6.0 m. The arrangement of these centers, together with that of the doors and windows, determines the type of kitchen. Some of the common types are shown in figure 12.18. Note that in all but one case the work centers are placed side by side with a continuous counter connecting them.

Most kitchens require 2 doors; one to the dining area and one to the service entrance. Unnecessary doors break up the assembly of the work centers and thus decrease the efficiency of the kitchen.

A serving hatch from the cook center counter through to the dining room is often a great asset and makes the serving of meals easier.

The following figures are suggested for kitchen storage requirements:

Wall cabinets, 2.5-3.0 m in length
Base cabinets, 2.5-3.0 m in length

Additional storage space is needed for cleaning equipment. There should be counter-top work surfaces:

1. Beside the refrigerator (note which way door opens). (Mix Center)
2. At both sides of the sink. (Sink Center)
3. At least on one side of the stove. (Cook Center)
4. On one side of a washing machine and built-in ironer, if this equipment is included.

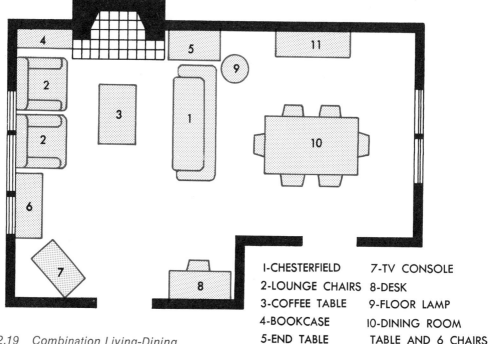

Figure 12.19   Combination Living-Dining Room

1-CHESTERFIELD   7-TV CONSOLE
2-LOUNGE CHAIRS   8-DESK
3-COFFEE TABLE   9-FLOOR LAMP
4-BOOKCASE   10-DINING ROOM
5-END TABLE   TABLE AND 6 CHAIRS
6-STEREO   11-BUFFET

LIVING AND DINING ROOM

This is the room where the character of the family is expressed and where friends are received. It should combine the requirements for quiet relaxation, for active entertainment, for study, and for children's play.

Unlike other rooms, which are enclosed by four walls and a door, the living room is often the open central core of the house. In contemporary houses it is often of irregular shape with openings revealing the other parts of the house and adding to its sense of freedom, accessibility and informality. For this reason the selection and placing of furniture is an essential part of the planning and design of the house. This determines the real shape and uses of the space within the living room.

The floor areas of a combined dining and living space may average 24 m². About half of this space will usually be occupied by the following pieces of furniture:

1 Chesterfield	1.0 × 2.1	2.1 m²
2 Lounge Chairs	0.8 × 0.9	1.4 "
2 Occasional Chairs	0.7 × 0.7	1.0 "
1 Coffee Table	0.7 × 0.9	0.6 "
1 End Table	0.4 × 0.7	0.3 "
1 Desk	0.6 × 1.2	0.7 "
1 Hi-Fi Set	0.4 × 1.5	0.6 "
1 Floor Lamp	0.3 × 0.3	0.1 "
1 T.V. Set	0.6 × 0.6	0.4 "
1 Book Case	0.3 × 0.9	0.3 "
1 Buffet	0.5 × 1.2	0.6 "
1 Dining Table	1.1 × 1.8	2.0 "
6 Dining Chairs	0.4 × 0.4	1.0 "
	Total	11.1 m²

References

1. Central Mortgage and Housing Corporation.
2. *Standard on Architectural Drawing practices*, by Canadian Government Specifications Board.
3. Canadian Wood Council.

Review Questions

1. Name the five basic house types and give the distinguishing features of each.
2. What is the purpose of presentation drawings?
3. What are side, front, and back views called in architectural drawings?
4. What information does the presentation floor plan drawing give?
5. What does a typical set of working drawings for a house include?
6. How are location dimensions of doors and windows given on a working drawing?
7. How are location dimensions for interior partitions given?
8. What room in the house receives the hardest use, and why?
9. What is meant by a *work triangle* in the kitchen?
10. Where should counter-top work surfaces be located?

PROBLEMS

PRESENTATION DRAWING PROBLEMS

1. Make a presentation plan drawing of the summer cottage shown in figure 12.20.
2. Make a presentation plan drawing of bungalow #1 shown in figure 12.21.
3. Make a presentation plan drawing of bungalow #2 shown in figure 12.22.
4. Make a presentation plan drawing of bungalow #3 shown in figure 12.23.
5. A prospective customer is interested in having a 4.3 x 6.7 m garage built. The garage is to have two windows with 460/920 mm lights, double hung; one door, 810 x 2030 mm; and one garage door 2740 mm wide and 2130 mm high. Make a presentation plan drawing of the garage.
6. Mr. Hines is interested in building a 16-unit motel. Construction is to be of 250 mm concrete block except for the front wall, which will be 100 mm angel stone backed by 200 mm block. The maximum width of the motel is to be 5.5 m. The units will each have a 3-piece bath, a telephone, and a television set, and will be suitable to accommodate two double beds. Make a plan drawing, complete with dimensions, of a unit which you would present to Mr. Hines. (Scale 1:50).

7. Make a presentation drawing of the floor plan of a summer cottage having the following details: floor area between 75 and 100 m², 3 bedrooms, kitchen with eating area, bathroom with basin and w.c., and a large living room. Other details may be selected by the student. (Scale 1:50).

WORKING DRAWING PROBLEMS

1. Make the working drawing (floor plan) of the garage described in presentation drawing problem 5.
2. Make the working drawing (floor plan) of the motel unit described in presentation drawing problem 6.
3. Make the working drawing (floor plan) of the summer cottage described in presentation drawing problem 7.

FURNITURE LAYOUT PROBLEMS

Draw one of the floor plans shown in figure 12.24 to the scale 1:50 and draw in the furniture that you recommend each room should have.

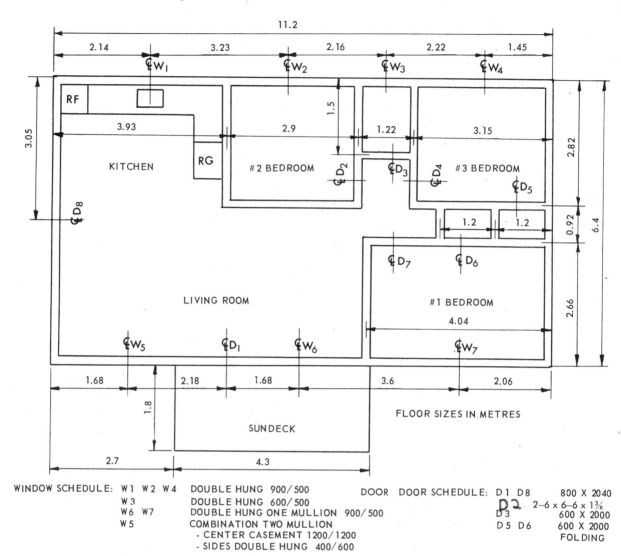

Figure 12.20   Summer Cottage

PROBLEM 1
SUMMER COTTAGE

NOTE:
A. For linear dimensions calculate to the nearest 0.01 m.
B. For area dimensions calculate to the nearest 0.1 m².
C. For calculation purposes use a nominal wall thickness of 0.16 m.

1. What are the overall dimensions of the cottage?
2. Calculate the size of (A) the largest bedroom, (B) the smallest bedroom, (C) the living room.

3. How many windows has the cottage?
4. How many doors has the cottage?
5. What is the rated floor area of (A) the bathroom, (B) the combined living room and kitchen?
6. Sketch the proper door convention showing a section of the wall for (A) Door D¹, (B) Door D⁵, (C) Door D⁷.
7. Sketch the proper window convention showing a section of the wall for (A) Window W¹, (B) Window W³, (C) Window W⁵, (D) Window W⁶.

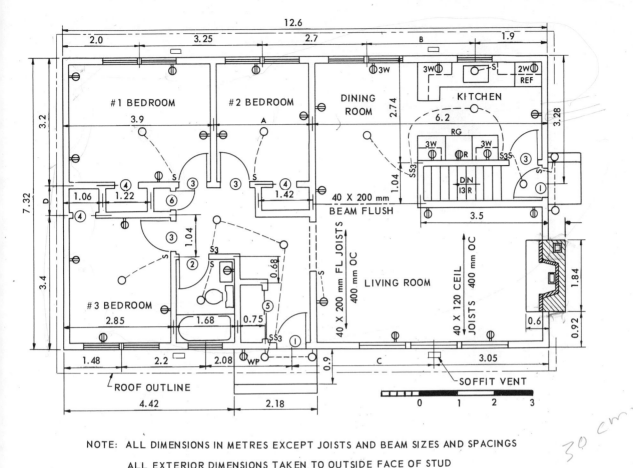

NOTE: ALL DIMENSIONS IN METRES EXCEPT JOISTS AND BEAM SIZES AND SPACINGS

ALL EXTERIOR DIMENSIONS TAKEN TO OUTSIDE FACE OF STUD

Figure 12.21   Floor Plan Bungalow #1

PROBLEM 2
BUNGALOW NO. 1

NOTE:

    A. For linear dimensions calculate to the nearest 0.01 m.

    B. For area dimensions calculate to the nearest 0.1 m².

    C. For calculation purposes use a nominal wall thickness of 0.14 m.

1. Calculate dimensions A to D.
2. What type of exterior wall is shown?
3. What are the overall dimensions of the house?
4. What is the rated floor area of (A) the house, (B) the bathroom, (C) #1 bedroom?
5. Calculate the size of (A) the #3 bedroom, (B) the front hall closet, (C) the front porch, (D) the chimney, (E) the combined chimney and hearth.
6. What is the size and spacing of (A) the floor joists, (B) the ceiling joists?
7. How many closets are there?
8. Of which basic type is the kitchen layout?
9. What type of door is used on the bedroom closets?
10. How many swinging doors are there?
11. What is the length of the living room?
12. Where is the archway located?
13. Using the scale on the drawing, what is the total length of the kitchen counters? (Use counter front measurements. Do not include the refrigerator or range frontage).

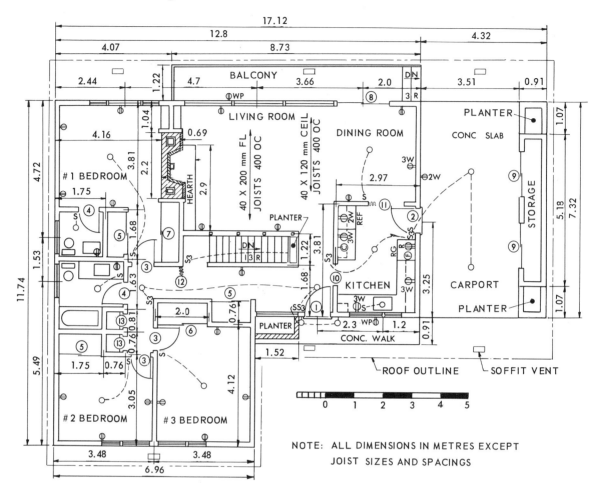

Figure 12.22   Floor Plan Bungalow #2

PROBLEM 3
BUNGALOW NO. 2

NOTE:

   A. For linear dimensions calculate to the nearest 0.01 m.

   B. For area dimensions calculate to the nearest 0.1 m².

   C. For calculation purposes use a nominal frame wall thickness of 0.14 m.

1. What type of exterior wall is shown?
2. What is the rated floor area of (A) the house, (B) the smallest bedroom, (C) the kitchen?
3. How many closets are there?
4. What type of door is used on the bedroom closets?

5. How many swinging doors are there?
6. What is the size and spacing of (A) the floor joists, (B) the ceiling joists?
7. Give the location of built-in book shelves.
8. Calculate the size of (A) the main bathroom, (B) the washroom off the master bedroom, (C) the kitchen, (D) the carport storage unit.
9. Using the scale on the drawing, what is the total length of (A) the kitchen counter (do not include range or refrigerator), (B) the kitchen wall cabinet, (C) the living room window, (D) the kitchen window?
10 What is the length of the balcony? (Include the stair treads).

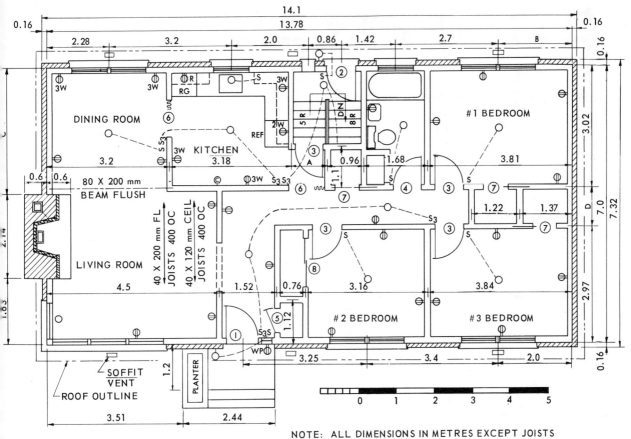

Figure 12.23   Floor Plan Bungalow #3

NOTE: ALL DIMENSIONS IN METRES EXCEPT JOISTS
AND BEAM SIZES AND SPACINGS

PROBLEM 4
BUNGALOW NO. 3

NOTE:

A. For linear dimensions calculate to the nearest 0.01 m.

B. For area dimensions calculate to the nearest 0.1 m².

C. For calculation purposes use a nominal wall thickness of 0.14 m.

1. What type of exterior wall is shown?
2. Calculate dimensions A to D.
3. What are the overall framing dimensions?
4. What is the rated floor area of (A) the house, (B) the largest bedroom, (C) the halls, (D) the living room?
5. What is the size and spacing of (A) the ceiling joists, (B) the floor joists?

6. Calculate the size of (A) the combined chimney and hearth, (B) the kitchen (C) the front entrance closet, (D) the combined front porch and planter?
7. How many closets are there?
8. How many swinging doors are there?
9. Where are the folding doors located?
10. Where are the sliding doors located?
11. Where is the milk-box located?
12. Using the scale on the drawing, what is the total length of the kitchen (A) wall cabinets, (B) base cabinets, (C) archway? (use counter front measurements for (A) and (B) and include range and refrigerator frontage).
13. What types of window are shown for (A) the living room, (B) the dining room?

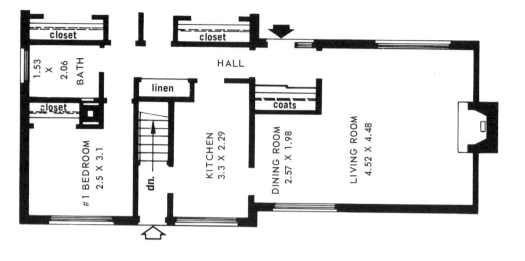

C

B

DIMENSIONS IN METRES

A

Figure 12.24   Furniture Layout Problems

Central Mortgage and Housing Corporation

Plan C

closet

BATH
1.53
X
2.06

closet

HALL

linen

coats

#1 BEDROOM
2.5 X 3.1

dn.

KITCHEN
3.3 X 2.29

DINING ROOM
2.57 X 1.98

LIVING ROOM
4.52 X 4.48

Plan B

LIVING ROOM
3.96 X 7.19

DINING ROOM
3.43 X 3.96

KITCHEN
3.43 X 3.2

dn.

HALL
2.9 X 2.29

coats

linen

BATH
1.52 X 2.52

BATH
1.27
X
2.52

closet

closet

BEDROOM
2.92 X 3.46

closet

closet

Plan A

#2 BEDROOM
2.9 X 2.62

closet

BATH
1.52 X 2.23

linen

HALL

dn.

coats

#1 BEDROOM
2.9 X 3.66

closet

closet

#3 BEDROOM
2.9 X 2.62

KITCHEN
2.9 X 2.29

LIVING-DINING ROOM
5.9 X 3.66

CHAPTER THIRTEEN

ELECTRICAL DRAFTING

ELECTRICAL REQUIREMENTS FOR THE HOME[1,2,]

The modern household contains dozens of electrical appliances. Many of them are used almost exclusively by the homemaker, particularly in the work areas of the home. In addition, the entire family uses lights, television and radio, plus many other electrical items which contribute to health, comfort, and safety. A modern homemaker, therefore, should understand the electrical requirements of the home and the location of the electrical outlets in each room.

Lighting Outlets are the openings for fixed lights. We seldom think of them as "outlets" because they are concealed behind the lighting fixtures.

Convenience Outlets are available in several forms, most common of which is the standard *duplex convenience outlet.* Lamps and plug-in appliances should be plugged directly into the convenience outlets.

Special Purpose Outlets are the openings through which certain major appliances are con-

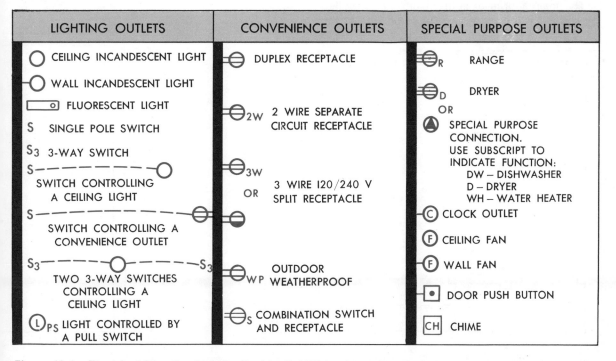

Figure 13.1 *Electrical Plan Symbols for Residential Wiring Layouts*   Ontario Hydro and Edison Electric Institute

nected. There are specially designed plug-in outlets for some major appliances (the electric range or clothes dryer, for example).

LOCATION OF OUTLETS, LIGHTS AND SWITCHES

Figure 13.1 shows the electrical outlet symbols used in the floor plans of homes and other buildings. The symbols shown are those adopted as a standard throughout the United States and Canada.

LIGHTS AND SWITCHES

S— — — —O

Rooms used for general living purposes need some source of general permanent illumination in addition to lamp light. This light can come from central ceiling fixtures, from wall brackets, or from coves, cornices, or valances. When such a feature is absent, a receptacle must be switched at the entrance.

Switches cut off or restore the flow of electricity to lights and appliances without disconnecting them from the outlets. They also contribute to safety. When there are enough switches, properly located, you can "light your way" through dark rooms, and up and down stairways. This reduces the possibility of stumbling in the dark. *Multiple switch control* is a term you should understand. It means control of a single light source from two or more locations.

The main source of light should be controlled by a wall switch located on the latch side of the

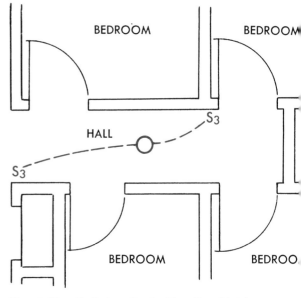

Two 3-Way Switches Controlling One Light

room's main entrance. When the room has more than one doorway, there should be a switch at each door. Switches that control a light from two places are called 3-way switches.

These make it possible to turn on the light when entering by one door, and to turn it off when leaving by the other, without retracing one's steps. It also reduces the possibility of tripping over objects which may have been left in the middle of the floor. For the same reason, there should be switches at both the head and foot of a stairway.

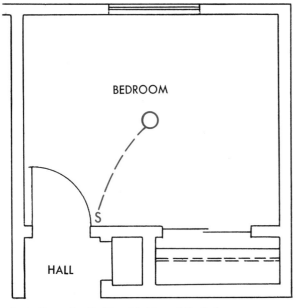

Location of a Ceiling Light and Switch

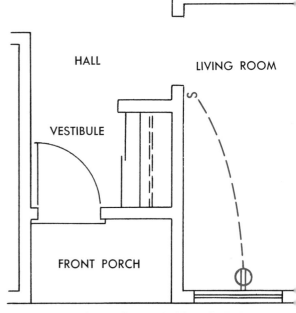

Convenience Outlet Controlled by a Switch

CONVENIENCE OUTLETS

Convenience outlets found in the home are classified according to their use. For safety reasons, new regulations call for convenience outlets to have a third opening for a third leg of the plug to ground the appliance.

DUPLEX RECEPTACLES

The cords on most appliances, table and floor lamps are about 2 metres long. You will have an ideal arrangement if duplex receptacles are placed so that:

(a) no part of any large unbroken wall space is more than 2 m from an outlet, and

(b) every small usable wall space which measures 0.7 m or more contains an outlet. ("Usable wall space" means any wall or window space which could contain a piece of furniture. The wall space against which a door stands when open is not considered "usable wall space").

Wherever possible, at least one outlet should be left free for connecting the vacuum cleaner and attachments, an electric fan, or other occasionally used appliance. Outlets selected for this purpose should be in locations which can be easily reached without moving furniture.

SEPARATE CIRCUIT RECEPTACLES

⊖2W

Duplex receptacles on separate circuits should be provided in areas such as workshop and garage where heavy wattage appliances may be used and also for automatic motor operated appliances such as refrigerator, freezer, room air conditioner, washing machine, sump and water pumps etc.

3-WIRE SPLIT RECEPTACLES

⊖ OR ⊖3W

In the kitchen, 3-wire split duplex receptacles should be installed along the counter top and in the eating area. Such receptacles allow the use of two high wattage kitchen appliances in the same outlet at the same time without the inconvenience of blowing fuses or tripping breakers. Each is supplied by a separate circuit. A minimum of three 3-wire split duplex receptacles, each of a separate circuit, must be installed in each kitchen. Two are located at the counter, separated by a distance of at least 2 m, and the third is at the location of the kitchen table.

SPECIAL PURPOSE OUTLETS OR RECEPTACLES ▲R OR ⊖R

Wiring Connection Provisions

Wiring provisions for the connection of appliances, such as range, dryer, dishwasher, water heater, is made at the time of initial construction. Each is supplied by a separate circuit. Depending on the local electrical code, the appliance may plug directly into a special appliance receptacle or adequate cable may be provided at the appliance area so that connections may be made inside the appliance.

Clock Receptacle -©

This is a recessed receptacle equipped with a clock hangar. It eliminates the untidy appearance of the clock cord hanging down a wall.

Exhaust Fan Ⓕ

Wall- or ceiling-mounted and/or range-hood fans are essential for maintaining a good humidity level as well as effectively removing cooking odors. It is recommended that some means of humidity control be used; this can best be achieved with the use of a humidistat or time switch.

Bell Push and Chime

A bell push should be located (with transformer and necessary wiring) at each main and secondary entrance, and it is recommended that the illuminated type be used. The door chime is located so that it may be heard throughout the house.

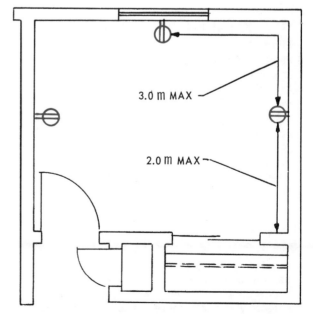

Location and Spacing of Convenience Outlets

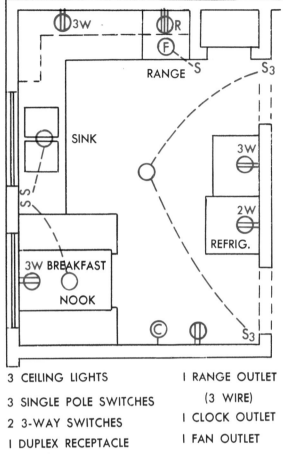

3 CEILING LIGHTS

3 SINGLE POLE SWITCHES

2 3-WAY SWITCHES

I DUPLEX RECEPTACLE

I SEPARATE CIRCUIT RECEPTACLE

3 3-WIRE SPLIT RECEPTACLE

I RANGE OUTLET

(3 WIRE)

I CLOCK OUTLET

I FAN OUTLET

Figure 13.2 Typical Electrical Requirements for a Kitchen

KITCHEN REQUIREMENTS

Figure 13.2 illustrates the electrical outlet requirements for a typical kitchen. There are convenience outlets at the counters and one for the refrigerator. Special outlets are shown for the electric range, clock, exhaust fan, and dishwasher. For permanent lighting there is the main ceiling light, one light over the sink, and another light over the eating area. See the chart, figure 13.3, for a complete list of the minimum requirements for the number and placement of outlets, lights, and switches.

OUTDOOR REQUIREMENTS
⊖WP

In view of the increasing popularity of outdoor decorative lighting, electric lawn mowers and hedge clippers, power operated barbecues, etc., outdoor weather-proof receptacles installed at the front and rear of the house are very necessary.

For convenient control of outdoor lighting, the receptacle at the front should be switched from inside the house. A receptacle should also be placed at the rear of the house; and a receptacle inside the garage is necessary for the use of portable tools, and garden equipment such as mower, hedge clipper, snow blower, etc.

If some convenience outlets are controlled by switches, the outlets so controlled should not be used for electric clocks or for radios. The reason for this is that in switching off the lamp, you would stop the clock or cut off power from the radio.

Outdoor lighting of driveways, garages, and rear entrances controlled inside the house contributes greatly to safety and security.

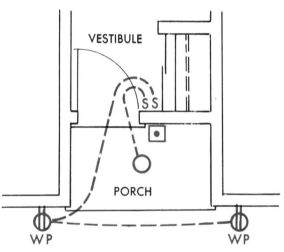

Outside Electrical Outlets

ELECTRICAL CIRCUITS

Shown is a schematic diagram showing how electricity is brought into the home. Electrical power flows from the main power lines along the *service entrance wires.* These wires may be brought in through a pipe or conduit, or they may be combined into a cable. After passing through a meter that records the amount of electricity used, the

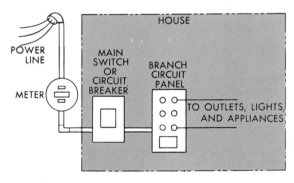

Bringing Electricity into the Home

service entrance wires are connected to the *service entrance equipment*, which consists of a main switch or circuit breaker. From the main switch, the electricity flows to the *branch-circuit panel* for distribution throughout the home. Each branch circuit delivers electricity to one or more *outlets*, to which lights and appliances are connected.

The sizes of fuses and circuit breakers are given in *amperes*. However, because appliances and lamps are generally rated in watts, the number of watts which can be connected simultaneously on a single circuit must be known. A 15 ampere circuit cannot safely carry more than 1500 watts continuously. For a house of 50 m² or more floor area, the number of branch circuits is 24, which includes two range blocks. In modern homes the maximum number of outlets in a branch circuit is 12.

APPLIANCE	WATTAGE RATING
Electric Kettle	1500 watts
Automatic Toaster	1100 "
Coffee Maker	Up to 1100 "
Waffle Iron or Sandwich Grill	Up to 1100 "
Mixer	100 "
Radio	100 "
Television	300 "
Built-in Ventilating Fan	100 "
Electric Roaster	1500 "
Refrigerator*	150 "
Automatic Hand Iron	1000 "
Ironer	1500 "
Floor Lamps (each)	150–300 "
Table Lamps (each)	50–150 "
Vacuum Cleaner	125 "
Room Air Conditioner	1000 "

Figure 13.4   Typical Wattage Ratings of Home Appliances

AREA	RECEPTACLE REQUIREMENTS
Living, Dining, Recreation and Bedrooms	Duplex receptacles shall be installed every 4 m of usable wall space around room perimeter so that no point along floor line is more than 2 m from an outlet. In the living room where no structural lighting outlet is installed, at least one receptacle must be switched at entrance. Note: usable wall space shall be considered as wall space 0.6 m wide not including doorways — areas occupied by door when fully opened — windows less than 0.3 m above the floor — fireplaces or other permanent installation that would limit the use of the wall space.
Kitchen	One duplex receptacle for each 2 m or fraction of each counter work space, including space occupied by sink. All receptacles at counter work surface shall be wired for 120/240V 3 wire split type, each supplied by a separate circuit. One 120/240V 3 wire split duplex receptacle at table height and location. One duplex receptacle for refrigerator. Installed exhaust fan or range hood.
Halls	One duplex receptacle in each hall.
Bathroom	One duplex receptacle convenient to mirror and approx. 1.2 m from floor.
Laundry-Utility, Workshop	One duplex receptacle on separate circuit is required at table height in each of these areas.
Garage	One duplex receptacle on separate circuit.
Outdoors	Two outdoor weatherproof duplex receptacles — one at front entrance switched, second location optional.

AREA	LIGHTING REQUIREMENTS
Living Room	See Receptacle Requirements.
Dining Room	Ceiling outlet or wall brackets controlled by switch at entrance.
Kitchen	Ceiling Outlet controlled by switch at entrance. Lighting outlet over sink controlled by wall switch.
Bedrooms	Lighting outlet or wall receptacle controlled by switch at entrance.
Bathroom (Main)	Ceiling outlet and outlet over or outlets at either side of vanity mirror or medicine cabinet controlled by switch at entrance.
Halls	Ceiling outlet controlled by wall switch in each separate hall area. Where hall is over 4.5 m in length, 3 way switching is required.
Stairways	The Lighting of all stairways including basement to be controlled from both upper and lower levels.
Entrances	Outdoor lighting outlet at each entrance controlled by switch. Bell wire circuit with transformer to front and rear or side entrances.
Recreation Room	One ceiling outlet for each 14 m² of floor space or part thereof.
Laundry-Furnace or Utility Room	If these are separate rooms a ceiling outlet controlled by wall switch at entrance.
Garage	Lighting outlet controlled by switch at entrance.

Ontario Electrical League and Ontario Hydro

Figure 13.3   Recommended Wiring Standards

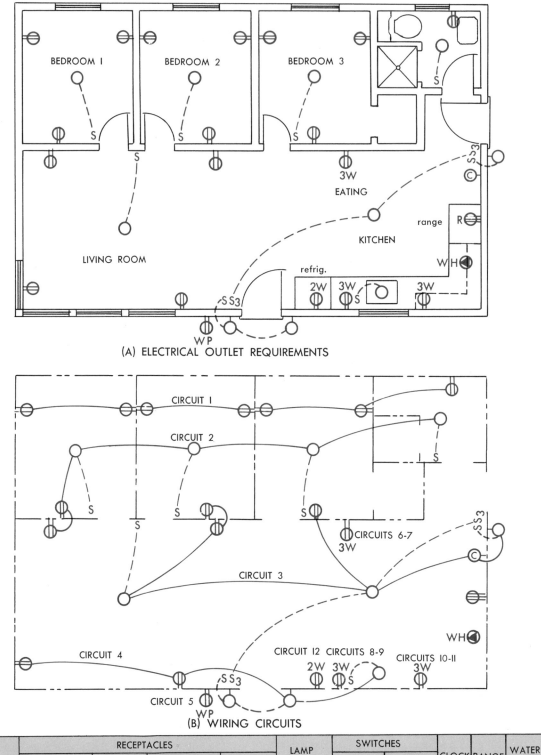

(A) ELECTRICAL OUTLET REQUIREMENTS

(B) WIRING CIRCUITS

	RECEPTACLES						LAMP OUTLETS			SWITCHES				CLOCK	RANGE	WATER HEATER
	DUPLEX				WEATHER PROOF	3-WIRE SPLIT		SEPARATE CIRCUIT				SINGLE POLE			3-WAY			
CIRCUIT	1	2	3	4	5	6-7	8-9	10-11	12	2	3	4	2	3	4	3	3	240 V	120 V
QUANTITY	7	2	3	2	1		3		1	4	3	3	4	2	2	2	1	1	1

(C) SCHEDULE OF OUTLETS

Figure 13.5   Circuiting and Scheduling Electrical Outlets for a Summer Cottage

Figure 13.5 shows the electrical outlets in a typical summer cottage and the technique for circuiting and scheduling them. Note that the circuits are planned so that no one room area has both the convenience outlets and the lighting outlets completely on one circuit. Note also that circuits and outlets are planned in such a manner that the circuit "run" is reasonably straight without frequent zig-zagging. A scheduling diagram is necessary in planning circuits for economy of wiring and proper distribution of outlets per circuit.

References

1. Ontario Hydro   2. Ontario Electric League

Review Questions

1. How is the loading of circuits expressed?

2. What is the purpose of three-way switches?

3. What special outlets may be required in a kitchen?

4. What special outlets may be required in a laundry room?

5. Give several important factors concerning circuiting.

6. Why is a scheduling diagram important?

PROBLEMS

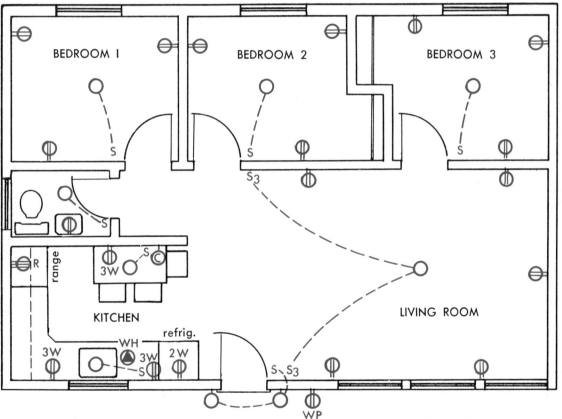

Floor Plan — Summer Cottage #1

PROBLEM 13.1
SUMMER COTTAGE #1

1. How many ceiling outlets are shown?
2. How many outside lights are there?
3. How many duplex receptacles are shown?
4. How many switches are there?
5. How many of these are three-way switches?
6. How many outside convenience outlets are shown?

7. How many separate circuit receptacles are required?
8. Where are these located?
9. How many 3-wire split receptacles are required?
10. How many wall outlets are shown?
11. Are there any outlets not referred to in the previous questions?

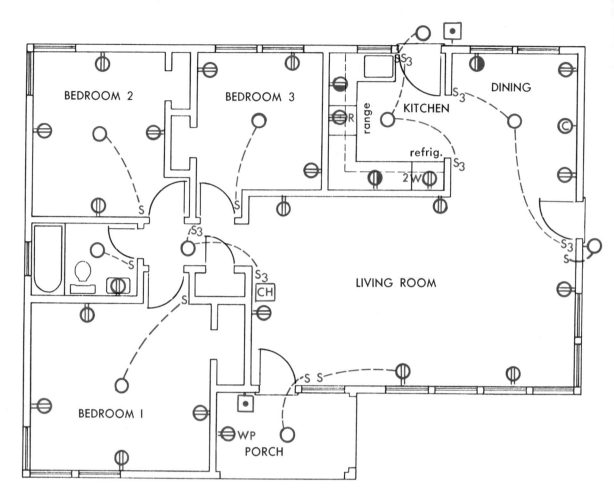

Floor Plan — Summer Cottage #2

PROBLEM 13.2
SUMMER COTTAGE #2

1. How many duplex receptacles are shown?
2. How many separate circuit receptacles are shown?
3. How many 3-wire split receptacles are shown?
4. Are there any duplex receptacles controlled by a switch; if so, where?
5. How many ceiling outlets are shown?
6. How many outside lights are shown?
7. How many switches are there?
8. How many of these are three-way switches?
9. Which room has the least number of outlets?
10. How many branch circuits would be necessary for this plan, keeping well within the maximum of 12 outlets on a general-purpose circuit?

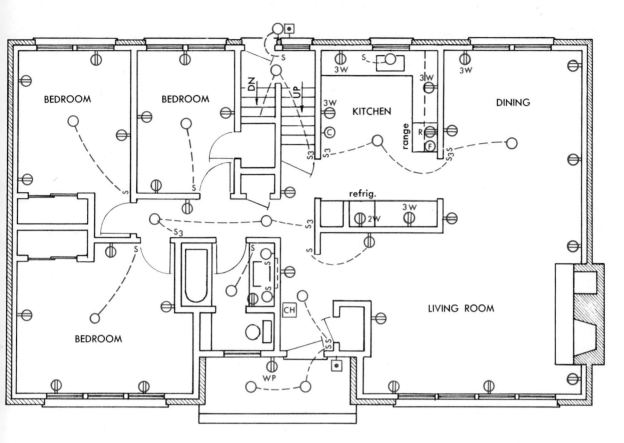

Floor Plan — Bungalow #1

PROBLEM 13.3   BUNGALOW #1

1. What is the total number of outlets?
2. How many ceiling outlets are there?
3. How many duplex receptacles are there?
4. What is the total number of switches shown?
5. How many of these are three-way switches?
6. Name the places where more than one light is controlled by the same switch.
7. How many separate circuit receptacles are used in the kitchen-dining area?
8. How many 3-wire split receptacles are required?
9. What is the purpose of having convenience outlets in the halls?
10. Name several uses for the outside convenience outlet.

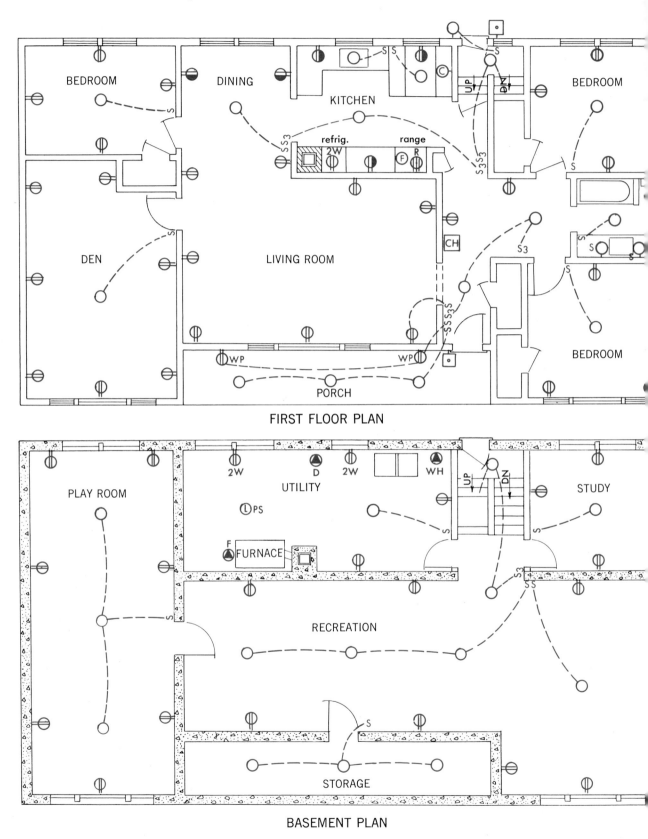

FIRST FLOOR PLAN

BASEMENT PLAN

Floor Plan — Bungalow #2 (see Problem 13.4)

PROBLEM 13.4 BUNGALOW #2

1. How many ceiling outlets are shown on the first-floor plan?
2. How many ceiling outlets are shown on the basement plan?
3. How many duplex receptacles are shown on the first-floor plan?
4. How many duplex receptacles are shown on the basement plan?
5. How many switches are in the home?
6. How many of these are three-way switches?
7. What is the greatest number of lights controlled by any one switch?
8. What room in the house has the greatest number of duplex receptacles?
9. Which rooms have separate circuit receptacles?
10. Which room does not have a ceiling light?
11. Which room has a duplex receptacle controlled by a switch?
12. How many outside lights are shown?
13. How many outside duplex receptacles are shown?
14. Are the outside duplex receptacles controlled by a switch?
15. How many separate circuit receptacles are shown?

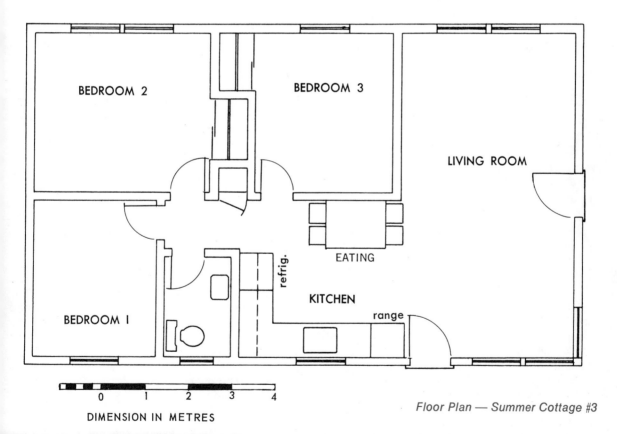

DIMENSION IN METRES

Floor Plan — Summer Cottage #3

PROBLEM 13.5 SUMMER COTTAGE #3

Make a schedule of outlets, and sketch the necessary circuit diagrams for summer cottage #3; follow the good practices shown on previous assignments and the standards given in chapter 13.

CHAPTER FOURTEEN

BASIC METALLURGY AND SHOP PROCESSES

In addition to drafting skills, a draftsman must have basic knowledge of the materials used in the manufacture of component parts, the common manufacturing processes for the production of parts, and the various machines and shop operations involved in manufacturing.

MATERIALS

FERROUS METALS

Metals that contain iron and are magnetic are called ferrous metals. The three general classes of ferrous metals are cast iron, steel, and wrought iron.

The first step in the manufacture of any iron or steel is the conversion of the iron ore into pig iron by mixing the iron ore, coke fuel, and limestone (to carry off impurities), in a blast furnace.

The iron melts from the ore and drops into a pool at the bottom of the furnace. Then it is drawn off into an iron ladle and poured into molds called *pigs.* The limestone combines with the impurities to form a scum called *slag.* The slag, which is lighter than the molten iron, floats to the top and is drawn off into a slag ladle.

About 93% of pig iron is pure iron and about 3% to 5% is carbon. The rest is silicon, phosphorus, sulphur, and other elements. Pig iron is used in foundries for the manufacture of iron castings.

Carbon content is a very important factor in the classification and uses of ferrous metals.

Cast iron, used in foundries for the making of various castings, has a carbon content of up to 5%. It is used extensively for machine frames and bases, and for a wide variety of machine parts such as gears, levers, and pulleys.

Wrought Iron has most of the carbon removed, and is therefore, very ductile. It is made up into common bar stock and sheet sizes, and is used mainly for ornamental and structural shapes and for making pipe and wire.

Steel is a name given to many iron based metals that differ greatly from each other in their chemical and physical qualities. The basic ingredient for all steel is pig iron. Before molten pig iron can be converted into steel, some of the impurities must be burned out, and other ingredients added, to give the metal the desired chemical composition. About 90% of all steel is now produced in open hearth furnaces. Electric furnaces are used primarily to make fine alloy and tool steel. Carbon content has a great influence on the classification and uses of the various kinds of steel.

Low carbon steel, commonly called machinery or mild steel, contains from 0.1 to 0.3% carbon. This steel, which can be easily forged, welded, and machined, is used for making such things as rivets, shafting, and chains.

Medium carbon steel contains from 0.3 to 0.6% carbon and is commonly used for axles, rails, and heavy forgings.

High carbon steel, commonly called tool steel, contains from 0.6 to 1.5% carbon and can be hardened and tempered. It is primarily used for making tools such as drills, reamers, hammers, and crowbars.

Alloy steels are made by adding metals such as chromium, nickel, tungsten, and vanadium to give the steel certain new and specific characteristics such as resistance to rust, corrosion, heat, shock, and fatigue.

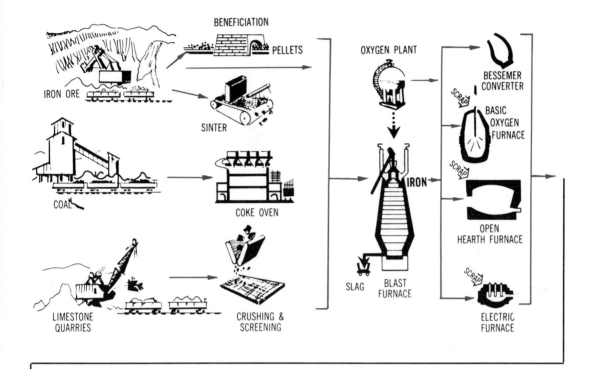

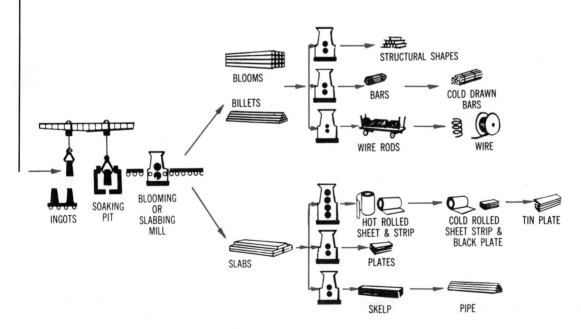

Figure 14.1   Flow Chart of Steelmaking

American Iron and Steel Institute

TYPE OF STEEL	NUMBER SYMBOL	PRINCIPLE PROPERTIES	COMMON USES
CARBON STEELS			
—Plain Carbon	10XX		
—Low Carbon Steel (0.6% to 0.20% Carbon)	1006 to 1020	Toughness and Less Strength	Chains, Rivets, Shafts, Pressed Steel Products
—Medium Carbon Steel (0.20% to 0.50% Carbon)	1020 to 1050	Toughness and Strength	Gears, Axles, Machine Parts, Forgings, Bolts and Nuts
—High Carbon Steel (Over 0.50% Carbon)	1050 and over	Less Toughness and Greater Hardness	Saws, Drills, Knives, Razors, Finishing Tools, Music Wire
—Sulphurized (Free Cutting)	11XX	Improves Machinability	Threads, Splines, Machined Parts
—Phosphorized	12XX	Increases Strength and Hardness but Reduces Ductility	
—Manganese Steels	13XX	Improves Surface Finish	
NICKEL STEELS	2XXX	Toughness and Strength	Crankshafts, Connecting Rods, Axles
—3.50% Nickel	23XX		
—5.00% Nickel	25XX		
NICKEL - CHROMIUM STEELS	3XXX	Toughness and Strength	Gears, Chains, Studs, Screws, Shafts
—0.70% Nickel 0.70% Chromium	30XX		
—1.25% Nickel 0.60% Chromium	31XX		
—1.75% Nickel 1.00% Chromium	32XX		
—3.50% Nickel 1.50% Chromium	33XX		
MOLYBDENUM STEELS	40XX	High Strength	Axles, Forgings, Gears, Cams, Mechanism Parts
—Chromium - Molybdenum Steels	41XX		
—Nickel - Chromium Molybdenum Steels	43XX		
—1.65% Nickel 0.25% Molybdenum	46XX		
—3.25% Nickel 0.25% Molybdenum	48XX		
CHROMIUM STEELS	5XXX	Hardness, Great Strength and Toughness	Gears, Shafts, Bearings, Springs, Connecting Rods
—Low Chromium	50XX		
—Medium Chromium	51XX		
—Chromium High Carbon	52XX		
CHROMIUM VANADIUM STEELS	61XX	Hardness and Strength	Punches and Dies, Piston Rods, Gears, Axles
NICKEL - CHROMIUM - MOLYBDENUM STEELS	86XX	Rust Resistance, Hardness and Strength	Food Containers, Surgical Equipment
SILICON - MANGANESE STEELS	92XX	Springiness and Elasticity	Springs

Figure 14.2   *Steel Designations, Properties and Uses of Steels*

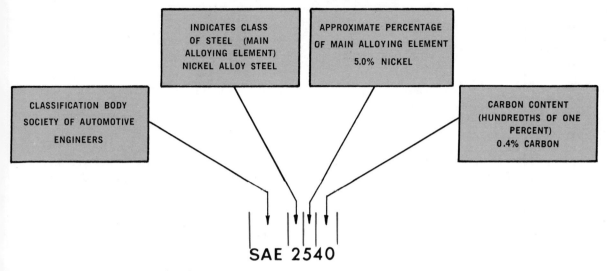

Figure 14.3   Steel Designation System

A system of symbols standardized by S.A.E. (Society of Automotive Engineers), and the A.I.S.I. (American Iron and Steel Institute), is used to identify the grades of standard carbon and alloy steels. A steel designated S.A.E. 1020 indicates a low carbon steel. The first two digits (10) indicate a plain carbon steel; the last two digits (20) indicate the average carbon content in points of one hundredth of one percent (0.2% carbon). S.A.E. 2440 designates a nickel alloy steel, with an average of 4% nickel and 0.4% carbon.

NON-FERROUS METALS

Metals that contain little or no iron and are non-magnetic and resistant to corrosion are called non-ferrous metals.

Aluminum is made from *bauxite* ore, and is used extensively in aircraft manufacture because it has only one third the weight of steel. Because it is very soft in its pure state, aluminum is usually alloyed with other metals to increase its strength and stiffness.

Brass is an alloy of about 66% copper and 33% zinc. A small quantity of lead (about 3%), is sometimes added to the alloy to make it easier to machine. Brass is commonly used for plumbing fittings, small bushings, radiator.parts, hardware, cartridge shells, and many cast parts.

Bronze is an alloy of copper, tin, and zinc. Other ingredients such as lead, phosphorus, manganese, and aluminum are often added to the alloy to give it special qualities of strength, toughness, ductility, and resistance to corrosion. Bronze is used extensively for machine bearings, propellers, gears, marine hardware, and weather-stripping.

Copper is a soft, ductile, tough metal, with the special properties of resistance to corrosion and excellent conductivity of electricity and heat. Some of its many uses include wiring, tubing, screening, roofing, radio parts, electric contacts, and piping.

Babbitt is an alloy of tin, copper and antimony. It is easily machined and is primarily used for the linings of bearings in automobiles and machines.

Review Questions

1. Name the three general classes of ferrous metal.
2. How does wrought iron differ from cast iron?
3. What is the basic ingredient of all steel?
4. How is steel produced?
5. Distinguish between low, medium, and high carbon steel.
6. Why are other metals added to steel?
7. How do non-ferrous metals differ from ferrous metals?
8. What is the purpose of alloying various metals with aluminum?
9. How does brass differ from bronze?
10. List the metals that are alloyed to produce babbitt.

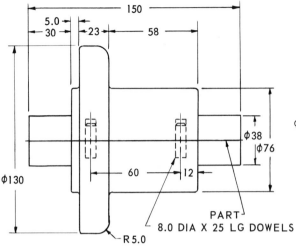

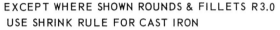

EXCEPT WHERE SHOWN ROUNDS & FILLETS R3.0
USE SHRINK RULE FOR CAST IRON

(A) PATTERN DRAWING

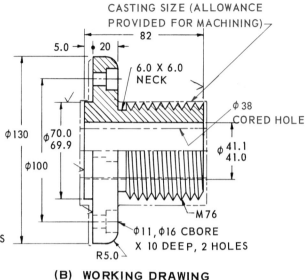

(B) WORKING DRAWING

Figure 14.4 Cast Part Drawings

MANUFACTURING PROCESSES

Most machine parts are produced by casting, forging, machining from standard stock, welding, or forming from sheet stock.

CASTING

Castings are made by pouring molten metal into cavities of the desired shape.

Sand-Casting

When the cavity for a casting is made in a mixture of sand and damp clay, the casting is called a sand casting. Patterns are used to produce the cavity in the sand mold. These are usually made of wood or metal. The pattern, normally made in two parts, is slightly larger in every dimension than the part to be cast to allow for shrinkage when the metal cools. *Draft* or *slight angles* are placed on the pattern to allow for easy withdrawal from the sand mold. Additional metal, known as machining or finish allowance, is also provided on the casting, where a surface is to be finished. Between 2.0 and 4.0 mm, depending on the material being cast, is usually allowed on small castings for each surface that requires finishing.

A typical sand mold is illustrated in figure 14.6. Sand molds consist of two or more sections: bottom (drag), top (cope), and intermediate sections (cheeks) when required. The sand is contained in flasks equipped with pins and lugs to ensure alignment of cope and drag. Molten metal is poured into the sprue (passage for molten metal).

Connecting runners provide flow channels for the metal to enter the mold cavity through gates. Riser cavities are located over the heavier sections of the casting to allow for the addition of liquid metal to the casting during solidification. The whole gating system not only provides for the molten metal to enter the mold, but also functions as a venting system for the removal of gases. When the metal has hardened, the sand is broken and the casting removed. The excess metal, gates and risers, are then removed and remelted. In sand casting, a new mold must be made for each part.

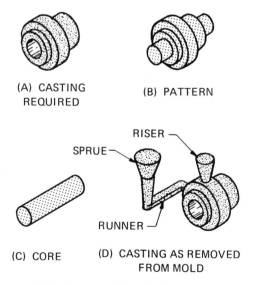

(A) CASTING REQUIRED

(B) PATTERN

(C) CORE

(D) CASTING AS REMOVED FROM MOLD

Figure 14.5 Sand Casting Parts

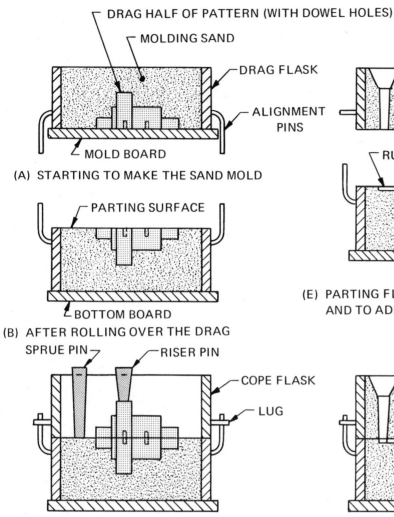

DRAG HALF OF PATTERN (WITH DOWEL HOLES)

MOLDING SAND

DRAG FLASK

ALIGNMENT PINS

MOLD BOARD

(A) STARTING TO MAKE THE SAND MOLD

PARTING SURFACE

BOTTOM BOARD

(B) AFTER ROLLING OVER THE DRAG

SPRUE PIN — RISER PIN

COPE FLASK

LUG

(C) PREPARING TO RAM MOLDING SAND IN COPE

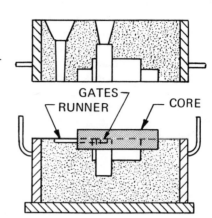

GATES

RUNNER CORE

(E) PARTING FLASKS TO REMOVE PATTERN AND TO ADD CORE AND RUNNER

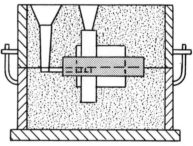

(F) SAND MOLD READY FOR POURING

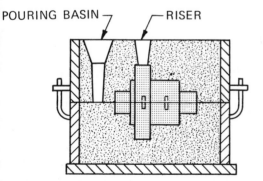

POURING BASIN RISER

(D) REMOVING RISER AND GATE SPRUE PINS AND ADDING POURING BASIN

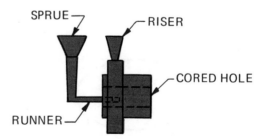

SPRUE RISER

CORED HOLE

RUNNER

SPRUE, RISER, AND RUNNER TO BE REMOVED FROM CASTING.

(G) CASTING AS REMOVED FROM THE MOLD

Figure 14.6   Sequence in Preparing a Sand Casting

Die Casting

This fairly new process uses a permanent metal mold or die. The die is usually made of steel and is in two parts, with a vertical parting line. The stationary half of the die is called the cover die; the movable half is called the ejector die. Molten metal is forced into the die cavity under pressure. After the molten metal has solidified, the die is opened and the casting is ejected from the ejector die. Parts produced by this method are very accurate in size, and are often completely finished when taken from the die. This factor eliminates or reduces machining costs.

Large production quantities are necessary to justify the large capital expenditure for machines and dies. At the present time, only non-ferrous alloys can economically be die cast, because of the lack of a suitable die material to withstand the higher temperatures required for casting steel and iron.

The die casting process is also used for the assembly of small parts. The parts are placed in an assembly die either by hand or automatically from vibratory feeders or magazines. The die is then closed, locating all parts in exact position. Molten metal, usually a lead, tin, or zinc alloy, is injected into a suitably arranged cavity to lock the parts together. The gate or sprue is sheared as the die opens, and the assembly is removed from the die.

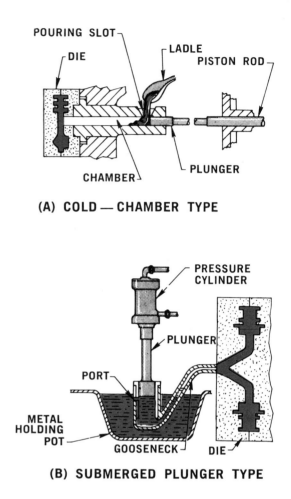

(A) COLD — CHAMBER TYPE

(B) SUBMERGED PLUNGER TYPE

Die Casting Machines

Machine Design, Vol. 37, No. 21, 1965

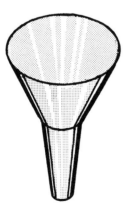

Forming from Sheet Stock

FORMING FROM SHEET STOCK

Many parts can be produced from a standard thickness of sheet or strip stock. The stock is first cut to size *in the flat* and then is bent, punched, or formed to the desired shape.

For limited quantities of simple parts, a template is made to control the shape in the flat, and the piece is formed using standard sheet metal equipment. See Chapter 11 for information on development techniques and examples of formed parts.

When very large quantities of a part are required, special dies are made and the parts are produced in punch presses. Such parts are often referred to as *stampings*.

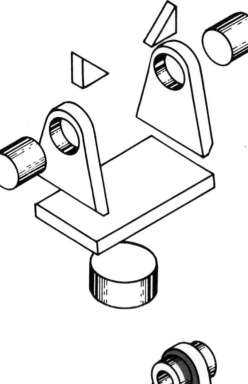

Welded Fabrication

FORGING

Forging is a process of squeezing or hammering a bar or billet into a desired shape. Materials to be forged must be ductile, and are usually heated to make them more plastic.

When a large quantity of parts is to be forged, a special steel die is used. The lower die is held on the bed of the drop hammer, and the upper die is fastened to the hammer mechanism. The hot billet is placed on the lower die, and the upper die is dropped several times, causing the metal to flow into the cavities of the dies. The small amount of excess material forms a thin web, or *flash,* surrounding the part between the two die faces. The flash is then removed in a trimming die. A generous draft angle must be provided for easy release of the forging from the die.

(A) BILLET

(B) TONGHOLD IS FORGED

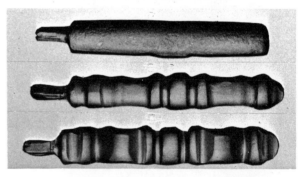

(C) THREE-STEP FORMING IMPRESSION

(D) BLOCKING AND FINISHING

(E) AFTER TRIMMING CRANKS ARE TWISTED INTO POSITION

Forging a Crankshaft   Wyman-Gordon Company

WELDING

Parts can be produced by welding simple pieces cut from standard rod, bar, or plate stock. Such parts are called welded fabrications. For many purposes this method provides a lighter and stronger part than can be obtained by casting or forging, often at less cost, particularly when the quantity of parts to be produced is not large enough to warrant the expense of making patterns or forging dies.

As with castings and forgings, some machining is usually necessary on the completed welded fabrications.

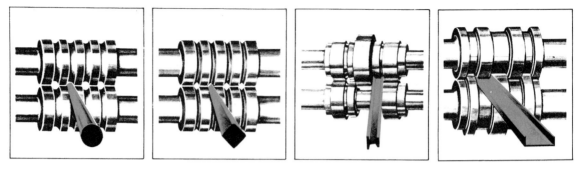

ROUNDS   SQUARES   RAILS   CHANNELS

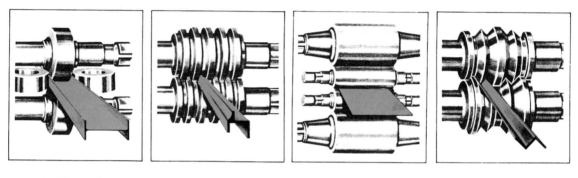

H COLUMNS   SPECIAL SECTIONS   SHEETS   ZEE BARS

The Forming of Standard Shapes

American Iron and Steel Institute

MACHINING FROM STANDARD STOCK

Many parts are designed so that they can be made from standard stock material by machining. Materials available in standard sizes include solid round, square, and rectangular bars; round and square pipe and tubing; a variety of structural steel shapes such as angle and channel; and plate and sheet.

All machining operations remove metal for one or more of the following reasons:

1. To produce a smooth surface or an accurate size.

2. To give a desired shape.

3. To produce holes, slots, threads, keyways, keyseats, or other special features.

Machining operations to remove soft metal are performed by hardened steel or carbide cutting tools. Diamond cutting tools or abrasive wheels are necessary to remove metal that has been hardened.

The machines commonly used for the production of parts from standard stock, as well as machining operations on castings, forgings, welded and formed parts, are the lathe, horizontal and vertical milling machines, shaper, drill press, cylindrical and surface grinders, boring machine, planer, and band saw. See the chart on page 55 for the finishes obtained by the various operations performed by these machines.

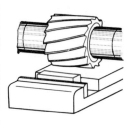

(A) PLAIN MILLING

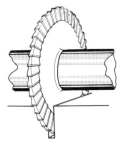

(B) SLITTING

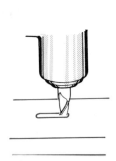

(C) SLOTTING

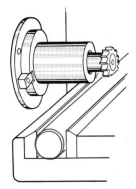

(D) KEY-SEAT

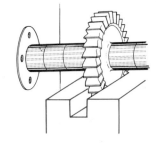

(E) SLOTTING — SIDE MILL

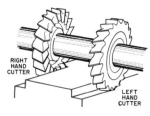

(F) STRADDLE MILLING

(G) DOVE-TAIL

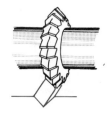

(H) DOUBLE ANGLE

Milling Machine Operations

Canadian Illinois Tool Works

Review Questions

1. What is the purpose of a pattern in sand casting?

2. Give two reasons for a pattern being larger than the finished part.

3. How do *die cast* parts differ from *sand cast* parts?

4. Why must materials be ductile to be forged?

5. Why is a generous draft angle provided on forging dies?

6. Give three reasons for machining operations to remove metal.

7. What cutting tools are used to remove metal that has been hardened?

8. What are some of the advantages of welded fabrications?

9. What is the purpose of a template in making parts from sheet stock?

10. How are stampings produced?

CHAPTER FIFTEEN

APPLIED GEOMETRY

Most of the lines forming the views on mechanical drawings can be drawn using the instruments and equipment described in chapter 2. However, geometrical constructions have important uses, both in making drawings and in solving problems by graphs and diagrams. It is sometimes necessary to use geometrical constructions, particularly if the draftsman does not have the advantages afforded by a drafting machine, an adjustable set square, or templates for drawing hexagonal and elliptical shapes.

The Spadina Interchange, Toronto, Canada

Ministry of Transportation and Communications, Ontario

TO DRAW A LINE OR LINES PARALLEL TO AND AT A GIVEN DISTANCE FROM AN OBLIQUE LINE

1. Given line AB, erect a perpendicular CD to AB.
2. Space the given distance from the line AB by scale measurement or by an arc, along line CD.
3. Adjust a set square, using a second set square or a T square as base, so that one side of the set square coincides with the given line.
4. Slide this set square along the base to the point at the desired distance from the given line, and draw the required line.

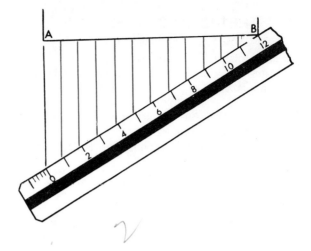

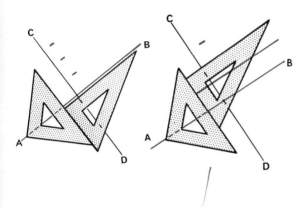

TO DIVIDE A LINE INTO A GIVEN NUMBER OF EQUAL PARTS

1. Given line AB and the number of equal divisions desired (12, for example), draw a perpendicular from A.
2. Place the scale so that the desired number of equal divisions are conveniently included between B and the perpendicular, then mark these divisions, using short vertical marks from the scale divisions as shown.
3. Draw perpendiculars through the points marked, dividing the line AB as required.

TO BISECT A STRAIGHT LINE

1. Given line AB, set the compass to a radius greater than ½ AB.
2. Using centers at A and B, draw intersecting arcs above and below line AB. A line CD drawn through the intersections will divide line AB into two equal parts and will be perpendicular (or at right angles) to line AB.

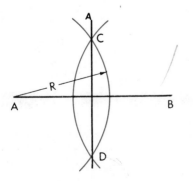

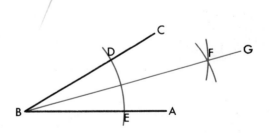

TO BISECT AN ANGLE

1. Given angle ABC; with center B and a suitable radius, draw an arc to cut BC at D and BA at E.
2. With centers D and E and equal radii, draw arcs to intersect at F.
3. Join BF and produce to G. Line BG is the required bisector.

TO DRAW A HEXAGON, GIVEN THE DISTANCE ACROSS THE CORNERS

1. Establish horizontal and vertical center lines, and draw a light construction circle with radius 50% of the distance across the corners.
2. With a 30°—60° set square, establish points on the circumference 60° apart.
3. Draw straight lines connecting these points.

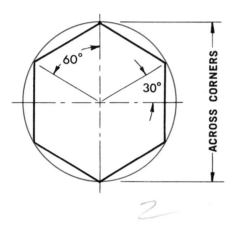

TO DRAW A HEXAGON, GIVEN THE DISTANCE ACROSS THE FLATS

1. Establish horizontal and vertical center lines for the hexagon.
2. Using the intersection of these lines as center, with radius 50% of the distance across the flats, draw a light construction circle.
3. Using the 30°—60° set square, draw six straight lines tangent to the circle and 120° apart.

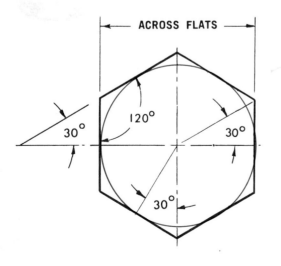

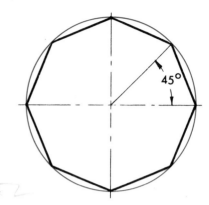

TO DRAW AN OCTAGON, GIVEN THE DISTANCE ACROSS THE CORNERS

1. Establish horizontal and vertical center lines and draw a light construction circle with radius 50% of the distance across the corners.
2. With the 45° set square, establish points on the circumference between the horizontal and vertical center lines.
3. Draw straight lines connecting these points to the points where the center lines cross the circumference.

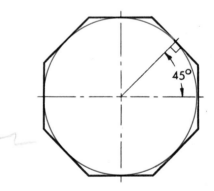

TO DRAW AN OCTAGON, GIVEN THE DISTANCE ACROSS THE FLATS

1. Establish horizontal and vertical center lines, and draw a light construction circle with radius 50% of the distance across the flats.
2. Draw horizontal and vertical lines tangent to the circle.
3. Using the 45° set square, draw lines tangent to the circle at a 45° angle from the horizontal.

TO INSCRIBE A REGULAR PENTAGON IN A GIVEN CIRCLE

1. Given circle with center O, draw the circle with diameter AB.
2. Bisect line OB at D.
3. With center D and radius DC, draw arc CE to cut the diameter at E.
4. With C as center and radius CE, draw arc CF to cut the circumference at F. Distance CF is one side of the pentagon.
5. With radius CF as a chord, mark off the remaining points on the circle. Connect the points with straight lines.

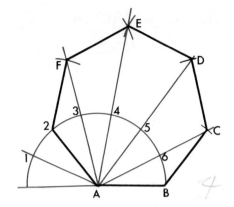

TO DRAW A REGULAR POLYGON, GIVEN THE LENGTH OF ONE SIDE

Let the polygon have seven sides.
1. Given the length of side AB, with radius AB and A as center, draw a semicircle, and divide it into 7 equal parts using a protractor.
2. Through the second division from the left, draw radial line A2.
3. Through points 3, 4, 5, and 6 extend radial lines as shown.
4. With AB as radius and B as center, cut line A6 at C. With the same radius and C as center, cut line A5 at D and so on at E and F.
5. Connect these points with straight lines.

These steps can be followed in drawing a regular polygon with any number of sides.

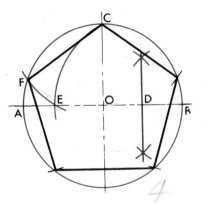

TO DRAW AN ARC TANGENT TO TWO LINES AT RIGHT ANGLES TO EACH OTHER

1. Given radius R of the arc, draw an arc having radius R with center at B cutting the lines AB and AC at D and E respectively.
2. With D and E as centers and with the same radius R, draw arcs intersecting at O.
3. With center O draw the required arc. The tangent points are D and E.

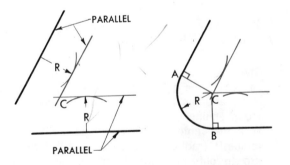

TO DRAW AN ARC TANGENT TO THE SIDES OF AN ACUTE ANGLE

1. Given radius R of the arc, draw lines inside the angle, parallel to the given lines, at distance R away from the given lines. The center of the arc will be at C.
2. Set the compass to radius R, and with center C draw the arc tangent to the given sides. The tangent points A and B are found by drawing perpendiculars through point C to the given lines.

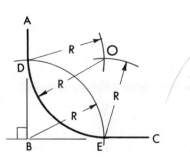

TO DRAW AN ARC TANGENT TO TWO SIDES OF AN OBTUSE ANGLE

Follow the same procedure as for an acute angle, that is:

1. Given radius R of the arc, draw lines inside the angle, parallel to the given lines, at distance R away from the given lines. The center of the arc will be at C.
2. Set the compass to radius R, and with center C draw the arc tangent to the given sides. The tangent points A and B are found by drawing perpendiculars through point C to the given lines.

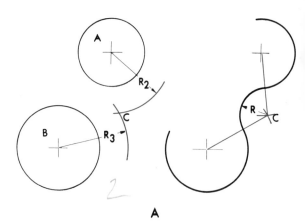

A

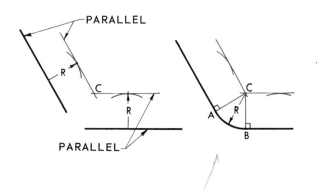

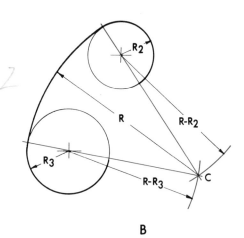

B

TO DRAW AN ARC TANGENT TO A GIVEN CIRCLE AND STRAIGHT LINE

1. Given R, the radius of the arc, draw a line parallel to the given straight line between the circle and the line at distance R away from the given line.
2. With the center of the circle as center and radius R_2 (radius of the circle + R), draw an arc to cut the parallel straight line at C.

TO DRAW AN ARC TANGENT TO TWO CIRCLES

(A)

1. Given the radius of arc R, with the center of circle A as center and radius R_2 (radius of circle A + R), draw an arc in the area between the circles.
2. With the center of circle B as center and radius R_1 (radius of circle B + R), draw an arc to cut the other arc at C.
3. With center C and radius R, draw the required arc tangent to the given circles.

(B)

1. Given radius of arc R, with the center of circle A as center and radius $(R - R_2)$, draw an arc in the area between the circles.
2. With the center of circle B as center and radius $(R - R_3)$ draw an arc to cut the other arc at C.
3. With center C and Radius R, draw the required arc tangent to the given circles.

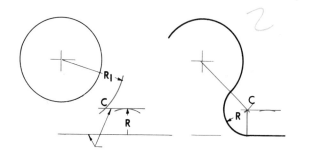

TO DRAW AN ELLIPSE

1. Given the major and minor diameters, construct two concentric circles with diameters equal to AB and CD.
2. Divide the circles into a convenient number of equal parts. The illustration shows 12.

3. Where the radial lines intersect the outer circle, as at 1, draw lines parallel to line CD inside the outer circle.
4. Where the radial lines intersect the inner circle, as at 2, draw a line parallel to axis AB away from the inner circle. The intersection of these lines, as at 3, gives points on the ellipse.
5. Draw a smooth curve through these points.

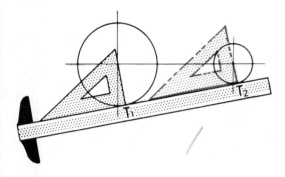

TO DRAW A STRAIGHT LINE TANGENT TO TWO CIRCLES

Place a T square so that the top edge just touches the edges of the circles, and draw the tangent line. Perpendiculars to this line from the centers of the circles give the tangent points T_1 and T_2.

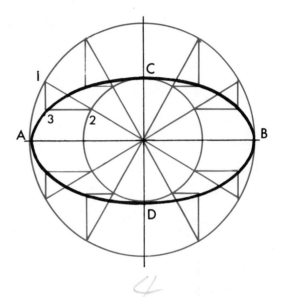

CHAPTER SIXTEEN

PROBLEMS IN INTERPRETING MECHANICAL DRAWINGS

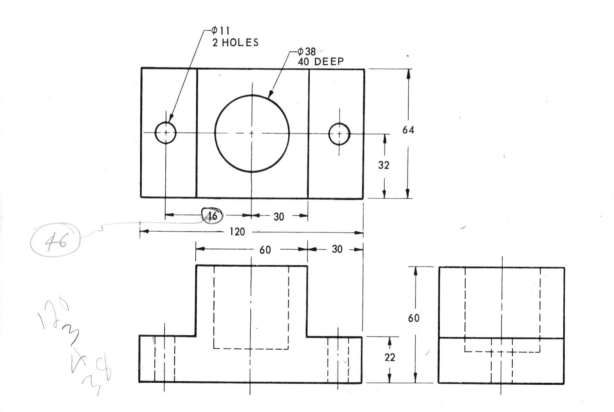

PROBLEM 16.1
MOUNTING BLOCK

1. What is the overall length of the part? *120*
2. How many holes are there? *3*
3. What is the depth of the large hole? *40*
4. What is the diameter of the large hole? *38*
5. How many different types of line are used *6* on the drawing?
6. What is the height of the 60 mm center portion above the step?
7. What is the assumed distance from the center hole to the hole near the right side?
8. Is the large hole in the exact center of the part? *YES.*

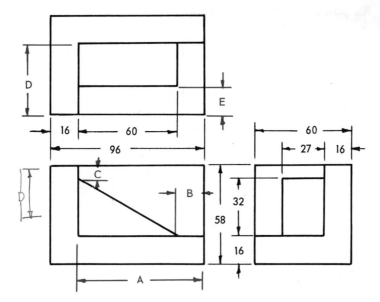

96 96
76 76
20

PROBLEM 16.2
WEDGE BLOCK *96x60x58*

1. What is the overall length, width and height?
2. In what two views are lengths seen? *F T×S*
3. In what two views are heights seen? *F.S.*
4. In what two views are widths seen? *T-S*
5. Name two detail length dimensions.
6. Name two detail height dimensions.
7. Name two detail width dimensions.
8. Calculate dimensions A to E.

A-80 C~10 E-1"
B-20 D-44

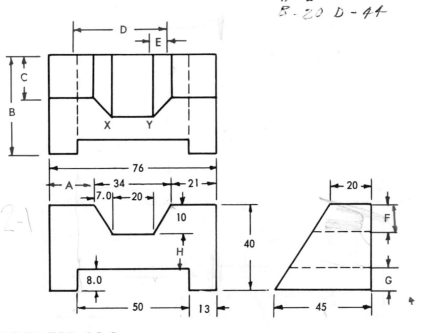

21
-45
-20 A-2-1
-42
-7
/0
8

PROBLEM 16.3
GROOVED SLIDE BLOCK

1. Calculate dimensions A to H.
2. What is the overall length, width and height?
3. Name six different dimensions that are detail lengths.
4. Name two different dimensions that are detail heights.
5. How many detail width dimensions are there?
6. In what view is the shape of the grooves seen most clearly?
7. What view shows that the whole front face is sloped?
8. How would points X and Y in the top view be established?

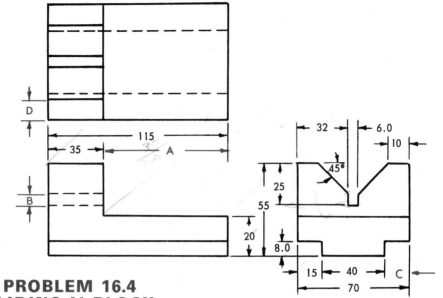

PROBLEM 16.4
SLIDING V BLOCK

1. How many different types of line are used on the drawing?
2. What do the hidden lines in the top view represent?
3. What is the included angle of the V opening?
4. What is the width of the V opening at the top of the block?
5. What purpose does the slot at the bottom of the V serve?
6. What is the horizontal distance from the corner of the V to the edge of the slot?
7. Calculate dimensions A to D.

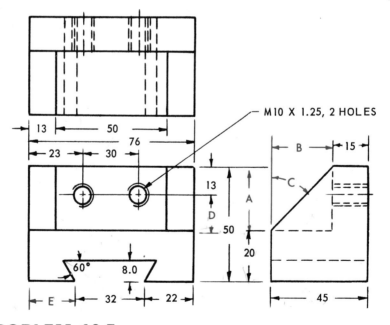

PROBLEM 16.5
DOVETAIL BRACKET

1. What is the angle of the side of the dovetail to the vertical?
2. What two functions does the dovetail serve?
3. Calculate dimensions A to E.
4. Explain each part of the note: M10 x 1.25.
5. Give the overall length, height, and width of the part.
6. Name five different detail length dimensions.

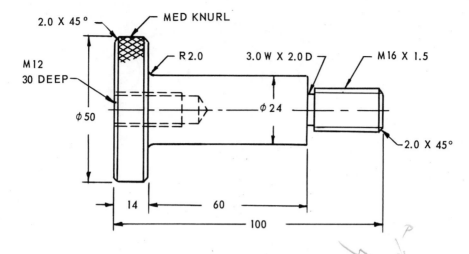

PROBLEM 16.6
KNURLED SHOULDER
CLAMP

1. What is the shape of the piece? *CYL.*
2. What is the largest diameter? *50*
3. What is the overall length? *100*
4. What is the length of thread on the right end portion? *23*

5. Explain the note: M16 x 1.5.
6. What is the depth of the tapped hole? *30*
7. What operation is required to provide a better grip for turning the part?
8. Why are the edges of the 50 diameter chamfered?
9. Why is the right end of the part chamfered?
10. Why is a necking operation called for between the 16 and the 24 diameters?

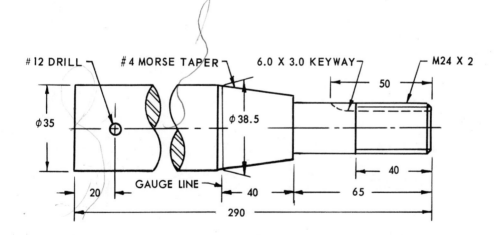

PROBLEM 16.7
TAPERED DRAW BAR

1. What is the largest diameter?
2. What is the width of the keyway?
3. What is the depth of the keyway?
4. Calculate the length from the left-hand end to the gauge line.
5. Explain each part of the note: M24 x 2.

6. What symbol is used to show the actual length of the 40 diameter is not drawn?
7. What is the diameter of a #12 drill?
8. What is the diameter at the gauge line?
9. Is there an indication of the material from which the part is made? If so, what is that material?

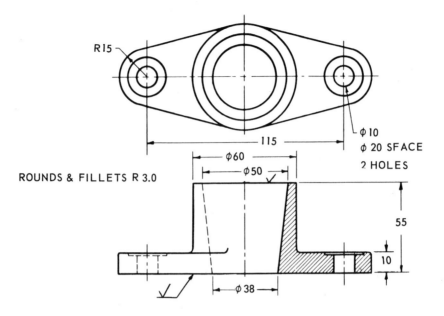

ROUNDS & FILLETS R 3.0

PROBLEM 16.8
TAPERED SHAFT SUPPORT

1. What is the overall length of the part?
2. What is the greatest width?
3. What is the diameter of the two small holes?
4. What is the diameter of the spotface?
5. What does the symbol ✓ indicate?
6. What is the difference between the large and small diameters of the tapered hole?

7. What does the symbol φ represent?
8. What type of section view is used?
9. What material is indicated by the hatching lines?
10. What is the purpose of the spotfacing operation?

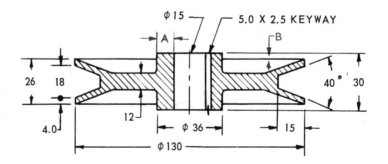

PROBLEM 16.9
V BELT PULLEY

1. What is the width of the keyway?
2. What is the depth of the keyway?
3. What purpose does the keyway serve?
4. Calculate the diameter at the bottom of the V.

5. What is the length of the hub?
6. Calculate dimensions A and B.
7. What is the outside radius of the pulley?
8. What is the radius for the hub?
9. What material is indicated by the hatching lines?

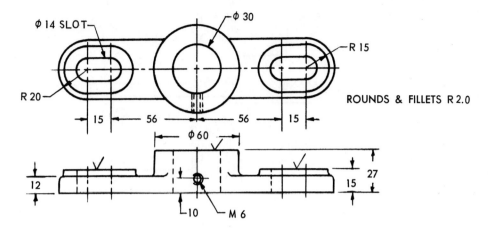

ROUNDS & FILLETS R 2.0

PROBLEM 16.10
ADJUSTABLE BASE PLATE

1. What is the overall length of the part?
2. What is the greatest width of the part?
3. What is the height of the top surface of the boss from the base?
4. What is the length of each boss?
5. What is the width of each boss?
6. What is the total length of the 14 dia. slots?
7. How many surfaces are to be finished?
8. How high does the center portion protrude above the side bosses?
9. What is the distance from the top of the center boss to the center of the tapped hole?
10. In the note M6, what does the M signify?

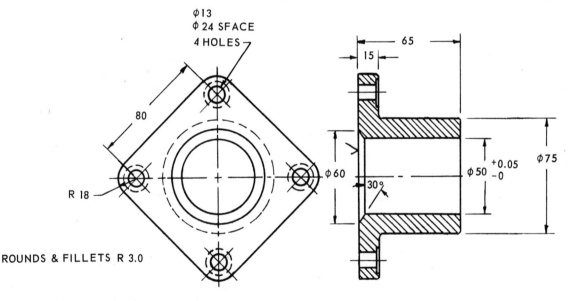

ROUNDS & FILLETS R 3.0

PROBLEM 16.11
FLANGED SHAFT SUPPORT

1. What kind of section is drawn?
2. What material is indicated by the hatching lines?
3. The four holes would be a clearance for what diameter bolt?
4. Why are these holes spotfaced on the under-side?
5. What are the limit sizes of the center hole?
6. At what angle is the chamfer face to the axis of the hole?
7. What would be the maximum dimensions of the part?
8. How long is the hub?
9. What is the wall thickness of the hub?

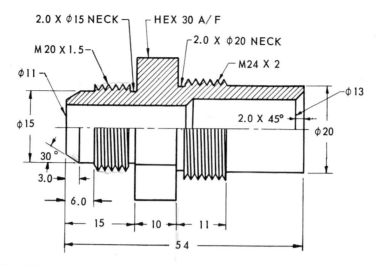

PROBLEM 16.12
COUPLING

1. What does M20 x 1.5 mean?
2. What is the total length of thread on the left side of the hexagon shape?
3. What is the total length of thread on the right side of the hexagon shape?
4. What is the distance from the right end of the part to the right side face of the hexagon shape?
5. How many different-sized holes are there?
6. What are their sizes?
7. How many chamfers are there on the part?
8. This view is drawn as what kind of section?
9. What dimension is missing on this drawing?
10. What purpose do the necking operations serve?

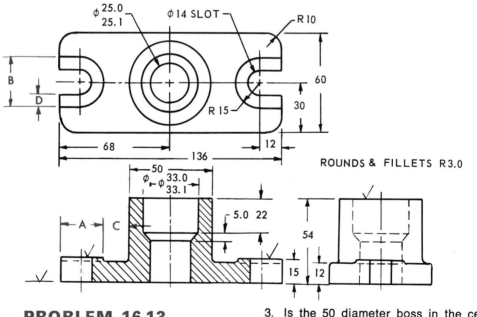

PROBLEM 16.13
ADJUSTABLE SHAFT
SUPPORT

1. What is the tolerance on the 33 nominal diameter hole?
2. What is the length of the 25 diameter hole?
3. Is the 50 diameter boss in the center of the part?
4. What is the tolerance on the 25 diameter hole?
5. How many surfaces are to be finished?
6. What is the radius of the slots?
7. Calculate dimensions A to D.

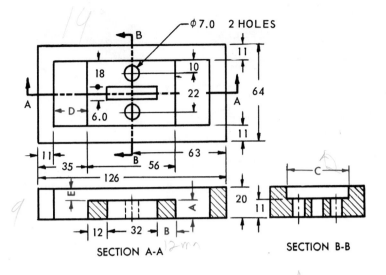

SECTION A-A

SECTION B-B

PROBLEM 16.14
LOCATING PIECE

1. Which of the two section views is referred to as a longitudinal section?
2. Which of the two sections is referred to as a cross section?
3. Is the object symmetrical about cutting-plane line A-A?
4. Is the object symmetrical about cutting-plane line B-B?
5. For what size bolts would the two 7.0 dia. holes be a clearance?
6. Calculate dimensions A to E.

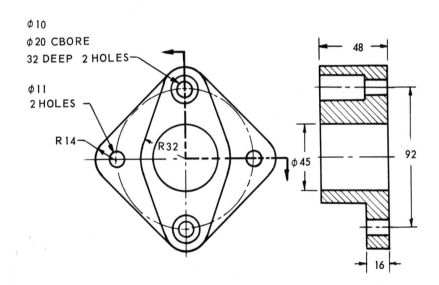

PROBLEM 16.15
BASE SUPPORT

1. What type of section view is used for the side view?
2. What is the overall length and width?
3. What is the purpose of the counterboring operation?
4. What is the distance between the two counter-bored holes?
5. How many degrees apart are they?
6. What material is indicated by the hatching line symbol?

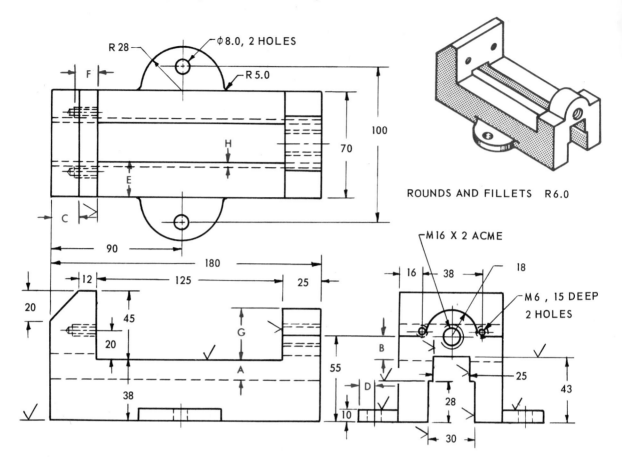

ROUNDS AND FILLETS   R6.0

PROBLEM 16.16
VISE BODY

1. How many distinctly separate surfaces are to be finished?
2. What is the overall width?
3. How many circular holes are there?
4. What is the size of the bolting down holes?
5. What is the size of the small tapped holes?
6. What is the thread series of the small tapped holes?
7. What is the thread series of the larger tapped hole?
8. What is the overall height of the left-side portion?
9. What is the overall height of the right-side portion?
10. How many filleted corners are shown on the drawing?
11. Calculate dimensions A to H.

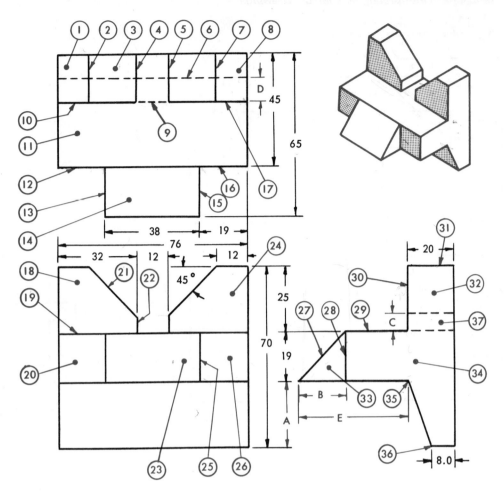

PROBLEM 16.17
SLIDE BRACKET

1. Calculate dimensions A to E.
2. What line in the top view is represented by surface 18 in the front view?
3. What surfaces in the top view are represented by line 31 in the side view?
4. What line in the front view is represented by surface 3 in the top view?
5. What surface in the side view is represented by surface 3 in the top view?
6. What line in the side view is represented by surface 14 in the top view?
7. What line in the side view is represented by line 12 in the top view?
8. What line in the top view is represented by point 35 in the side view?
9. What line in the front view is represented by surface 11 in the top view?
10. What surface in the front view is represented by line 27 in the side view?

11. What surface in the top view is represented by line 29 in the side view?
12. What line in the side view is represented by surface 8 in the top view?
13. What lines in the top view are represented by line 28 in the side view?
14. What surfaces in the front view are represented by line 30 in the side view?
15. What line in the front view is represented by line 29 in the side view?
16. What lines in the top view are represented by line 30 in the side view?
17. What surface in the side view is represented by line 4 in the top view?
18. What surfaces in the front view are represented by line 28 in the side view?
19. What lines in the top view are represented by surface 33 in the side view?
20. What line in the top view is represented by point 36 in the side view?
21. What line in the front view is represented by line 4 in the top view?

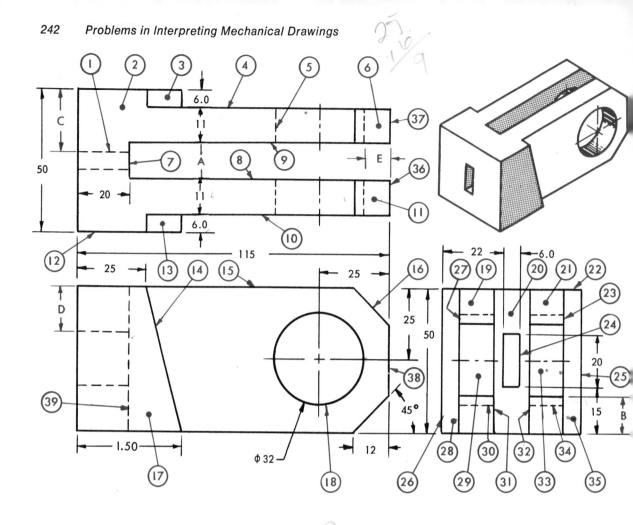

PROBLEM 16.18
GUIDE BLOCK

1. Calculate dimensions A to E.
2. What line in the side view is represented by surface 2 in the top view?
3. What line in the top view is represented by line 24 in the side view?
4. What line in the front view is represented by surface 35 in the side view?
5. What surface in the top view is represented by surface 28 in the side view?
6. What surface in the top view is represented by surface 21 in the side view?
7. What surface in the side view is represented by line 7 in the top view?
8. What line in the front view is represented by surface 2 in the top view?
9. What line in the front view is represented by line 5 in the top view?
10. What surface in the top view is represented by surface 35 in the side view?

11. What lines in the side view are represented by surface 17 in the front view?
12. What line in the front view is represented by surface 28 in the side view?
13. What line in the side view is represented by line 1 in the top view?
14. What surfaces in the side view are represented by surface 16 in the front view?
15. What line in the top view is represented by line 26 in the side view?
16. What surfaces in the top view are represented by line 14 in the front view?
17. What line in the top view is represented by line 27 in the side view?
18. What lines in the side view are represented by line 18 in the front view?
19. What surface in the side view is represented by line 37 in the top view?
20. What line in the top view is represented by line 31 in the side view?
21. What line in the top view is represented by surface 29 in the side view?

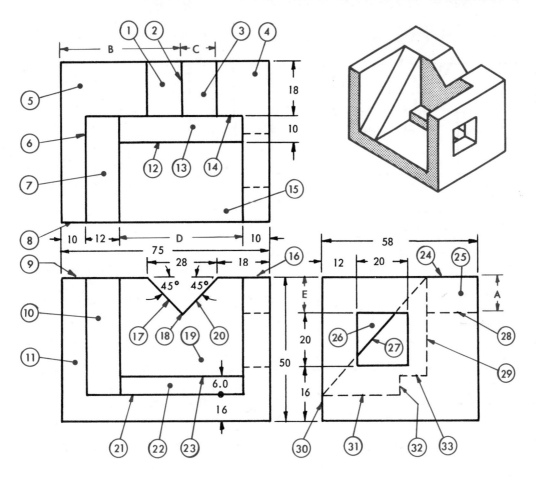

PROBLEM 16.19
V BRACKET

1. Calculate dimensions A to E.
2. What line in the front view is represented by surface 1 in the top view?
3. What line in the side view is represented by surface 11 in the front view?
4. What surface in the top view is represented by line 31 in the side view?
5. What line in the side view is represented by line 2 in the top view?
6. What surface in the front view is represented by line 12 in the top view?
7. What lines in the front view are represented by line 24 in the side view?
8. What line in the side view is represented by point 18 in the front view?
9. What surface in the front view is represented by line 27 in the side view?
10. What line in the front view is represented by surface 3 in the top view?
11. What line in the side view is represented by line 8 in the top view?
12. What line in the top view is represented by line 32 in the side view?
13. What line in the side view is represented by line 21 in the front view?
14. What line in the top view is represented by line 29 in the side view?
15. What line in the side view is represented by surface 7 in the top view?
16. What surfaces in the top view are represented by line 24 in the side view?
17. What line in the front view is represented by surface 15 in the top view?
18. What surface in the front view is represented by line 29 in the side view?
19. What line in the top view is represented by surface 19 in the front view?
20. What surface in the side view is represented by line 6 in the top view?
21. What surface in the top view is represented by line 16 in the front view?

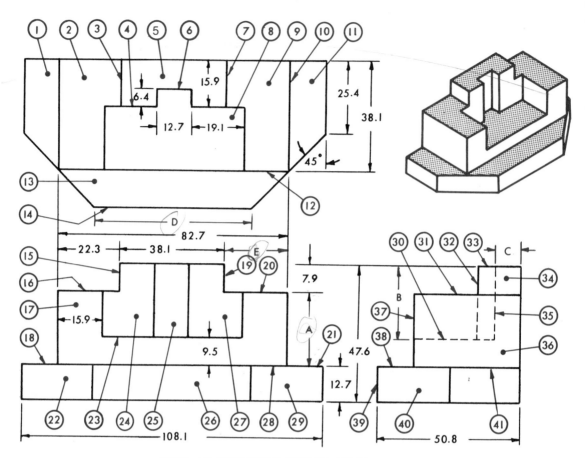

NOTE: ALL DIMENSIONS SHOWN ARE IN MILLIMETERS

PROBLEM 16.20
STEP BLOCK

1. Calculate dimensions A to E.
2. What surfaces in the top view are represented by line 41 in the side view?
3. What line in the side view is represented by surface 5 in the top view?
4. What line in the side view is represented by line 4 in the top view?
5. What lines in the front view are represented by surface 34 in the side view?
6. What line in the side view is represented by surface 25 in the front view?
7. What surfaces in the front view are represented by surface 40 in the side view?
8. What surface in the top view is represented by line 30 in the side view?
9. What line in the side view is represented by surface 13 in the top view?
10. What lines in the front view are represented by line 41 in the side view?

11. What lines in the front view are represented by line 31 in the side view?
12. What line in the side view is represented by line 12 in the top view?
13. What surface in the side view is represented by line 10 in the top view?
14. What line in the side view is represented by line 14 in the top view?
15. What surface in the front view is represented by line 12 in the top view?
16. What lines in the top view are represented by surface 34 in the side view?
17. What line in the front view is represented by surface 8 in the top view?
18. What line in the side view is represented by line 6 in the top view?
19. What line in the front view is represented by surface 13 in the top view?
20. What surfaces in the top view are represented by line 31 in the side view?
21. What line in the top view is represented by surface 25 in the front view?

SURFACE IDENTIFICATION PROBLEMS 16.21 to 16.25

Draw a chart similar to the one shown and place in the chart the appropriate numbers corresponding to the letters shown in the pictorial drawing. The letters represent surfaces in the pictorial drawings.

The numbers enclosed by a circle refer to a hidden surface or a hidden line. In some instances an enclosed number may refer to more than one surface.

SURFACE IDENTIFICATION CHART			
Pictorial Drawing Letters	Orthographic Drawing		
	Top View	Front View	Side View
A			
B			
C			
D			
E			
F			
G			
H			
I			
J			
K			
L			
M			
N			

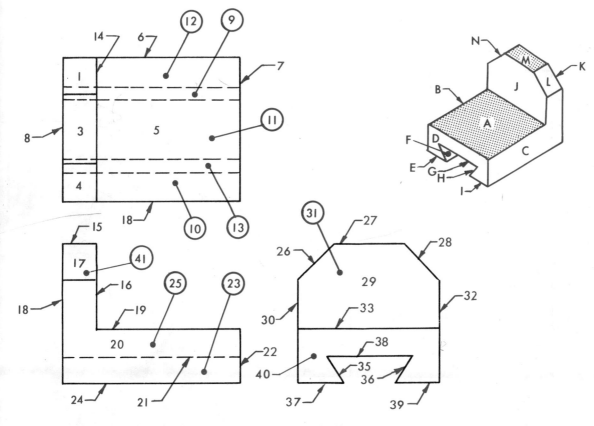

PROBLEM 16.21   DOVETAIL GUIDE

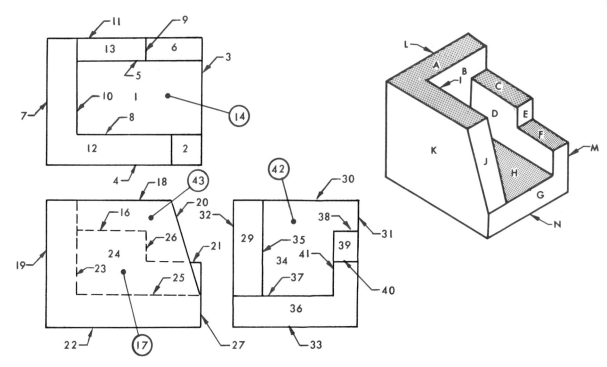

PROBLEM 16.22   BRACKET

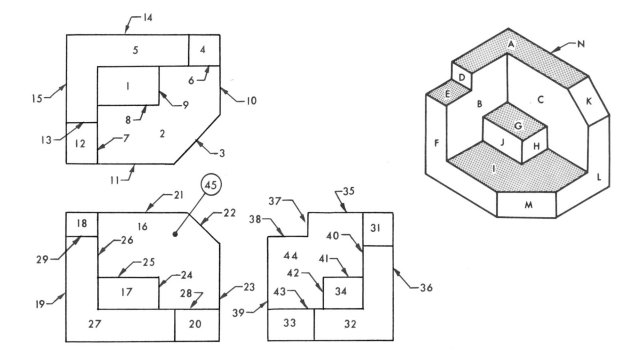

PROBLEM 16.23   CORNER BRACKET

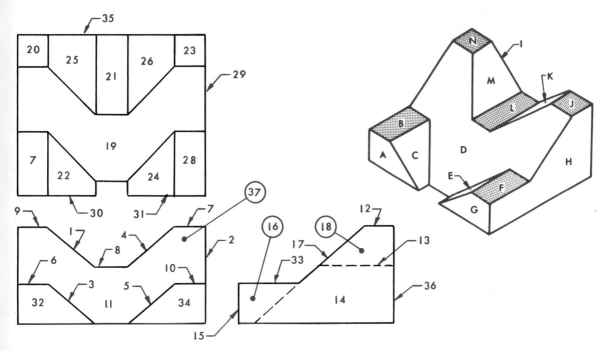

PROBLEM 16.24   ANGLE STOP

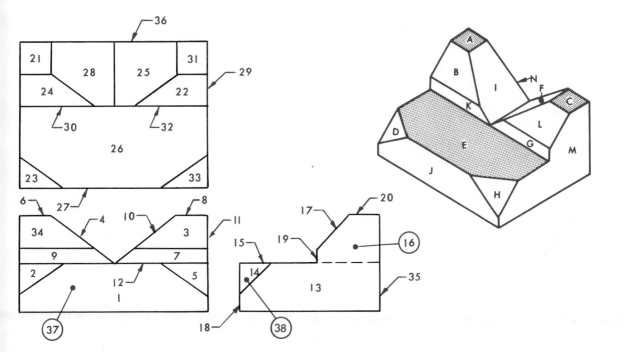

PROBLEM 16.25   ANGLED STEP BRACKET

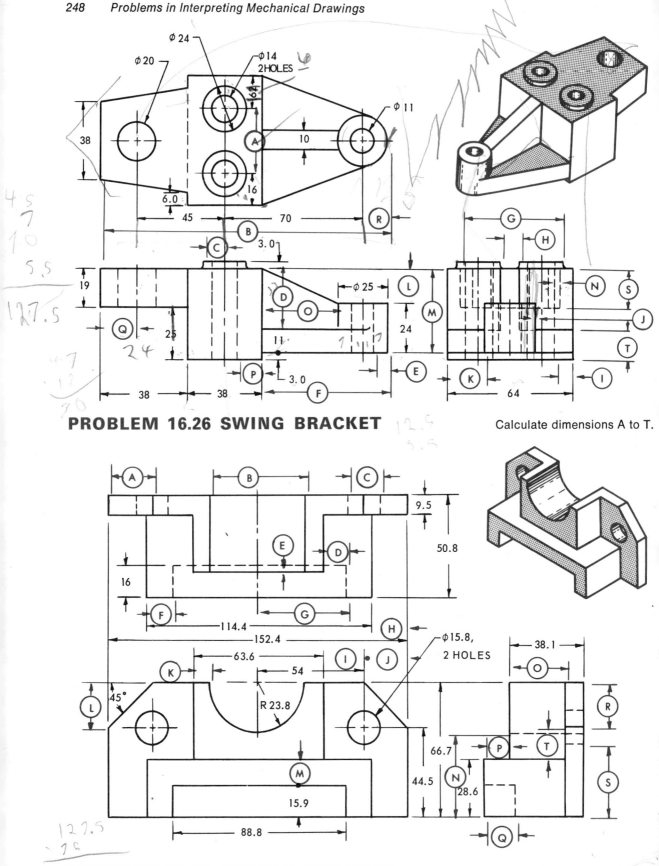

PROBLEM 16.26 SWING BRACKET

Calculate dimensions A to T.

PROBLEM 16.27 CRADLE BRACKET

Calculate dimensions A to T.

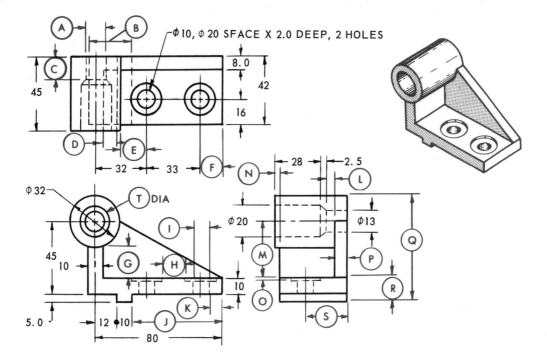

ϕ10, ϕ20 SFACE X 2.0 DEEP, 2 HOLES

PROBLEM 16.28 BEARING GUIDE

Calculate dimensions A to T.

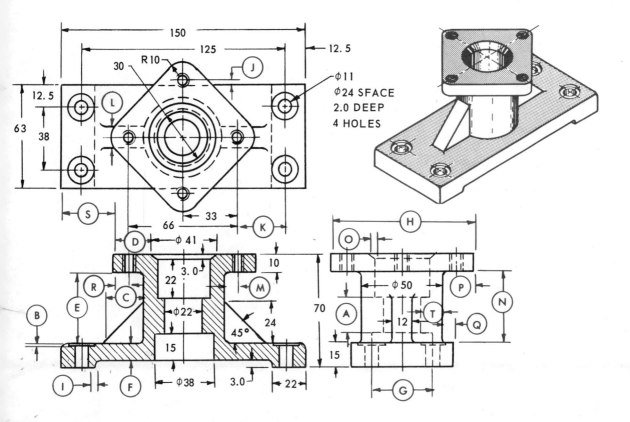

ϕ11
ϕ24 SFACE
2.0 DEEP
4 HOLES

PROBLEM 16.29 VERTICAL GUIDE

Calculate dimensions A to T.

APPENDIX

ANSI AND CSA PUBLICATIONS

ANSI — AMERICAN NATIONAL STANDARDS

ANSI	Y14.1	SIZE AND FORMAT
*ANSI	Y14.2-1957	LINE CONVENTIONS, SECTIONING AND LETTERING
*ANSI	Y14.3-1957	PROJECTIONS
*ANSI	Y14.4-1957	PICTORIAL DRAWING
*ANSI	Y14.5-1966	DIMENSIONING AND TOLERANCING FOR ENGINEERING DRAWINGS
*ANSI	Y14.6-1957	SCREW THREADS
ANSI	Y14.7	GEARS, SPLINES AND SERRATIONS
ANSI	Y14.7.1	GEAR DRAWING STANDARDS — PART 1, FOR SPUR, HELICAL, DOUBLE HELICAL AND RACK
ANSI	Y14.9	FORGINGS
ANSI	Y14.10	METAL STAMPINGS
ANSI	Y14.11	PLASTICS
ANSI	Y14.14	MECHANICAL ASSEMBLIES
ANSI	Y14.15	ELECTRICAL AND ELECTRONICS DIAGRAMS
ANSI	Y14.15A	INTERCONNECTION DIAGRAMS
ANSI	Y14.17	FLUID POWER DIAGRAMS
ANSI	Y32.2	GRAPHIC SYMBOLS FOR ELECTRICAL AND ELECTRONICS DIAGRAMS
ANSI	Y32.9	GRAPHIC ELECTRICAL WIRING SYMBOLS FOR ARCHITECTURAL AND ELECTRICAL LAYOUT DRAWINGS

(Continued)

*WHERE INDICATED IN THE TEXT, EXTRACTS HAVE BEEN MADE FROM THESE AMERICAN NATIONAL STANDARDS WITH THE PERMISSION OF THE PUBLISHERS, THE AMERICAN SOCIETY OF MECHANICAL ENGINEERS, UNITED ENGINEERING CENTER, 345 EAST 47TH STREET, NEW YORK, N.Y. 10017.

Table 1   ANSI and CSA Publications

ANSI — AMERICAN NATIONAL STANDARDS (CONTINUED)

ANSI	B1.1	UNIFIED SCREW THREADS
ANSI	B18.2.1	SQUARE AND HEX BOLTS AND SCREWS
ANSI	B18.2.2	SQUARE AND HEX NUTS
ANSI	B18.3	SOCKET CAP, SHOULDER AND SET SCREWS
ANSI	B18.6.2	SLOTTED HEAD CAP SCREWS, SQUARE HEAD SET SCREWS, SLOTTED HEADLESS SET SCREWS
ANSI	B18.6.3	MACHINE SCREWS AND MACHINE SCREW NUTS
ANSI	B17.2	WOODRUFF KEY AND KEYSLOT DIMENSIONS
ANSI	B17.1	KEYS AND KEYSEATS
ANSI	B18.21.1	LOCK WASHERS
ANSI	B27.2	PLAIN WASHERS
ANSI	B46.1	SURFACE TEXTURE

CSA — CANADIAN STANDARDS

CSA	B1.1	UNIFIED AND AMERICAN SCREW THREADS
CSA	B19.1	PLAIN WASHERS
CSA	B33.1	SQUARE AND HEXAGON BOLTS AND NUTS, STUDS AND WRENCH OPENINGS
CSA	B35.1	MACHINE SCREWS, STOVE BOLTS AND ASSOCIATED NUTS
CSA	B78.1	DRAWING STANDARD — GENERAL PRINCIPLES
CSA	B78.2	DRAWING STANDARD — DIMENSIONING AND TOLERANCING
CSA	B95	SURFACE TEXTURE
CSA	B97.1	LIMITS AND FITS FOR ENGINEERING AND MANUFACTURING
CSA	Z85	ABBREVIATIONS FOR SCIENTIFIC AND ENGINEERING TERMS
33-GP-7		ARCHITECTURAL DRAWING PRACTICES (NATIONAL RESEARCH COUNCIL, OTTAWA, CANADA)

THE ABOVE STANDARDS MAY BE PURCHASED FROM:

ANSI	AMERICAN NATIONAL STANDARDS INSTITUTE, INC. 1430 BROADWAY, NEW YORK, N.Y. 10018
	THE AMERICAN SOCIETY OF MECHANICAL ENGINEERS UNITED ENGINEERING CENTER 345 EAST 47TH STREET, NEW YORK, N.Y. 10017
CSA	CANADIAN STANDARDS ASSOCIATION 178 REXDALE BOULEVARD REXDALE, ONTARIO, CANADA, M9W 1R3

Table 1 (Continued) ANSI and CSA Publications

TABLE 2   ISO Metric Screw Threads   253

SERIES WITH GRADED PITCHES (Coarse, Fine) and **SERIES WITH CONSTANT PITCHES**

Nominal Size DIA (mm) Preferred	COARSE Thread Pitch	COARSE Tap Drill Size	FINE Thread Pitch	FINE Tap Drill Size	4 Thread Pitch	4 Tap Drill Size	3 Thread Pitch	3 Tap Drill Size	2 Thread Pitch	2 Tap Drill Size	1.5 Thread Pitch	1.5 Tap Drill Size	1.25 Thread Pitch	1.25 Tap Drill Size	1 Thread Pitch	1 Tap Drill Size	0.75 Thread Pitch	0.75 Tap Drill Size	0.5 Thread Pitch	0.5 Tap Drill Size	0.35 Thread Pitch	0.35 Tap Drill Size
1.6	0.35	1.25																				
1.8	0.35	1.45																				
2	0.4	1.6																				
2.2	0.45	1.75																				
2.5	0.45	2.05																			0.35	2.15
3	0.5	2.5																			0.35	2.65
3.5	0.6	2.9																			0.35	3.15
4	0.7	3.3																	0.5	3.5		
4.5	0.75	3.7																	0.5	4.0		
5	0.8	4.2																	0.5	4.5		
6	1	5.0															0.75	5.2				
8	1.25	6.7	1	7.0											1	7.0	0.75	7.2				
10	1.5	8.5	1.25	8.7									1.25	8.7	1	9.0	0.75	9.2				
12	1.75	10.2	1.25	10.8							1.5	10.5	1.25	10.7	1	11						
14	2	12	1.5	12.5							1.5	12.5	1.25	12.7	1	13						
16	2	14	1.5	14.5							1.5	14.5			1	15						
18	2.5	15.5	1.5	16.5					2	16	1.5	16.5			1	17						
20	2.5	17.5	1.5	18.5					2	18	1.5	18.5			1	19						
22	2.5	19.5	1.5	20.5					2	20	1.5	20.5			1	21						
24	3	21	2	22					2	22	1.5	22.5			1	23						
27	3	24	2	25					2	25	1.5	25.5			1	26						
30	3.5	26.5	2	28					2	28	1.5	28.5			1	29						
33	3.5	29.5	2	31					2	31	1.5	31.5										
36	4	32	3	33					2	34	1.5	34.5										
39	4	35	3	36					2	37	1.5	37.5										
42	4.5	37.5	3	39	4	38	3	39	2	40	1.5	40.5										
45	4.5	39	3	42	4	41	3	42	2	43	1.5	43.5										
48	5	43	3	45	4	44	3	45	2	46	1.5	46.5										

TABLE 2 ISO Metric Screw Threads

NUMBER OR LETTER SIZE DRILL	SIZE		NUMBER OR LETTER SIZE DRILL	SIZE		NUMBER OR LETTER SIZE DRILL	SIZE		NUMBER OR LETTER SIZE DRILL	SIZE	
	mm	INCHES		mm	INCHES		mm	INCHES		mm	INCHES
80	0.343	.014	50	1.778	.070	20	4.089	.161	K	7.137	.821
79	0.368	.015	49	1.854	.073	19	4.216	.166	L	7.366	.290
78	0.406	.016	48	1.930	.076	18	4.305	.170	M	7.493	.295
77	0.457	.018	47	1.994	.079	17	4.394	.173	N	7.671	.302
76	0.508	.020	46	2.057	.081	16	4.496	.177	O	8.026	.316
75	0.533	.021	45	2.083	.082	15	4.572	.180	P	8.204	.323
74	0.572	.023	44	2.184	.086	14	4.623	.182	Q	8.433	.332
73	0.610	.024	43	2.261	.089	13	4.700	.185	R	8.611	.339
72	0.635	.025	42	2.375	.094	12	4.800	.189	S	8.839	.348
71	0.660	.026	41	2.438	.096	11	4.851	.191	T	9.093	.358
70	0.711	.028	40	2.489	.098	10	4.915	.194	U	9.347	.368
69	0.742	.029	39	2.527	.100	9	4.978	.196	V	9.576	.377
68	0.787	.031	38	2.578	.102	8	5.080	.199	W	9.804	.386
67	0.813	.032	37	2.642	.104	7	5.105	.201	X	10.084	.397
66	0.838	.033	36	2.705	.107	6	5.182	.204	Y	10.262	.404
65	0.889	.035	35	2.794	.110	5	5.220	.206	Z	10.490	.413
64	0.914	.036	34	2.819	.111	4	5.309	.209			
63	0.940	.037	33	2.870	.113	3	5.410	.213			
62	0.965	.038	32	2.946	.116	2	5.613	.221			
61	0.991	.039	31	3.048	.120	1	5.791	.228			
60	1.016	.040	30	3.264	.129	A	5.944	.234			
59	1.041	.041	29	3.354	.136	B	6.045	.238			
58	1.069	.042	28	3.569	.141	C	6.147	.242			
57	1.092	.043	27	3.658	.144	D	6.248	.246			
56	1.181	.047	26	3.734	.147	E	6.350	.250			
55	1.321	.052	25	3.797	.150	F	6.528	.257			
54	1.397	.055	24	3.861	.152	G	6.629	.261			
53	1.511	.060	23	3.912	.154	H	6.756	.266			
52	1.613	.064	22	3.988	.157	I	6.909	.272			
51	1.702	.067	21	4.039	.159	J	7.036	.277			

Table 3   Number and Letter-Size Drills

TABLE 4 Twist Drill Sizes 255

METRIC DRILL SIZES (mm)[1]		DECIMAL EQUIV-ALENT IN INCHES	METRIC DRILL SIZES (mm)[1]		DECIMAL EQUIV-ALENT IN INCHES
PREFERRED	AVAILABLE	(REF)	PREFERRED	AVAILABLE	(REF)
	0.40	.0157	1.70		.0669
	0.42	.0165		1.75	.0689
	0.45	.0177	1.80		.0709
	0.48	.0189		1.85	.0728
0.50		.0197	1.90		.0748
	0.52	.0205		1.95	.0768
0.55		.0217	2.00		.0787
	0.58	.0228		2.05	.0807
0.60		.0236	2.10		.0827
	0.62	.0244		2.15	.0846
0.65		.0256	2.20		.0866
	0.68	.0268		2.30	.0906
0.70		.0276	2.40		.0945
	0.72	.0283	2.50		.0984
0.75		.0295	2.60		.1024
	0.78	.0307		2.70	.1063
0.80		.0315	2.80		.1102
	0.82	.0323		2.90	.1142
0.85		.0335	3.00		.1181
	0.88	.0346		3.10	.1220
0.90		.0354	3.20		.1260
	0.92	.0362		3.30	.1299
0.95		.0374	3.40		.1339
	0.98	.0386		3.50	.1378
1.00		.0394	3.60		.1417
	1.03	.0406		3.70	.1457
1.05		.0413	3.80		.1496
	1.08	.0425		3.90	.1535
1.10		.0433	4.00		.1575
	1.15	.0453		4.10	.1614
1.20		.0472	4.20		.1654
1.25		.0492		4.40	.1732
1.30		.0512	4.50		.1772
	1.35	.0531		4.60	.1811
1.40		.0551	4.80		.1890
	1.45	.0571	5.00		.1969
1.50		.0591		5.20	.2047
	1.55	.0610	5.30		.2087
1.60		.0630		5.40	.2126
	1.65	.0650	5.60		.2205
				5.80	.2283

[1] METRIC DRILL SIZES LISTED IN THE "PREFERRED" COLUMN ARE BASED ON THE R'40 SERIES OF PREFERRED NUMBERS SHOWN IN THE ISO STANDARD R497. THOSE LISTED IN THE "AVAILABLE" COLUMN ARE BASED ON THE R80 SERIES FROM THE SAME DOCUMENT.

Table 4   Twist Drill Sizes

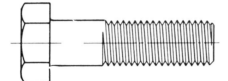

NOMINAL SIZE (MILLIMETRES)	WIDTH ACROSS FLATS	THICKNESS
1.6	3.2	1.1
2	4	1.4
2.5	5	1.7
3	5.5	2
4	7	2.8
5	8	3.5
6	10	4
8	13	5.5
10	17	7
12	19	8
14	22	9
16	24	10
18	27	12
20	30	13
22	32	14
24	36	15
27	41	17
30	46	19
33	50	21
36	55	23
39	60	25

Table 5   Hexagon Head Bolts, Regular Series

TABLE 6 Hexagon Head Nuts   257

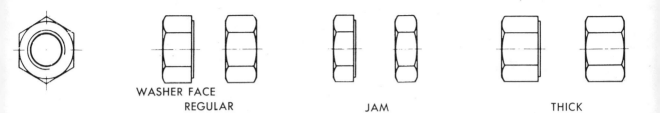

WASHER FACE
REGULAR   JAM   THICK

NOMINAL SIZE (MILLIMETRES)	DISTANCE ACROSS FLATS	THICKNESS		
		REGULAR	JAMB	THICK
1.6	3.2	1.3		
2	4.0	1.6	1.2	
2.5	5.0	2.0		
3	5.5	2.4	1.6	4.0
4	7.0	3.2	2.0	5.0
5	8.0	4.0	2.5	5.0
6	10	5.0	3.0	6.0
8	13	6.5	5.0	8.0
10	17	8.0	6.0	10
12	19	10	7.0	12
14	22	11	8.0	14
16	24	13	8.0	16
18	27	15	9.0	18.5
20	30	16	9.0	20
22	32	18	10	22
24	36	19	10	24
27	41	22	12	27
30	46	24	12	30
33	50	26		
36	55	29		
39	60	31		

Table 6   Hexagon Head Nuts

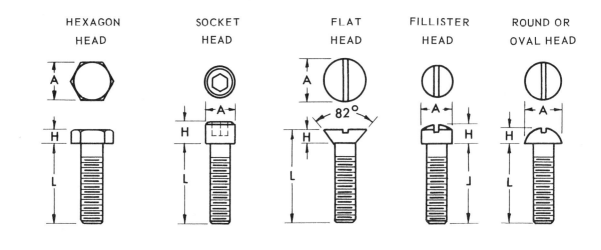

NOMINAL SIZE	HEXAGON HEAD		SOCKET HEAD			FLAT HEAD		FILLISTER HEAD		ROUND OR OVAL HEAD	
	A	H	A	H	KEY SIZE	A	H	A	H	A	H
M3	5.5	2.0	5.5	3.0	2.5	5.6	1.6	6.0	2.4	5.6	
4	7.0	2.8	7.0	4.0	3.0	7.5	2.2	8.0	3.1	7.5	
5	8.5	3.5	9.0	5.0	4.0	9.2	2.5	10	3.8	9.2	
6	10	4.0	10	6.0	5.0	11	3.0	12	4.6	11	
8	13	5.5	13	8.0	6.0	14.5	4.0	16	6.0	14.5	
10	17	7.0	16	10	8.0	18	5.0	20	7.5	18	
12	19	8.0	18	12	10						
14	22	9.0	22	14	12						
16	24	10	24	16	14						
18	27	12	27	18	14						
20	30	13	30	20	17						
22	36	15	33	22	17						
24	36	15	36	24	19						
27	41	17	40	27	19						
30	46	19	45	30	22						

Table 7   Common Cap Screws

TABLE 8 *Set Screws* 259

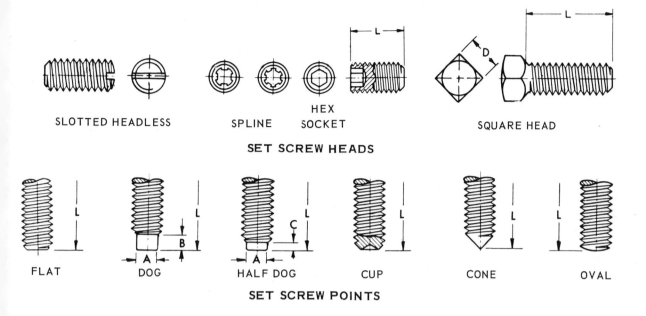

SLOTTED HEADLESS   SPLINE   HEX SOCKET   SQUARE HEAD

SET SCREW HEADS

FLAT   DOG   HALF DOG   CUP   CONE   OVAL

SET SCREW POINTS

NOMINAL SIZE	KEY SIZE
M 1.4	0.7
2	0.9
3	1.5
4	2.0
5	2.5
6	3.0
8	4.0
10	5.0
12	6.0
16	8.0

Table 8   Set Screws

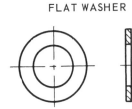
FLAT WASHER

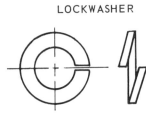
LOCKWASHER

SPRING LOCKWASHER

BOLT SIZE	FLAT WASHERS			LOCKWASHERS			SPRING LOCKWASHERS		
	I.D.	O.D.	THICK.	I.D.	O.D.	THICK.	I.D.	O.D.	THICK.
2	2.2	5.5	0.5	2.1	3.3	0.5			
3	3.2	7.0	0.5	3.1	5.7	0.8			
4	4.3	9.0	0.8	4.1	7.1	0.9	4.2	8.0	0.3 0.4
5	5.3	11	1.0	5.1	8.7	1.2	5.2	10.0	0.4 0.5
6	6.4	12	1.5	6.1	11.1	1.6	6.2	12.5	0.5 0.7
7	7.4	14	1.5	7.1	12.1	1.6	7.2	14.0	0.5 0.8
8	8.4	17	2.0	8.2	14.2	2.0	8.2	16.0	0.6 0.9
10	10.5	21	2.5	10.2	17.2	2.2	10.2	20	0.8 1.1
12	13	24	2.5	12.3	20.2	2.5	12.2	25	0.9 1.5
14	15	28	2.5	14.2	23.2	3.0	14.2	28.0	1.0 1.5
16	17	30	3.0	16.2	26.2	3.5	16.3	31.5	1.2 1.7
18	19	34	3.0	18.2	28.2	3.5	18.3	35.5	1.2 2.0
20	21	36	3.0	20.2	32.2	4.0	20.4	40.0	1.5 2.25
22	23	39	4.0	22.5	34.5	4.0	22.4	45	1.75 2.5
24	25	44	4.0	24.5	38.5	5.0			
27	28	50	4.0	27.5	41.5	5.0			
30	31	56	4.0	30.5	46.5	6.0			

Table 9   Common Washer Sizes

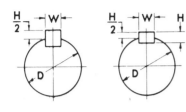

SQUARE   FLAT

DIAMETER OF SHAFT (mm)		SQUARE KEY NOMINAL SIZE		FLAT KEY NOMINAL SIZE	
OVER	UP TO	W	H	W	H
6	8	2	2		
8	10	3	3		
10	12	4	4		
12	17	5	5		
17	22	6	6		
22	30	7	7	8	7
30	38	8	8	10	8
38	44	9	9	12	8
44	50	10	10	14	9
50	58	12	12	16	10

Table 10   Square and Flat Stock Keys

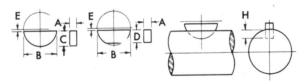

KEY NO.	NOMINAL (A × B)		KEY			KEY SEAT
	MILLIMETRES	INCHES	E	C	D	H
204	1.6 × 6.4	0.062 × 0.250	0.5	2.8	2.8	4.3
304	2.4 × 12.7	0.094 × 0.500	1.3	5.1	4.8	3.8
305	2.4 × 15.9	0.094 × 0.625	1.5	6.4	6.1	5.1
404	3.2 × 12.7	0.125 × 0.500	1.3	5.1	4.8	3.6
405	3.2 × 15.9	0.125 × 0.625	1.5	6.4	6.1	4.6
406	3.2 × 19.1	0.125 × 0.750	1.5	7.9	7.6	6.4
505	4.0 × 15.9	0.156 × 0.625	1.5	6.4	6.1	4.3
506	4.0 × 19.1	0.156 × 0.750	1.5	7.9	7.6	5.8
507	4.0 × 22.2	0.156 × 0.875	1.5	9.7	9.1	7.4
606	4.8 × 19.1	0.188 × 0.750	1.5	7.9	7.6	5.3
607	4.8 × 22.2	0.188 × 0.875	1.5	9.7	9.1	7.1
608	4.8 × 25.4	0.188 × 1.000	1.5	11.2	10.9	8.6
609	4.8 × 28.6	0.188 × 1.250	2.0	12.2	11.9	9.9
807	6.4 × 22.2	0.250 × 0.875	1.5	9.7	9.1	6.4
808	6.4 × 25.4	0.250 × 1.000	1.5	11.2	10.9	7.9

NOTE: METRIC KEY SIZES WERE NOT AVAILABLE AT THE TIME OF PUBLICATION. SIZES SHOWN ARE INCH-DESIGNED KEY-SIZES SOFT CONVERTED TO MILLIMETRES. CONVERSION WAS NECESSARY TO ALLOW THE STUDENT TO COMPARE KEYS WITH SLOT SIZES GIVEN IN MILLIMETRES.

Table 11   Woodruff Keys

Gauge	U.S. STANDARD (USS) mm	U.S. STANDARD (REVISED) mm	BIRMINGHAM (BWG) mm	NEW BIRMINGHAM (BG) mm	BROWNE AND SHARPE (B & S) mm	IMPERIAL STANDARD (SWG) mm	ELECTRICAL STEEL mm
3		6.01			5.83		
4	5.95	5.70	6.05	6.35	5.19	5.89	
5	5.56	5.31	5.59	5.65	4.62	5.39	
6	5.16	4.94	5.16	5.03	4.12	4.88	
7	4.76	4.55	4.57	4.48	3.67	4.47	
8	4.37	4.18	4.19	3.99	3.26	4.06	
9	3.97	3.80	3.76	3.55	2.91	3.66	
10	3.57	3.42	3.40	3.18	2.59	3.25	
11	3.18	3.04	3.05	2.83	2.30	2.95	3.18
12	2.78	2.66	2.77	2.52	2.05	2.64	2.77
13	2.38	2.78	2.41	2.24	1.83	2.34	2.39
14	1.98	1.90	2.11	1.99	1.63	2.03	1.98
15	1.79	1.71	1.83	1.78	1.45	1.83	1.78
16	1.59	1.52	1.65	1.59	1.29	1.63	1.59
17	1.43	1.37	1.47	1.41	1.15	1.42	1.42
18	1.27	1.21	1.25	2.58	1.02	1.22	1.27
19	1.11	1.06	1.07	1.19	0.91	1.02	1.11
20	0.95	0.91	0.89	1.00	0.81	0.91	0.95
21	0.87	0.84	0.81	0.89	0.72	0.81	
22	0.79	0.76	0.71	0.79	0.65	0.71	0.79
23	0.71	0.68	0.64	0.71	0.57	0.61	0.71
24	0.64	0.61	0.56	0.63	0.51	0.56	0.64
25	0.56	0.53	0.51	0.56	0.46	0.51	0.56
26	0.48	0.46	0.46	0.50	0.40	0.46	0.47
27	0.44	0.42	0.41	0.44	0.36	0.42	0.43
28	0.40	0.38	0.36	0.40	0.32	0.38	0.39
29	0.36	0.34	0.33	0.35	0.29	0.35	
30	0.32	0.31	0.31	0.31	0.25	0.32	0.36
31	0.28	0.27	0.25	0.28	0.23		
32	0.26	0.25	0.23		0.20	0.27	0.32
33	0.24	0.23	0.20	0.22	0.18	0.25	
34	0.22	0.21	0.18	0.20	0.16	0.23	
35			0.13	0.18		0.21	
36	0.18	0.17	0.10	0.16	0.13		
37						0.17	
38	0.16	0.15		0.12	0.10	0.15	
40				0.10		0.12	
42						0.10	

N.B. METRIC STANDARDS GOVERNING GAUGE SIZES WERE NOT AVAILABLE AT THE TIME OF PUBLICATION. THE SIZES GIVEN IN THE ABOVE CHART ARE "SOFT CONVERSION" FROM CURRENT INCH STANDARDS, AND ARE NOT MEANT TO BE REPRESENTATIVE OF THE PRECISE METRIC GAUGE SIZES WHICH MAY BE AVAILABLE IN THE FUTURE. CONVERSIONS ARE GIVEN ONLY TO ALLOW THE STUDENT TO COMPARE GAUGE SIZES READILY WITH METRIC DRILL SIZES.

Table 12 Sheet Metal Gauges and Thicknesses

TABLE 13 Wire Gauges and Diameters 263

IMPERIAL STANDARD				AMERICAN				STEEL			
GAUGE	mm	GAUGE	mm	GAUGE	mm	GAUGE	mm	GAUGE	mm	GAUGE	mm
7/0	12.70							7/0	12.45		
6/0	11.79							6/0	11.72		
5/0	10.97							5/0	10.94		
4/0	10.16			4/0	11.68			4/0	10.00		
3/0	9.45			3/0	10.40			3/0	9.21		
2/0	8.84			2/0	9.27			2/0	8.41		
1/0	8.23			1/0	8.25			1/0	7.79		
1	7.62	26	0.46	1	7.35	26	0.40	1	7.19	26	0.46
2	7.01	27	0.42	2	6.54	27	0.36	2	6.67	27	0.44
3	6.40	28	0.38	3	5.83	28	0.32	3	6.19	28	0.41
4	5.89	29	0.35	4	5.19	29	0.29	4	5.72	29	0.38
5	5.39	30	0.32	5	4.62	30	0.25	5	5.26	30	0.36
6	4.88	31	0.30	6	4.12	31	0.27	6	4.88	31	0.34
7	4.47	32	0.27	7	3.67	32	0.20	7	4.50	32	0.33
8	4.06	33	0.25	8	3.26	33	0.18	8	4.12	33	0.30
9	3.66	34	0.23	9	2.91	34	0.16	9	3.77	34	0.26
10	3.25	35	0.21	10	2.59	35	0.14	10	3.43	35	0.24
11	2.95	36	0.19	11	2.30	36	0.13	11	3.06	36	0.23
12	2.64	37	0.17	12	2.05	37	0.11	12	2.68	37	0.22
13	2.34	38	0.15	13	1.83	38	0.10	13	2.32	38	0.20
14	2.03	39	0.13	14	1.63	39	0.09	14	2.03	39	0.19
15	1.83	40	0.12	15	1.45	40	0.08	15	1.83	40	0.18
16	1.63	41	0.11	16	1.29	41	0.07	16	1.59		
17	1.42	42	0.10	17	1.15	42	0.06	17	1.37		
18	1.22	43	0.09	18	1.02	43	0.06	18	1.21		
19	1.02	44	0.08	19	0.91	44	0.05	19	1.04		
20	0.91	45	0.07	20	0.81	45	0.05	20	0.88		
21	0.81	46	0.06	21	0.72	46	0.04	21	0.81		
22	0.71	47	0.05	22	0.64	47	0.04	22	0.73		
23	0.61	48	0.04	23	0.57	48	0.03	23	0.66		
24	0.56	49	0.03	24	0.51	49	0.03	24	0.58		
25	0.51	50	0.02	25	0.46	50	0.02	25	0.52		

N.B. METRIC STANDARDS GOVERNING GAUGE SIZES WERE NOT AVAILABLE AT THE TIME OF PUBLICATION. THE SIZES GIVEN IN THE ABOVE CHART ARE "SOFT CONVERSIONS" FROM CURRENT INCH STANDARDS, AND ARE NOT MEANT TO BE REPRESENTATIVE OF THE PRECISE METRIC GAUGE SIZES WHICH MAY BE AVAILABLE IN THE FUTURE. CONVERSIONS ARE GIVEN ONLY TO ALLOW THE STUDENT TO COMPARE GAUGE SIZES READILY WITH METRIC DRILL SIZES.

Table 13 Wire Gauges and Diameters in Millimetres

ANGLE	SINE	COSINE	TAN	COTAN	ANGLE
0°	.0000	1.0000	.0000	θ	90°
1°	.0175	.9998	.0175	57.290	89°
2°	.0349	.9994	.0349	28.636	88°
3°	.0523	.9986	.0524	19.081	87°
4°	.0698	.9976	.0699	14.301	86°
5°	.0872	.9962	.0875	11.430	85°
6°	.1045	.9945	.1051	9.5144	84°
7°	.1219	.9925	.1228	8.1443	83°
8°	.1392	.9903	.1405	7.1154	82°
9°	.1564	.9877	.1584	6.3138	81°
10°	.1736	.9848	.1763	5.6713	80°
11°	.1908	.9816	.1944	5.1446	79°
12°	.2079	.9781	.2126	4.7046	78°
13°	.2250	.9744	.2309	4.3315	77°
14°	.2419	.9703	.2493	4.0108	76°
15°	.2588	.9659	.2679	3.7321	75°
16°	.2756	.9613	.2867	3.4874	74°
17°	.2924	.9563	.3057	3.2709	73°
18°	.3090	.9511	.3249	3.0777	72°
19°	.3256	.9455	.3443	2.9042	71°
20°	.3420	.9397	.3640	2.7475	70°
21°	.3584	.9336	.3839	2.6051	69°
22°	.3746	.9272	.4040	2.4751	68°
23°	.3907	.9205	.4245	2.3559	67°
24°	.4067	.9135	.4452	2.2460	66°
25°	.4226	.9063	.4663	2.1445	65°
26°	.4384	.8988	.4877	2.0503	64°
27°	.4540	.8910	.5095	1.9626	63°
28°	.4695	.8829	.5317	1.8807	62°
29°	.4848	.8746	.5543	1.8040	61°
30°	.5000	.8660	.5774	1.7321	60°
31°	.5150	.8572	.6009	1.6643	59°
32°	.5299	.8480	.6249	1.6003	58°
33°	.5446	.8387	.6494	1.5399	57°
34°	.5592	.8290	.6745	1.4826	56°
35°	.5736	.8192	.7002	1.4281	55°
36°	.5878	.8090	.7265	1.3764	54°
37°	.6018	.7986	.7536	1.3270	53°
38°	.6157	.7880	.7813	1.2799	52°
39°	.6293	.7771	.8098	1.2349	51°
40°	.6428	.7660	.8391	1.1918	50°
41°	.6561	.7547	.8693	1.1504	49°
42°	.6691	.7431	.9004	1.1106	48°
43°	.6820	.7314	.9325	1.0724	47°
44°	.6947	.7193	.9657	1.0355	46°
45°	.7071	.7071	.0000	1.0000	45°
ANGLE	COSINE	SINE	COTAN	TAN	ANGLE

Table 14   *Trigonometric Functions*

TABLE 15 Functions of Numbers 265

NUMBER	SQUARE	CUBE	SQUARE ROOT	CUBE ROOT	CIRCUMFERENCE OF CIRCLE	AREA OF CIRCLE
1	1	1	1.0000	1.0000	3.142	0.7854
2	4	8	1.4142	1.2599	6.283	3.1416
3	9	27	1.7321	1.4422	9.425	7.0686
4	16	64	2.0000	1.5874	12.566	12.5664
5	25	125	2.2361	1.7100	15.708	19.6350
6	36	216	2.4495	1.8171	18.850	28.2743
7	49	343	2.6458	1.9129	21.991	38.4845
8	64	512	2.8284	2.0000	25.133	50.2655
9	81	729	3.0000	2.0801	28.274	63.6173
10	100	1000	3.1623	2.1544	31.416	78.5398
11	121	1331	3.3166	2.2240	34.558	95.0332
12	144	1728	3.4641	2.2894	37.699	113.097
13	169	2197	3.6056	2.3513	40.841	132.732
14	196	2744	3.7417	2.4101	43.982	153.938
15	225	3375	3.8730	2.4662	47.124	176.715
16	256	4096	4.0000	2.5198	50.265	201.062
17	289	4913	4.1231	2.5713	53.407	226.980
18	324	5832	4.2426	2.6207	56.549	254.469
19	361	6859	4.3589	2.6684	59.690	283.529
20	400	8000	4.4721	2.7144	62.832	314.159
21	441	9261	4.5826	2.7589	65.973	346.361
22	484	10648	4.6904	2.8020	69.115	380.133
23	529	12167	4.7958	2.8439	72.257	415.476
24	576	13824	4.8990	2.8845	75.398	452.389
25	625	15625	5.0000	2.9240	78.540	490.874
26	676	17576	5.0990	2.9625	81.681	530.929
27	729	19683	5.1962	3.0000	84.823	572.555
28	784	21952	5.2915	3.0366	87.965	615.752
29	841	24389	5.3852	3.0723	91.106	660.520
30	900	27000	5.4772	3.1072	94.248	706.858
31	961	29791	5.5678	3.1414	97.389	754.768
32	1024	32768	5.6569	3.1748	100.531	804.248
33	1089	35937	5.7446	3.2075	103.673	855.299
34	1156	39304	5.8310	3.2396	106.814	907.920
35	1225	42875	5.9161	3.2711	109.956	962.113
36	1296	46656	6.0000	3.3019	113.097	1017.88
37	1369	50653	6.0828	3.3322	116.239	1075.21
38	1444	54872	6.1644	3.3620	119.381	1134.11
39	1521	59319	6.2450	3.3912	122.522	1194.59
40	1600	64000	6.3246	3.4200	125.66	1256.64
41	1681	68921	6.4031	3.4482	128.81	1320.25
42	1764	74088	6.4807	3.4760	131.95	1385.44
43	1849	79507	6.5574	3.5034	135.09	1452.20
44	1936	85184	6.6332	3.5303	138.23	1520.53
45	2025	91125	6.7082	3.5569	141.37	1590.43
46	2116	97336	6.7823	3.5830	144.51	1661.90
47	2209	103823	6.8557	3.6088	147.65	1734.94
48	2304	110592	6.9282	3.6342	150.80	1809.56
49	2401	117649	7.0000	3.6593	153.94	1885.74
50	2500	125000	7.0711	3.6840	157.08	1963.50

Table 15   Function of Numbers

SIZE		THREADS PER INCH AND TAP DRILL SIZES												
		GRADED PITCH SERIES						CONSTANT PITCH SERIES						
		COARSE UNC		FINE UNF		EXTRA FINE UNEF		8 UN		12 UN		16 UN		
NUMBER OR FRACTION	DECI-MAL	THREADS PER INCH	TAP DRILL DIA	THREADS PER INCH	TAP DRILL DIA	THREADS PER INCH	TAP DRILL DIA	THREADS PER INCH	TAP DRILL DIA	THREADS PER INCH	TAP DRILL DIA	THREADS PER INCH	TAP DRILL DIA
0	.060	—	—	80	$\frac{3}{64}$	—	—	—	—	—	—	—	—
2	.086	56	No. 50	64	No. 49	—	—	—	—	—	—	—	—
4	.112	40	No. 43	48	No. 42	—	—	—	—	—	—	—	—
5	.125	40	No. 38	44	No. 37	—	—	—	—	—	—	—	—
6	.138	32	No. 36	40	No. 33	—	—	—	—	—	—	—	—
8	.164	32	No. 29	36	No. 29	—	—	—	—	—	—	—	—
10	.190	24	No. 25	32	No. 21	—	—	—	—	—	—	—	—
¼	.250	20	7	28	3	32	.219	—	—	—	—	—	—
⁵⁄₁₆	.312	18	F	24	I	32	.281	—	—	—	—	—	—
⅜	.375	16	.312	24	Q	32	.344	—	—	—	—	UNC	—
⁷⁄₁₆	.438	14	U	20	.391	28	Y	—	—	—	—	16	V
½	.500	13	.422	20	.453	28	.469	—	—	—	—	16	.438
⁹⁄₁₆	.562	12	.484	18	.516	24	.516	—	—	UNC	—	16	.500
⅝	.625	11	.531	18	.578	24	.578	—	—	12	.547	16	.562
¾	.750	10	.656	16	.688	20	.703	—	—	12	.672	UNF	—
⅞	.875	9	.766	14	.812	20	.828	—	—	12	.797	16	.812
1	1.000	8	.875	12	.922	20	.953	UNC	—	UNF	—	16	.938
1⅛	1.125	7	.984	12	1.047	18	1.078	8	1.000	UNF	—	16	1.062
1¼	1.250	7	1.109	12	1.172	18	1.188	8	1.125	UNF	—	16	1.188
1⅜	1.375	6	1.219	12	1.297	18	1.312	8	1.250	UNF	—	16	1.312
1½	1.500	6	1.344	12	1.422	18	1.438	8	1.375	UNF	—	16	1.438
1⅝	1.625	—	—	—	—	18	—	8	1.500	12	1.547	16	1.562
1¾	1.750	5	1.562	—	—	—	—	8	1.625	12	1.672	16	1.688
1⅞	1.875	—	—	—	—	—	—	8	1.750	12	1.797	16	1.812
2	2.000	4.5	1.781	—	—	—	—	8	1.875	12	1.922	16	1.938
2¼	2.250	4.5	2.031	—	—	—	—	8	2.125	12	2.172	16	2.188
2½	2.500	4	2.250	—	—	—	—	8	2.375	12	2.422	16	2.438
2¾	2.750	4	2.500	—	—	—	—	8	2.625	12	2.672	16	2.688
3	3.000	4	2.750	—	—	—	—	8	2.875	12	2.922	16	2.938
3¼	3.250	4	3.000	—	—	—	—	8	3.125	12	3.172	16	3.188
3½	3.500	4	3.250	—	—	—	—	8	3.375	12	3.422	16	3.438
3¾	3.750	4	3.500	—	—	—	—	8	3.625	12	3.668	16	3.688
4	4.000	4	3.750	—	—	—	—	8	3.875	12	3.922	16	3.938

NOTE: THE TAP DIAMETER SIZES SHOWN ARE NOMINAL. THE CLASS AND LENGTH OF THREAD WILL GOVERN THE LIMITS ON THE TAPPED HOLE SIZE.

Table 16 Inch Screw Threads

TABLE 17 Abbreviations and Symbols   267

And	&		Machine Steel	MS or MACH ST
Across Flats	A/F		Material	MATL
Angular	ANG		Maximum	MAX
Approximate	APPROX		Maximum Material	
Assembly	ASSY		Condition	M or MMC
Basic	BASIC		Metre	m
Bill of Material	B/M		Metric Thread	M
Bolt Circle	BC		Micrometre	μm
Brass	BR		Millimetre	mm
Brown and Sharpe Gauge	B & S GA		Minimum	MIN
Bushing	BUSH		Minute (Angle)	MIN
Casting	CSTG		Nominal	NOM
Cast Iron	CI		Not to Scale	NTS or ___
Centimetre	cm		Number	NO
Center Line	℄		Outside Diameter	OD
Center to Center	C to C		Parallel	PAR
Chamfered	CHAM		Perpendicular	PERP
Circularity	CIR		Pitch	P
Cold Rolled Steel	CRS		Pitch Circle Diameter	PCD
Concentric	CONC		Pitch Diameter	PD
Counterbore	CBORE		Plate	PL
Countersink	CSK		Radian	rad
Cubic Centimetre	cm^3		Radius	R
Cubic Metre	m^3		Reference or	
			Reference Dimension	REF
Datum	DATUM		Revolutions per Minute	RPM
Degree (Angle)	° or DEG		Right Hand	RH
Diameter	DIA or ϕ		Second (Arc)	(")
Diametral Pitch	DP		Second (Time)	SEC
Dimension	DIM		Section	SECT
Drawing	DWG		Slotted	SLOT
Eccentric	ECC		Socket	SOCK
Figure	FIG		Spherical	SPHER
Finish All Over	FAO		Spotface	SFACE
Gauge	GA		Square	SQ
Heat Treat	HT TR		Square Centimetre	cm^2
Head	HD		Square Metre	m^2
Heavy	HY		Steel	ST
Hexagon	HEX		Straight	STR
Hydraulic	HYD		Symmetrical	SYM
Inside Diameter	ID		Thread	THD
International Organization			Through	THRU
for Standardization	ISO		Tolerance	TOL
Iron Pipe Size	IPS		True Profile	TP
Kilogram	kg		Undercut	UCUT
Kilometre	km		U.S. Sheet-Metal Gauge	USS GA
Large End	LE		Wrought Iron	WI
Left Hand	LH			
Machined	√ or √			

ISO A   ANSI -A-

Table 15   Abbreviations and Symbols

INDEX

A

Abbreviations, 49, 268
Adjacent parts in section, 120
Adjustable set square, 6
Aligned system, dimensioning, 44
Alignment of parts and holes, 80
Allowances for joints and seams, 166
Angle, bisecting, 227
Angular units, 47
ANSI, 2
    publications, 251, 252
ASME publications, 251, 252
Arc,
    constructions, 11, 20
    in isometric, 151
    in oblique, 156
    tangent to circle and straight line, 230
    tangent to sides of acute angle, 229
    tangent to sides of obtuse angle, 230
    tangent to two circles, 230
    tangent to two lines, 229
Architect's scale, 12, 13
Architectural dimensioning, 195
Architectural drafting, 181
Arms in section, 123
Arrow heads, 45
Arrowless dimensioning, 93
Assembly drawings, 64, 67
Auxiliary views, 137

B

Bedrooms, 196
Bill of materials, 68, 69

Bisecting, 227
Bolts
    hexagon head, 256
Break lines, 17, 19, 81
Breaks, 154
Broken-out sections, 116
Brushes, 14

C

Cabinet oblique, 154
Casting, 220
Cavalier oblique, 154
Center lines, 16, 18
Chamfers, 48
Circles
    constructions, 11, 20
    in isometric, 150, 151
    in oblique, 156
Circuits, electrical, 208, 210
Civil engineer's scale, 12, 13
Classes of thread, 105
Compass, 11
Cones, 170, 171
Convenience outlets, 207
Construction lines, 19
Conventional representation, 76
Counterbore, 52
Counterbored hole, 107
Countersink, 52
Countersunk hole, 107
Cross-hatching, 119
CSA
    publications, 252
    standards, 2

Cutting-plane line, 17, 112
Cylindrical intersection, 81, 173
Cylindrical Parts, dimensioning, 50

D

Decimal dimensions, 43
Detail assembly drawing, 66
Developing a house plan, 196
Development drawings, 163
  cone, 170, 171
  frustrum of a cone, 170, 171
  parallel line, 167
  radial line, 170
  straight line, 164
Detail drawings, 65
Diameter, 49, 50
Die casting, 222
Dimension lines, 16
Dimensioning, 44
  aligned system, 45
  angular units, 47
  architectural, 195
  auxiliary views, 140
  basic rules, 46
  cylindrical parts, 50
  datum, 73
  fillets and rounds, 72
  formed parts, 47
  holes, 49, 52, 53, 197
  isometric drawings, 153
  limited spaces, 47
  notes, 48
  not-to-scale dimensions, 72
  oblique drawings, 156
  point-to-point, 73
  polar system, 72
  placing of, 45, 46
  radii, 51
  repetitive parts, 73
  sections, 120
  systems, 45
  tabular, 94
  unidirectional systems, 45
Dimensions, 42, 70
  decimal inch, 13, 43
  dual, 43
  fractional, 13, 43
  not-to-scale, 72
  reference, 72
  SI (metric) 42
Dining room, 198
Dividers, 14
Dividing a line into equal parts, 227

Door symbols, 192
Drafting
  architectural, 181
  defined, 1
  electrical, 205
  machine, 6
  paper, 8
  pencils, 9
  simplified, 92
Drawings
  assembly, 64, 67
  detail, 65
  detail assembly, 66
  development, 163
  dimensioning oblique, 156
  one-view, 31
  orthographic, 29, 30
  pictorial, 146
  presentation, 181
  reproduction of, 82
  simplified, 95
  three-view, 32
  two-view, 32
  working, 44
Drill size, 254, 255

E

Electrical drafting, 205
  circuits, 208, 210
  convenience outlets, 207
  lights and switches, 206
  wiring standards, 209
Electrical requirements for the home, 205
Ellipse, 231
Enlarged scale, 12, 74
Enlarged views, 74
Erasing shields, 14
Extension lines, 16

F

Fastening, 100
Ferrous metals, 216
Fillets and rounds, 72, 78, 79
Fit, thread, 105
Fits
  types of, 71
Floor plan symbols, 186
Foreshortened projection, 80
Forging, 223

Forming from sheet stock, 222
Fractional dimensions, 13, 43
Frustrum of a cone, development of,
    170, 171
Full scale, 12
Full section, 113, 114
Function of numbers, 265

G

Geometrical constructions, 35
Guide lines, 21

H

Half section, 113
Hatching lines, 112
Helix, 100
Hexagon constructions, 228
Hidden lines, 16, 18
Holes, 76
    alignment, 80, 124
    counterbored, 52, 107
    countersunk, 52, 107
    dimensioning, 49, 52, 53, 107
    in section, 121
    slotted, 53
    spotface, 52, 107
    symbols, 96
House plan, development, 196
    House types, 182, 183

I

Inches,
    conversion to millimetres, inside covers.
Inclined surfaces, 138
Incomplete view, 138
Intersection
    lines of, 172
    of cylinders, 77, 81
    of flat-side prisms, 172
    of unfinished surfaces, 77-79
    points of, 78
Iron, 216
Irregular curves, 14
    in isometric, 152

Isometric, 147
    drawings, dimensioning of, 153
    drawing circles and arcs in, 150, 151
    drawing irregular curves in, 152
    projection, 147
    sectioning, 154

J

Joints and seams, 166

K

Keys, 108, 261
Kitchens, 197
Knurling, 74

L

Leaders, 16, 48
Left-hand threads, 104
Lettering, 15, 187
    guides, 15
    sets, 15
Letters, 15
Limits and fits, 70
Line constructions, 16
Line division, 227
Line work, 16, 17
Lines
    break, 17, 19, 154
    center lines, 16, 18
    construction, 19
    cutting-plane, 17, 112
    dimension, 16
    drawing, 10
    element, 167
    extension, 16
    guide, 19
    hatching or section, 119
    hidden, 16, 18
    leaders, 16, 14
    miter, 33
    non-isometric, 149
    object, 16
    oblique, 22, 31
    oblique dimension, 156
    of intersection, 172

phantom, 17
radial, 170
section, 17
solid, 17
thickness of, 17
viewing plane, 17, 75
Lights and switches, 206
Living room, 198
Location of outlets, lights and switches, 206
Lugs in section, 125

M

Machining
from standard stock, 224
symbols, 54
Manufacturing process, 220
casting, 220
die casting, 222
forging, 223
forming from sheet stock, 222
welding, 223
machining from standard stock, 224
Materials, 216
Measurement units of, 42
Mechanical engineer's scale, 12, 13
Metals
ferrous, 216
non-ferrous, 219
thickness, 262
Metric scale, 12
Miter line, 33
Multiple threads, 106

N

Non-ferrous metals, 219
Non-isometric lines, 149
Not-to-scale dimensions, 72
Notes, 48
Numbers, 15
roughness, 56
Nuts
hexagon, 257

O

Object lines, 16

Oblique projection, 154
cabinet, 155
cavalier, 155
drawing circles and arcs in, 156
drawing, dimensioning an, 156
Obtuse angle, 230
Octagon constructions, 228
Offset sections, 114
One-view drawings, 31
Operational names, 49
Opposite-handed views, 74
Orthographic drawing, 29
Orthographic projection, 29

P

Parallel lines, 227
development, 167
Parallel straight edge, 5
Partial view, 75
Pattern drawing, 220
Pentagon, 229
Permanent fastenings, 100
Phantom lines, 17
Phantom sections, 114
Pictorial drawings, 146
Pitch, 104
Points of intersection, 78
Point-to-point dimensioning, 73
Polar dimensioning system, 72
Polygon, 229
Presentation drawings, 181
Prints, 82
Prisms, intersection of flat-sided, 172
Projections
foreshortened, 80
isometric, 147
oblique, 154
orthographic, 29
third angle, 29, 30
Publications
ANSI, 251
ASME, 251
CSA, 251

R

Radial lines development, 170
Radii, dimensioning, 51
Rear views, 30
Receding axis, 154

Receding plane, 154
Rectangular dimensioning system, 72
Reduced scale, 12
Reference dimensions, 72
Removable fastenings, 100
Removed sections, 117, 118
Repetitive parts, 73, 76
Representation, conventional, 76
Reproduction of drawings, 82
Revolved sections, 117
Ribs in section, 121, 122
Right-hand threads, 104
Rooms
    living and dining, 198
Roughness numbers, 56
Runouts, 77

S

Sand casting, 220
Sand mold, 220
Scale, 12, 13
    enlarged, 12
    foot and inch, 13
    full, 12
    metre, 12
    millimetre, 12
    reduced, 12
Screw
    fit of, 105
    threads, 100, 253, 266
Screws
    cap, 258
    machine, 259
    set, 259
Section lines, 17, 119
Sectioning, isometric, 154
Sections, 112
    adjacent parts, 120
    broken-out or partial, 116
    dimensions, 120
    full, 113,114
    half, 113, 114
    holes, 121
    large areas, 120
    lugs, 125
    offset, 114
    phantom or hidden, 114
    placement, 119
    revolved and removed, 117, 118
    ribs, 121, 122
    spokes and arms, 123

thin, 119
    through shafts, bolts, pins, keys, etc., 120
Set squares, 6
Sheet metal gauges and sizes, 262
Simplified drafting, 92
Single threads, 105
Sketching, 20, 96
Slant height of a cone, 170, 171
Sloping surfaces, 137
Slotted holes, 53
Spacing the views, 34
Spokes in section, 123
Spotface, 52
Sprue, 220
Stampings, 222
Steel, 216
Straight line
    development, 164
    tangent to two circles, 231
Steel designation, 218
Surface
    roughness range, 55
    symbols, 54
Symbols
    door, 192
    electrical, 205
    floor plan, 186, 190, 191, 193
    holes, 96
    surface, 54
    thread, 102, 103
    wall, 190, 191
    windows, 193
Systems
    aligned, 45
    polar dimensioning, 72
    rectangular dimensioning, 72
    unidirectional, 45

T

Tabular dimensioning, 94
Tangent,
    arcs, 229
    straight lines, 230
Tap drill size, 254
Tapers, 73,
Technical drawing, 1, 4
Templates, 14
Thickness of lines, 17
Thin sections, 119
Third angle orthographic projection, 29, 30
Three-view drawings, 32
Thread
    classes, 104

forms, 101
  internal symbol, 102, 103
  representation, 102, 103
  specifications, 105
  standards, 101, 104
  symbols, 102, 103
Threaded fasteners, 106, 107
  bolts, 106, 107
  cap screws, 106, 107
  machine screws, 106, 107
  studs, 106, 107
Threads
  right- and left-hand, 104
  single and multiple, 106
  screw, 101, 105, 253, 266
Title block, 8
'Title strip, 8
Tolerances and allowances, 70
Trigonometric functions, 264
T square, 6
Two-view drawings, 32

U

Unfinished surfaces, intersection of, 77-79
Unidirectional system, dimensioning, 45
Units of measurement, 42, 43
  decimal inch, 43
  feet and inches, 43
  fractional inch, 43
  metric, 42

V

Viewing plane line, 17
Views, 29
  auxiliary, 137
  enlarged, 74
  number of, 31
  opposite-handed, 74
  partial, 75
  placement of, 30
  rear, 30
  selection, 31
  spacing, 34

W

Washers, 260
Waviness numbers, 57
Webs and spokes, 123
Welding, 223
Whiteprints, 82
Window symbols, 193
Wire gauges & diameters, 263
Wiring standards, 209
Working drawings, 44
  architectural, 187, 190
  mechanical, 44